THE OAKWOOD PRESS

BROTHERI ENGINL...~ for POWER, TRANSPORT & WEAPONS

by
Sydney A.Leleux

Pearl in May 1961 after restoration.   *S.A.Leleux*

THE OAKWOOD PRESS

© Sydney A.Leleux, 2019

ISBN 978-0-85361-459-3

First Edition published as *Brotherhoods, Engineers*, 1965
Second Edition 2019

Printed by Blissetts, Roslin Road, Acton, W3 8DH

'The Contractor is Brotherhood – the best you could have to deal with.'
- I.K. Brunel

(*Brunel Letter Book, Vol II*, page 80 – postscript in a letter to C.Richardson dated 14th September, 1858 inviting him to be Resident Engineer for the Bristol & South Wales Junction Railway contract. Richardson took the post.)

Front cover: Set of 10 turbine discs, each with many blades for the steam to impact, on the single rotor shaft, and their designer Ernest Dewar. The discs increase in diameter from left to right to compensate for the drop in pressure as the steam passes along the length of the turbine. Later a set of fixed blades will be fitted between each disc to deflect the steam into the next stage.

Back cover: 8-cylinder diesel engine being lifted in the works. The end engine column is clearly visible. The 18in. gauge workshop railway for handling materials is clearly visible.

Published by
The Oakwood Press, 54-58 Mill Square, Catrine, KA5 6RD
Telephone: 01290 551122   Website: www.stenlake.co.uk

Contents

Appendices

RAILWAY WORKS, CHIPPENHAM.

A Catalogue of the

NEW STORES & MATERIALS

INCLUDING

200 TONS NEW BAR IRON,

BB, BBH, Lowmoor, Bowling, S.C. Crown, and the best Brands, 4½ tons New Cast and Shear Steel, *Brown & Co.*, and *Cammell & Co.*, 4 tons Scrap Steel, 40 tons New Bolts and Nuts, Rivets and nails, 5 tons Chain and Chain Slings, 1,650 feet run New 1½ and 2-inch Boiler Tubes, several tons useful Castings, 40 tons useful Iron, 60 patent Signal Lamps, 150 dozen New Files, 11 dozen Augers, Adzes, 33 cwt. Sledge and Stone Hammers, Picks, 10,000 feet Gutta Percha Fuse Galvanized Signal Wire, 54 cwt. Metal, an Assortment of Brass Work, 3 Lift and Force Pumps, 6 pairs Forge Bellows, 2 iron Bogies, Grindstones, 3 Portable Weighing Machines 7 to 40 cwt., Iron Wheel Cramps, 20 bolts Felt, 3 wrought iron Oil Tanks, 140 gallons Oil, Turps, Dry Colours, and Paints,

SIX NEW LOCOMOTIVE ENGINES AND ROLLING STOCK,

Manufactured by *Mr. Brotherhood,* including

FOUR 6-WHEEL SADDLE TANK LOCOMOTIVES,

With 4 Wheels coupled, 10 and 12-inch inside Cylinders, 4 feet 8½-inch Gauge, a 4-wheel ditto coupled, 10-inch outside Cylinders, a 6-wheel ditto coupled, 16⅝-inch inside Cylinders 7-feet Gauge,

20 NEW 8-TON OAK-FRAMED NARROW-GAUGE COAL WAGGONS,

Eight 6-ton Broad-gauge Railway Trucks, 2 Coal Trucks 10 and 6 tons, a 10-ton wrought iron Tilt Truck, Ten 6-ton Ballast Trucks, a Hay Truck,

21 NEW END-TIP EARTH WAGGONS

Narrow Gauge, 10 sets of Locomotive and Waggon Wheels finished, with Lowmoor and Blaenavon Weldless tyres, 16 sets ditto partly finished, 3 sets 30-inch Narrow-Gauge Wheels and Axles, 36 pairs Waggon Wheels and Axles, 16 tons Waggon Wheel Tyres partly Lowmoor, 7 tons Bufferhead Forgings, 5 tons new wrought iron Railway Waggon Work, 8 Broad and Narrow-Gauge Trolleys, 9 Earth Waggon Frames,

ENGINEERS', BOILER MAKERS' AND FOUNDERS' TOOLS,

Including 7 tons Steel Turning, Slotting, Drilling, and Shaping Tools, 3 sets *Whitworth's* Stocks and Dies, 4 *Adamson's* patent Hydraulic Jacks, 16 Lifting and Screw Jacks, 10 tons Lathe Straps and Bolts, 20 tons Smith's Tools, 22-tons Steam Hammer Heads and Anvils, 15 tons Steam Hammer Tools,

60 Tons LEVELLING SLABS and BENDING, SHAPING and SWAGE BLOCKS,

Nine pairs *Weston's* Differential Blocks, 26 pairs wrought iron Blocks with Rope Falls, a 2-ton Portable Crane, 74 tons Foundry Boxes, 22 Crane and Shank Ladles, 56 Water Boshes, 250 TONS WROUGHT AND CAST IRON SCRAP, 23 tons Pig Iron, 5 tons old Lowmoor Tyres, 20 tons useful Castings, 60 Anvils, 2 tons Core Barrels, 5 Straightening Presses, Hydraulic Pipe Proving Machine, 2 Proving Pumps, 16 Shop Trolleys, Hand Truck, Valuable Collection of IRON and WOOD PATTERNS, DRAWINGS and MODELS, Office Fittings,

CONTRACTORS' PLANT AND EFFECTS,

INCLUDING A CONTRACTORS' SEWAGE PUMP AND ENGINE COMBINED,

By *Kittoe* and *Brotherhood* with Vertical Boiler, a 4-horse power Portable Steam Engine by *Hornsby & Son*, a 12-inch Centrifugal Pump, by *Easton & Amos*, with 14-inch Outlet and Driving Gear, a 9-inch *Parsey's* patent ditto, 12 *Fowler's* Pumps, Four 6 and 7-inch cast iron Well Pumps, 3 sets Well-boring Tackle, cast iron Mortar Mill, 2 feet diameter, Clay Crushing Mill, a Fire Engine, by *Merryweather*, with Leather Hose, a 6-horse power Vertical Steam Engine and Cornish Boiler, Multitubular ditto, a Circular Saw Bench, 87 TONS BRIDGE and CONTRACTORS' RAILS, 1,400 Broad Gauge Sleepers, Pile-driving Engine, 5 tons Crow Bars and Platelayers' Tools, 44 wrought iron Skips, 230 Navvy, Off-bearing and Crowding Barrows, 9 Double and Single-purchase Crabs, 9 Dobbin and other Carts, Hay Waggon, 2 Timber Whims, Locomotive Bogie, 11 Boiler Carriages, 26 sets Harness, Winnowing and Chaff-cutting Machines, Trestles and Firewood.

THE STOCK OF WELL-SEASONED TIMBER,

Including 30,000 feet super of wide Pine Plank, 2,250 feet of 3-inch Pine Plank, 9,000 feet super Oak and Elm Planks and Boards, 700 feet of Honduras Mahogany, 1 log Honduras Mahogany, 63 logs Yellow Pine, 4,000 feet cube, 4,300 feet run Yellow Deals and Battens, 400 Larch Poles, new Sash Frames, &c.

To be Sold by Auction, by

MESSRS. FULLER, HORSEY, SON & Co.,

AT THE WORKS, CHIPPENHAM,

On MONDAY, 15th NOVEMBER, 1869, and 9 following days (Saturdays excepted), at 12 o'clock precisely each day.

May be Viewed three days preceding and mornings of Sale. Catalogues, 6d. each, may be had at the Works; and of Messrs. FULLER, HORSEY, SON & Co., 11, Billiter Square, London, E.C.

Approved Bills at Four Months will be taken from Purchasers to the extent of £50 and upwards.

Cover of the catalogue for the sale of the Railway Works in November 1869. Note the first item of Contractors' Plant, a Kittoe & Brotherhood combined pump and engine.

Courtesy Chippenham Museum

INTRODUCTION & ACKNOWLEDGEMENTS

Rowland Brotherhood was born in 1812 into a family of contractors who did assorted works for large houses and estates, mainly in Middlesex. His father obtained the contract for excavating the foundations of the Wharncliffe viaduct for the new Great Western Railway. Rowland supervised this contract, did a good job, and as a result obtained other contracts along the railway. His business as a railway contractor, with a factory at Chippenham, followed. His second son, Peter, began in his father's firm, being responsible for railway locomotive construction, but then set up as an engineer on his own account in London. He invented a 3-cylinder radial engine which had many uses, not least proving the ideal power plant for the new torpedo weapon. Peter's son Stanley inherited the business and later transferred it to Peterborough. At various times Peter Brotherhood Ltd, as the firm had become, constructed high quality motor cars, engines for First World War tanks and aircraft, agricultural tractors, steam lorries, airship engines, narrow gauge diesel locomotives and canal boats, although regrettably none of these projects lasted very long. General engineering, especially power plant and gas compressors, always continued alongside them.

This history of an engineering family shows that engineering can be very creative but also has pitfalls. In order to be successful the engineer requires a good factual knowledge, or the ability to recognise this talent in others and attract such people. However, engineering knowledge and skill alone are not enough. The successful engineer must also consider possibly more mundane, but vitally important, financial aspects like costs and cash flow. Despite several warnings, Rowland Brotherhood never did fully grasp this aspect, his son Peter trusted his able manager, while Peter's son Stanley was very reluctant to surrender financial control of his company and thereby avoided a crash. However, financial ability alone is not enough; some older members of staff felt that difficulties in more recent years arose because the firm was then run by accountants with little engineering knowledge!

What is an engineer? Put crudely, scientists discover new materials and physical phenomena, which they then investigate, measure their properties and derive laws to predict their behaviour. Engineers use this body of scientific knowledge to design useful things, and their contractors actually construct the engineers' designs. Inevitably there is a lot of overlap, particularly when engineers like Peter Brotherhood do research to improve their products and then manufacture them themselves.

I hope that the following account of the varied fortunes of an engineering family and their company, which after 150 years is still a respected manufacturer of engineering products, records some aspects of managing and employment in an engineering works which may otherwise fail to be recorded, particularly as I have had access to many Company records and retired employees.

The first edition of this book was written due to my interest in a large, obviously very old, model locomotive named *Pearl* which I soon discovered on the main staircase of King's College, London, when I entered as a student in October 1958. During my first year the College Railway Club was formed (not by me, I hasten to add!). Early in my second year a new member suggested that the Club ought to restore *Pearl* as it was in poor external condition. I, as Club Secretary, obtained the necessary permission and, as described later, the restoration was done. In the meantime I endeavoured to discover something of its builder, shown on a plate above the leading wheels as P.BROTHERHOOD CHIPPENHAM. In due course I made contact with Peter Brotherhood Ltd, Peterborough, and eventually *Brotherhoods, Engineers* was published by David & Charles in 1965.

Time passed, and then in 1975 the Company's Publicity Manager, Ernest Woodcock, invited me to update my book, in particular giving more detail of 20th century activity, which had formed rather less than 10 per cent of the contents. When doing this I was privileged to meet a number of long-serving employees: R.J. 'Rue' Hardy, F.Jordan, S.Laxton, B.Scott, Thomas F.Sewell and N.Sismey. Unfortunately updating took much longer than expected, due in part to moving house, changing job and additions to the family, so that by the time it was ready major changes had occurred in the firm and the book was no longer required.

More time passed. One day in the summer of 2005, out of the blue, Yvonne Newton, an administrator at Peter Brotherhood Ltd, rang me, saying there was to be a major event for sales agents and asking if my book could be copied on to CD ROM for distribution to them. My formal letter giving this permission noted that I still had the unpublished late 1970s version, and, updated, it could perhaps be published as part of any celebrations to commemorate the hundredth anniversary of the Company's move to Peterborough in 1907. The Chairman, Stephen FitzPatrick, liked this suggestion. A working group comprising Yvonne and Andrew Eyre, an engineer with strong interest in the firm's history, together with two senior retired employees, E. 'Ted' Brooks and Peter Roy, was formed to assist me, but again publication did not occur.

Over ten years later, with the assistance of Andrew Eyre, having tried to concentrate on power units, transport and weapons, particularly torpedoes, together with glimpses of shop-floor life, publication has at last taken place.

Note that before decimalization in 1971 the British currency used pounds (£) composed of 20 shillings (s.), and each shilling comprised 12 pence (d.). Sometimes money was expressed in guineas, one guinea being twenty one shillings (one pound one shilling). Sums of money were written 1-2-6 or 1/2/6 (one pound, two shillings and six pence) while three shillings was usually written 3/-. I have made little attempt to give modern equivalent values.

Most British engineering until the late 1960s was done using imperial units (feet, pounds, etc.). These units are used here unless the original used metric measures, but sometimes SI equivalents (*Système international (d'unités)*, modern metric system) are given in brackets. Personal protective clothing was scanty until quite recent times, which is obvious in the many old photographs used as illustrations. The soft cloth cap, or maybe a bowler for a foreman, was more an item of traditional class uniform than a means of protection.

I have been very fortunate to have been given access to many of the firm's old records, for example accounts, catalogues, letter and minute books. Their survival is all the more remarkable considering the several changes of both premises and management which have taken place. Many have been made available by the Northamptonshire Record Office.

Writing a book like this is a bit like ordering one of Brotherhoods' compressors or turbines. Sales, and maybe engineering, staff agree the order, and in due course the customer receives the product. The vital contribution of designers, pattern makers, moulders, turners, fitters etc. tends to be taken for granted. Here, I write the words which describe various facts and link them together, but all manner of other people have contributed those facts. Besides past and present staff at Brotherhoods, information has been received from sources as diverse as Charterhouse School and the College of Arms, ICI, members of the Industrial Railway and Road Locomotive Societies, the Institutions of Civil and Mechanical Engineers, the vicar of Werrington and Burghley House. To avoid a long list here I have tried to acknowledge sources in the text. As they would not otherwise appear, I would like to record the assistance given by the late Mr F.Simpkins of Chippenham, and Nottinghamshire County Library, particularly the helpful and efficient staff at the Stapleford branch, who obtained so many of the books I needed. I am indebted to everyone who has helped in any way with this project, and particularly to Yvonne Newton and her team who provided vast amounts of information, encouraged and criticized, and generally kept me going, and more recently to Andrew Eyre.

Lastly, and by no means least, I must thank my wife Zoe. She has lived with Brotherhoods for our entire married life, over 50 years! Without her encouragement, support and understanding there would be no book at all.

Sydney A.Leleux

This replica of GWR *North Star*, constructed at Swindon in 1925 utilizing some original parts, stood for many years above the Erecting Shop at Swindon Locomotive Works. Rowland unloaded this locomotive from a barge at Maidenhead in 1837 when it was delivered by ship from the builders, Robert Stephenson & Co., Newcastle.

S.A.Leleux, February 1960

CHAPTER ONE

ROWLAND BROTHERHOOD
EARLY LIFE 1812-1842

Rowland's grandfather, Harry Brotherhood, lived at Witton, near Hounslow, Middlesex. In the spring he cut oak for shipbuilders and in the summer cut turf on the commons for use as fuel. Turf cutting ceased after the Enclosure Acts were passed, so instead he made roads, planted hedges, made fences to enclose the fields, and did other similar work. This would appear to be the beginning of the family's contracting business. William, his eldest son, was born in 1788. By the early 1800s one of their most profitable tasks was emptying cesspits and using the contents as manure on Hounslow Heath. In 1811 William married a local girl, Charlotte Wilder; on his marriage he became a partner in his father's business which increased very slowly until after the Battle of Waterloo in 1815. When peace returned the gentry began to improve their estates; the Brotherhoods became known, and their business gradually grew.

Rowland Brotherhood was born at Witton Dean on 5th October, 1812. When he was old enough he was sent to a dame's school in the village; however, as there was a growing family he left school at $9^1/_4$, and did light jobs for his father and grandfather. To improve his education he went to night school in winter, and Sunday School nearly all the year round. By the time he was 16 work had increased to such an extent that he was put in charge of some jobs. William had a 'house on wheels' made for Rowland's use at the more distant works; by the end of 1834 he had done work of some description in most of the parks, towns, and principal estates between London, Uxbridge, Slough, Staines, and Windsor.

On Sunday 30th August, 1835, Rowland married Priscilla Penton, daughter of William Penton, an excise officer, formerly of Alresford, near Winchester, Hampshire. Shortly after his marriage, Rowland and his father cut out the Manchester Zoological Gardens. Soon after they returned home work began on the construction of the Great Western Railway (GWR).

William Brotherhood did trial borings for the company and obtained the contract for excavating the foundations of the piers of the Wharncliffe viaduct at Hanwell (the brickwork was let to Grissel & Peto). Rowland, assisted by a younger brother, was manager for the work which involved digging pits about 40ft square and 20ft deep into the London clay. The spoil was taken by barrow to form the approach

Rowland Brotherhood had the contract for excavating the foundations for the Wharncliffe viaduct over the River Brent at Hanwell. Painting *c.*1837.

Courtesy Ealing Local History Centre

Rowland built the Uxbridge Road under the skew bridge at Hanwell. Painting J.C.Bourne, 1846. *Courtesy Ealing Local History Centre*

embankments. This viaduct is 300 yards long, comprising eight spans of 70ft, with the rails a maximum of 65ft above the river. It was widened on the north side in 1877 to take an additional pair of tracks.

After finishing at Hanwell, Rowland made the new road under the Skew Bridge across the Uxbridge Road at Southall. (This bridge comprised cast-iron girders supported by two rows of eight pillars, the four central pairs being cast iron and the rest brick. The space between the main and cross girders was filled with brick arches, replaced with planking after a main girder failed in March 1839. In 1847 the bridge caught fire and was replaced by one made of wrought iron, possibly heeding the failure of the cast-iron bridge over the River Dee at Chester on 24th May, 1847.) Whilst working on this contract, Rowland's eldest son William was born, on 15th June, 1836. At the end of 1836 he moved from Hounslow to Maidenhead and began work on the embankment east of the Thames bridge. Again he was assisted by two brothers, their father having some separate work at West Drayton and Langley. In November 1837 Rowland unloaded the GWR locomotive *North Star* from a barge on the Thames.

On Whit Monday 1838 the railway opened to Maidenhead where Rowland's second son Peter had been born on 22nd April. Not long after the opening wet weather affected the track at the London end. Rowland

Brunel's bridge over the Thames at Maidenhead, whose arches, many alleged, were too flat to stand. It is still in use! Rowland constructed the approach embankments.
Courtesy National Railway Museum

replaced the bad burnt ballast and clay with gravel to a depth of 2ft. The original track had been laid with piles driven at intervals beneath the track cross timbers. However, experience soon showed that this gave an uneven ride, as the track timbers could yield under the weight of a train between the cross timbers but could not where the piles were located. Rowland helped to cut the track free from the piles so that the line rested equally on the ballast throughout.

At the end of September 1838 Rowland moved to Reading. A Mr Rainger had taken the contract for part of the Sonning cutting, embankments at Twyford and Reading, and also sections between Bath and Bristol. The GWR later removed him and gave Rowland the task of excavating half a mile of the centre of Sonning cutting, amounting to 80,000 cubic yards. Sometimes Rowland's father came to see the work. One night when he was riding home his horse shied and threw him, causing him to die a few days later, on 26th January, 1839, aged 51.

During the excavation all the labourers employed by the GWR, about 700 altogether, went on strike and said they wanted everyone out throughout the line to London. This was presumably the incident mentioned by George Henry Gibbs, a Director of the GWR, in his diary, dated 8th October, 1838:

GWR broad gauge express in Sonning Cutting near Maidenhead, as widened for four tracks (hence the retaining walls), with mixed broad and standard gauge tracks in the centre and standard gauge at the sides.   *National Railway Museum*

At Sonning two of the contractors were doing well, but the workmen had struck at the western end and we had to threaten Knowles that we should instantly take the contract from him unless things were placed immediately in a more satisfactory condition.

Rowland described the event as follows:

> I had a message as to what was going on. So I had a short consultation with a lot of our old men at the east end with my brother and found they were all satisfied, so we started and as we went along all the men followed, nearly six hundred and nearly all young, strong and active, we met the other men at the end of our work .... so a fight commenced and there were soon 8 or 900 men hard at it in various forms, and myself and brothers amongst them, and we drove them all into Reading, and I got nearly all of our back to work the same afternoon. The next day Mr. Wm Owen and the other engineers came and thanked us for what we had done, and within a fortnight from then I had possession of all the work between Twiford [sic] and Reading.

On 13th October Gibbs had written in his diary 'Knowles has been dismissed and the western end of the Sonning Cutting is in full work again.' After the fight Rowland had about 1,000 men employed at Sonning. There were 42 horse roads up each side of the cutting for the removal of spoil (a horse at the top pulled a rope attached to the man's barrow, so he could run it along a steeply sloping plank up the side of the cutting and dump the dirt at the top), and trains of earth wagons ran to the embankments at each end. Nearly 200 horses and a number of locomotives were in use. Much of the work continued day and night. Rowland established shops for his men so that they did not have to go into Reading for provisions. The railway was opened to Reading in May 1840. This was the last contract on which Rowland was assisted by his brothers. They did a little more further down the line and then returned to their old work. Soon after, thinking they could do better, they emigrated to the USA, taking their mother and sisters with them. Rowland was greatly distressed by their decision.

Rowland moved to Wootton Bassett (about six miles west of Swindon) at the end of 1840, taking over an unfinished contract. The railway was opened to Chippenham, 10 miles west of Wootton Bassett, in May 1841, after which he did a lot of ballasting and other work. That October he received an urgent message from Brunel asking him to go the Southall where rain had caused 9,000 tons of clay to slip into a cutting. Employing 400 men the job was done in 19 days and nights. At this time all permanent way maintenance on the GWR was done by contract. Having finished at Southall, Rowland saw that he could earn more money for less work, and obtained the maintenance contract for the Steventon (near Didcot) to Chippenham section, about 36 miles, which paid him very well.

In the spring of 1842 Rowland moved to Chippenham, where he lived for the next 30 years. In 1847 he 'bought [Orwell] house and garden from Mr Provis and put up the flag staff and cannons in front' but he appears to have retained his original house as well. Orwell House was reopened as the Brunel pub and restaurant in August 2006, retaining many key features of this listed building.

Soon after arriving at Chippenham he started a smith's shop to repair maintenance tools. From this small beginning grew the Chippenham Railway Works.

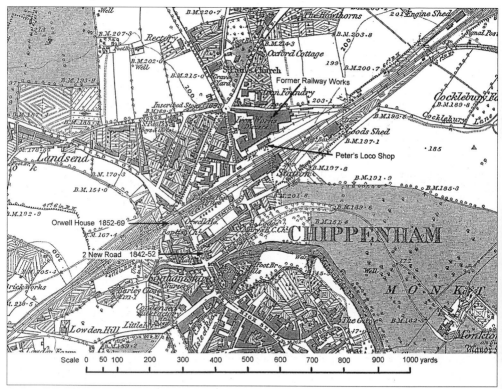

Map of Chippenham, with the Railway Works, then shown as Iron Works (Disused), just above the station, and Rowland's two homes identified. *Ordnance Survey*

CHAPTER TWO

ROWLAND BROTHERHOOD
RAILWAY CONTRACTOR 1842-69

Rowland's first maintenance contract for the GWR was for the 36 mile section from Steventon, about four miles west of Didcot, to Chippenham, and was for only one year, 1842 to 1843. There were many slips to be made up and other extra work the company had to pay for. The line in the clay country of the Vale of the White Horse required constant care and Rowland often had to work at night during the winter. The company asked him to continue for another year with the section from Bristol to Swindon. More heavy slips in cuttings and banks had to be made good, bad ballast was replaced, and a large quantity of stone made unsafe by frost action in Corsham cutting had to be removed. In 1844 he obtained the contract for the whole GWR line from Reading to Bristol for the three years ending June 1847.

In addition to his railway work, Rowland continued to have other contracts. He sank wells and in 1847 excavated a reservoir on Clifton Down, Bristol, which was supplied by a pumping engine drawing water from a spring near the low water mark. Brunel's steamship the *Great Britain* was built at Bristol. At her launching in July 1847 she stuck in the lock leading to the Avon, so Brunel sent for Rowland Brotherhood,

Launch of *Great Britain* at Bristol, 19th July, 1843 in the presence of Prince Albert.

SS GB Trust

15

whose men quickly cut away the stone and brickwork thus freeing the ship before the next tide.

The next GWR maintenance contract was for seven years, to June 1854. In addition to routine work Brotherhood had to make good all slips up to 500 cubic yards and therefore got a higher price. As the term was much longer than before he decided to improve the general condition of the line. The GWR company engineer agreed to provide stone or gravel for ballast (or cash in lieu) if Rowland would provide the labour. He began to construct deep side drains in all the bad cuttings and to remove burnt ballast and clay from the cutting bottoms, replacing it with flat stones covered with rubble and covered with good gravel ballast. For nearly seven years he had a broad gauge train carrying stone from Foxes Wood, near Bristol, and Tetbury Road, near Cirencester, to various parts of the line; another train with gravel from Reading and Maidenhead ran for nearly 15 years. The lines from Swindon to Cirencester and from Reading to Oxford were later added to this contract.

Rowland did various other works all over the GWR in the late 1840s, including trial shafts and borings on the South Wales and Salisbury sections. He planted trees and hedges beside the GWR between Bath and Steventon, and also the quickset hedges on the Coalpit Heath to Stonehouse Junction section of the Bristol & Gloucester Railway. On 1st May, 1851 he took the contract for maintaining 75 miles of the Lancashire & Yorkshire Railway between Wakefield, Goole, Bradford and Mirfield. The remaining sections were taken by Mr Brassey, another well-known contractor.

Brotherhood's last maintenance contracts, for seven years from June 1854 to June 1861, covered the following lines: Reading to Bristol, Didcot to Oxford (later extended to Birmingham and Wolverhampton), Swindon to Stonehouse and Cirencester, Thingley Junction (near Chippenham) to Frome and Radstock, and some branches including those to Salisbury and Devizes. Together they totalled about 350 route miles. By this time the rails were nearly worn out and the contract included the supply of switches, crossings and other track parts. Improvements to the drainage and general condition of the line continued. Rowland cut the hay and kept sheep and cattle on the embankments that comprised his '350 mile farm'. One year he raised and sold 40 oxen and 1,000 sheep. He also took first prize for the largest and best shorthorn cattle at the Chippenham and Warminster shows.

At the end of the contract in 1861 the chief engineer was very anxious that Brotherhood should continue, however, as much track relaying was required he required a slightly higher price:

but there had been some new directors come on the Board during the last few years and they 'the Company' thought they could do it for the Old price so I let them have it, and I sold them all my tools etc. to do it.

GWR branch lines opened after 1856 had been maintained by the company from their opening and this policy was extended to the main lines. It is probable that Brotherhood's final contract was the last one granted.

During the construction of the line from Oxford to Birmingham (1851-52) Rowland supplied gravel for ballast from a pit near Warwick Castle. One day an iron bridge collapsed beneath one of his ballast trains with the result that the opening was delayed while he made iron girders to strengthen several of the bridges. In 1854 he did over £30,000 worth of work at Paddington, moving 7,000 tons of earth from the site of the goods shed to Bulls Bridge, Hayes, building retaining walls, laying track, etc. At Bulls Bridge he made a small dock. The same year he began construction of the Uxbridge branch from West Drayton. He had bought many young horses in the West Country, thinking that, being so near London, they would sell well after his work was finished. He was not disappointed. At their auction in June 1854 at the Green Man, Uxbridge, horses he had bought for £30 to £40 sold for £60 to £70. He realized over £3,000.

He built the Didcot avoiding line in 1856, and also the fork line at Reading, connecting the main line with the Hungerford branch (his son William was the paymaster here). That August he undertook the construction, completed in 1858, of a new station, goods shed and engine shed at Chippenham. In November he began to replace timber bridges over the Thames at Nuneham and Appleford with wrought-iron girders on screw piles.

In addition to his railway work Brotherhood sent 500 navvies for work in Crimea (1854), and also submitted plans for the construction of huts from earth and turf.

One Christmas, probably 1858, Brotherhood received a letter from a London gentleman who knew he had done some large excavations. This man was associated with some Paris bankers who wanted an estimate from an English contractor for the construction of the Suez Canal. Two engineers had just returned from Egypt, bringing the plan and sections, so Rowland went to Paris to see them. On returning home he made an estimate for excavating the canal:

which came to over £8,000,000, which the then promoters thought could be done for less or at least they feared to bring it out before the Public at first with

that amount. So I withdrew from the matter and I saw an account made up
before the work was finished which amounted to over £11,000,000 sterling.

While in Paris one of the bankers asked him to tender for the
construction of a railway from Bordeaux to the sea, and so he went over
the line. However, at this time France was preparing for war against
Austria (1859) so he put 'war prices' on the railway in order to avoid
taking it.

About this time also there was a scheme for a railway from Halifax to
Quebec in conjunction with a steamship from Ireland. Rowland was to
have built the line but the idea fell through, although Peter had
surveyed the proposed route.

In England, Rowland had obtained the contract for the East Somerset
Railway from Frome to Shepton Mallet in April 1857. The cost was
£64,500 and the work was to be completed in 18 months. This was
achieved, and 40 horses used on this contract were offered for sale in
September 1858. Sometimes railway builders received shares in part
payment, and this was the first time Rowland had been so paid. He did
not care for it, and subsequently the practice was to cost him dearly.

A number of Bristol gentlemen wanted improved communication
with South Wales. At his own expense Rowland surveyed a line from
Bristol Temple Meads station through Queen Square, with an iron
bridge across the Floating Harbour, thence along Canons Marsh and
through a tunnel under St Vincent's Rock (part of Clifton Down). The
route then followed the Avon to its mouth, finally running behind the
sea wall to a pier at New Passage. A ferry took passengers across the
Severn to a pier at Portskewett where there was to be a short branch to
the South Wales main line. The plans and sections were all ready for
presentation to Parliament when the men who were expected to support
the scheme suddenly opposed it, so that Rowland had to survey a new
route running northwards from Bristol for the Bristol & South Wales
Union Railway (B&SWUR). Its Bill was passed and the contract let to
Brotherhood in September 1858. Work on the tunnel at Almondsbury
began a month later. Rowland subscribed £2,500 and Peter Brotherhood,
Engineer, £250. The new route, with its steamer service across the
Severn, shortened the distance between Bristol or the West of England
and South Wales by 34 miles. I.K.Brunel, in a letter to C.Richardson
about the B&SWUR, on 14th September, 1858 wrote: 'The Contractor is
Brotherhood – the best you could have to deal with'.

Once all the pile drivers working on the New Passage pier went on
strike for higher wages:

OPENING OF THE BRISTOL AND SOUTH WALES UNION RAILWAY AND FERRY : NEW PASSAGE HOTEL AND PIER

New Passage hotel and pier on the east (English) bank of the River Severn, at the opening of the Bristol & South Wales Union Railway and ferry, 1st January, 1864. The Brotherhood family had a holiday near here while the first hundred piles were driven.

S.K.Jones, collection S.A.Leleux

Rowland was also responsible for corresponding works on the west (Welsh) bank at Portskewett. This view in 1887 shows the ferry approaching the pier where a train (for Newport, Cardiff, etc.) is waiting. In the background are works at Sudbrook for constructing the Severn Tunnel.   *S.K.Jones, collection S.A.Leleux*

because they eat so much more than they did in land, I told them they aught to feel very much obliged to me for bringing them down to such a very healthy place, but they could not see it, and thought they aught to have sixpence per day more on account of their eating. So I proposed to give three pence per day and they should allow the other three on account of their good health, and after a little more reasoning they all went back to the work satisfied.

The work cost over £240,000, and Rowland had to take a quarter in shares and debentures. His third son, Rowland, was the paymaster on this contract.

> At the commencement of the (pier) on the south side, I took Mrs.B. and a lot of our children down to stay a short time at the Severn Lodge by the water side, it was arranged that they should stay there until the first hundred piles were driven in …. and the first hundred piles were driven quite as soon as our children wished them to be as they liked the spot and Oliver Norrises milk, bread and butter.

Years later, Oliver Norris of New Passage and Rowland's son Rowland had contracts to sink shafts for the construction of the Severn Tunnel. After work on the B&SWUR had begun the people who had opposed the original route

> went to the Chamber of Commerce office took a copy of my plan and section of the first line and made one on the very same ground, but only from the St. Vincent rock to the mud at the Avons mouth.

However, this line was a commercial failure and the pier rapidly became silted up. This railway, from Hotwells to Avonmouth, was opened in 1865.

Brotherhood, writing in 1882 of events around 1859, said:

> My tender for the first part of the Metropolitan under ground railway was accepted, which ran from the junction of the G.W.R. at Paddington to the further end of Euston Square, the price was about £295,000 a big price on account of there being so much gravel and sand. The price of building sand and gravel for concrete in London was 4s. to 5s. per cube yard...... In making my estimate for the brickwork, Concrete, and ballast I put in the London prices although I well knew nearly all the excavation would be gravel or sand, because I had helped to sink a well there in my younger days, and knew the ground well. When the line was first let there was no one in such a good position as myself and Mr.Jay, who was then a large builder and contractor on the Great Northern Railway.... I had my broad gauge plant on the G.W.R. and Mr.Jay his narrow on the Gt.Northern, so the Directors left it to us to divide the Contract, to suit our selves. Mr.Jay asked me how far I should like to go east, I

told him to the end of Euston Square, which he said would suit him very well, but he did not know the ground as well as me. He got into the London Clay at that point and then into the old rotten London, while I was on the maiden ground composed of what I required in the work, and from which he afterwards had to purchase.

My price for the earthworks was at the rate of 4/6d per cube yard, the greater part I should sell at 4/6 or 5/- so that I should get not less than 9/0 for my excavation, and as I had estimated the cost of gravel for ballast, concrete and sand for the building, I should get double price for that part also, The Total of the contract was £290,000 and I was quite confident I could do the whole for less than £200,000 so there would be a net profit over £90,000 and more on extras.

It was rather strange just at this time the contract for the Southern Outfall Sewer, for the London drainage came out, in it there was to be a tunnel under Woolwich, and knowing the ground there I tendered for it, at a high price, having made my estimate on the same principle as that of the railway, but I did not expect to get the contract, because there were so many of the big builders and others tendering. But my tender was accepted for it likewise the amount being £285,000 and a splendid job at the price, plenty of gravel and sand for the work and lots to be sold at good prices.

And just as I had worked up to the point to commence to make a large fortune my Bankers became frightened, and then I saw and felt the great Mistake I had made in letting a country bank have my account and security.... There was no reason on their part for such conduct. The amount I had over drawn was small when compared with the value of my deeds they had, and I had not asked them for a further advance. As both contracts were for cash and the payments due at the end of every month, after I had once made a start, I should soon have paid the bank off and the prices being so high, had plenty of cash to spare, but no reasoning would suit them and although both the contracting parties would have taken me without any bond. The two old gents thought I must have made some error in my estimates and to my dismay I had to give both contracts up, I turned the Railway over to Smith & Knight who made a large sum out of it.

I then saw Webster who was then in a very small way, and advised him as he had tendered at first to go in at my price, for the sewer, and that was the first foundation of his making so much money and afterwards doing so much of the London public works.

Mr.Gale Golding being my lawyer at the time, and knowing what a chance I had lost and seeing there was more London work to be done, and that my name still stood well with the engineers and others there, he brought Mr.Fowler who was then Chairman of the North Wilts Bank, to my house and it was then arranged to pay off the Wilts & Dorset Bank, which they did, and took my deeds etc as security for the amount and any further accommadation I may require.

Soon after that the contract for the great middle sewer over £300,000 came out and I tendered for it at a good price, but this time was the lowest but one and Mr.Brasseys tender was accepted at about £11,000 below me, So the great field for London work for making money was lost to me.

the neighborhood – the Country immediately north of Bristol I should think a delightful one to live in beautiful country – good society near Bristol & Clifton &c – I can't vouch for any cricketing but should think it highly probable.

Yours faithfully
IK Brunel

Richardson logic
The Contractor is Brotherhood – the best you could have to deal with.

End of letter from I.K.Brunel to C.Richardson about the B&SWUR, on 14th September, 1858

Rowland Brotherhood, *c.*1863.
Collection S.A.Leleux

Despite the loss of these London contracts he continued to build railways elsewhere, including the Thame & Oxford and part of the Andover & Redbridge. His son James was paymaster for both. He also made the Clifton Maybank Junction between the GWR and LSWR near Yeovil. All these lines opened in 1864. Brotherhood tried to buy rails for his contracts from Swindon where a rail-rolling mill had been established in 1860.

The late E.C.Lowther remembers being told by his mother, Kate Brotherhood, and Uncle Charles Brotherhood, about the visit of the Italian patriot Garibaldi to Chippenham as the guest of Lord Lansdowne. The date was not recorded but was probably 1864. When they heard of the proposed visit the Brotherhood boys decided to give him a hero's welcome by giving him a grand salute. They cast a cannon in the Works. On the day of the visit all the local notables were at the station to meet the great man. On his arrival, at a time the boys judged to be the right instant, they fired the gun. However, they had overdone the gunpowder and the detonation shattered the glass in the canopy over the platform, which fell in fragments. Garibaldi, however, was highly delighted and said it was the most wonderful reception he had ever been accorded, much better than the usual fanfare of trumpets and rolling of drums. Mrs Brotherhood laughed so much that she had to be revived with smelling salts several times, and Rowland undertook to replace the glass roof. When Garibaldi was told the episode was quite unofficial, and that the boys responsible would be well beaten, he said 'that must not happen to lads who had cast such a cannon that it did not burst when fired.'

Rowland was full of praise for his wife's help:

And I must say here that if I had not been blessed with one of the very best of wifes I never could have gone through all I have nor carried out the works I have done without her help. She acted as my cashier throughout nearly all the works, sometimes drawing the money from the Banks, and collecting silver from other sauces [sic] and often had to sit up until midnight, counting and tying up many hundreds of pounds in small bags for me to throw out of the trains to the gangs on the maintenance and other works along the line, This she continued to do until the family got too large and the work so increased when her Brother Mr.E.Penton came down and took it out of her hands.

And I am bound to say that if there was any credit due in carrying out work or bringing up our family the greater share belonged to my devoted Wife.

Brotherhood family cricket team outside the verandah at Orwell House, 1862. A family history produced by Mary L.Henderson and Maria van Stockum, American descendants of James, states that the identifications are as in a letter written by Alfred. They differ from those in the first edition of this book, except for those marked *. Standing, from left to right, are: Fred, Rowland Jnr, Alfred, James*, Rowland Snr*, John, Ernest, Peter*. In front, from left to right, are: George, Charles, Harry. Alfred wrote, 'the photograph was taken just before we went to play a Cricket match against the Marquis of Lansdowne's team at Bowood, near Chippenham. We were only beaten once.' Bowood House at Calne is about five miles from Chippenham. William was missing, apparently supervising the erection of a bridge in India, so Rowland Snr was wicket keeper.   *Collection S.A.Leleux*

CHAPTER THREE

CHIPPENHAM RAILWAY WORKS 1842-1869

General

As already described, Rowland Brotherhood established his Railway Works at Chippenham in 1842, initially to repair tools used in his maintenance contracts. It soon expanded to supply permanent way and other railway fittings, with rolling stock from the late 1840s, bridges and signalling equipment from 1851, and locomotives from 1858. The works were on the north side of the GWR main line, east of the viaduct, and level with the station. The family home, Orwell House, was/is almost opposite the end of Station Hill, and the works only a few yards away through the viaduct. The site was almost triangular, bounded to the south by the railway, Old Road to the west and Foundry Lane to the north. Although standard gauge did not reach Chippenham until 1874, the works had mixed gauge track at least by 1864/66 and probably earlier, once standard gauge locomotives were being built. Any standard

A familiar sight to both Rowland and Peter Brotherhood. GWR locomotives at Chippenham shed in 1864, which was at the other end of the siding serving Rowland's Railway Works. From left to right the locomotives are: 2-2-2 *Polar Star*, 0-6-0 *Pyrachan* and 2-2-2 *Javelin*. The photograph is said to have been taken by the pioneer photographer Fox Talbot, who lived at nearby Laycock, although the curator of the Fox Talbot Museum doubted this, as he took very few local photographs apart from in Laycock itself.

Courtesy National Railway Museum

gauge locomotive or wagon would have been transported from the works loaded on a broad gauge wagon.

According to *The Catalogue of the Great Exhibition*, in 1851 Rowland exhibited a broad gauge iron wagon with his patent tilt (canvas covering), and on the GWR stand

> a model of a safety stop or switch for a siding, worked together with the signal by the same lever as the switch for the siding; also of double signals for a junction line worked by the switchman. Manufactured by Mr Richard [sic] Brotherhood, Great Western Railway, Chippenham, Wiltshire.' (Class 5, Exhibits 501, 502, 506).

Without going into the details of railway signalling history, it was some years before the control for points and signals at a station were largely collected together into one place (the signal box), and Rowland Brotherhood was among the first to operate signals by long wires. Even then it took more time before they were interlocked to prevent conflicting movements. He supplied capstans to operate points, initially on main lines but later (from about 1865) they were relegated to sidings where they lasted to the end of the broad gauge in 1892. A replica has been made and installed on the broad gauge lines at Didcot Railway Centre.

Although his business was generally profitable, by the early 1860s Rowland had the need for more capital, partly as a result of the cost of developing the Railway Works and partly because he had been paid in shares for some contracts, in particular for the B&SWUR and the East Somerset Railway, which together gave a cash shortfall of some £70,000. He sought a further overdraft from the North Wilts Bank, giving various shares etc as security. However,

> they had lost my old friend Mr Fowler their Chairman, who was not only a Quaker & a rich man, but was also a man of business, and connected with Dimsdales & Co Bankers of London who understood such matters. But two or three of the N.W.B Directors, Shopkeepers & some others of the same class, Shareholders in Melksham, became nervous and pressed me for repayment, which could not be done just then, without a most ruinous sacrifice.

Rowland consulted his old business friend, Mr Charles Cammell, who had just converted his business to a limited company, and who strongly advised Rowland to do the same. (The creation and management of limited companies was covered by various Companies Acts from 1862 onwards, limiting the liability of members or subscribers of the

Victorian Railways (Australia) 5ft 3in.
gauge wagon apparently fitted with
Brotherhood's patent tilt, taken
around 1885.   *R.Davidson*

Replica Brotherhood point capstan –
here used only as a direction
indicator – beside mixed broad and
narrow (i.e. standard) gauge track at
the Didcot Railway Centre. Note the
point with no moving parts where
the standard gauge changes sides.
Something similar was required
where the two gauges joined and
became mixed.

S.A.Leleux, 24th June, 2006

company to what they have invested in it. In particular, shareholders are not liable for the company's debts, unlike a partnership or sole trader whose proprietor(s) are liable for their business' debts, to the full extent of their personal resources if necessary.) Following a meeting with 'several Gentlemen and friends' the prospectus for the General Contract Company Limited was printed, with Sir Daniel Gooch, locomotive engineer and later Chairman of GWR as Chairman. There were a number of

> other good names, as Directors & Shareholders. And it was thought with such a good list of names, and with the Interest that such could bring in both English and foreign, that the company would take and do well. But the Panic set in just at the time, and we were too late to float or raise the capital required. There were many Firms failed at that time.

However, Rowland had several large contracts for bridges and rolling stock and was able to keep the Railway Works in operation in 1866. Unfortunately some of the bank's local shareholders became uneasy and

> one day Mr G[abriel] Goldney & T.P[ocock] came to my house and wished to see me in private, So we went & sit under the walnut tree at the bottom of the garden, when they brought out an assignment, or bill of Sale [a mortgage including movable goods as well as land and buildings], and pressed me very much to sign it, and cheat my trade friends & creditors, who were very few but all first rate firms. I at once refused and sent for my friends, we had a private meeting and decided to call in Messrs Barnard Thomas & Co, Accountants of Bristol to examine the books & the State of affairs, and report there on, and on 25th of August we had another meeting, including those Connected with the Bank, when the accountants rendered their report, and after due consideration it was arranged that I should go on under an inspection, which would keep the Bank quiet until I could recover myself. And Mr Freeman, for the Lowmoor Co, Mr Almond for the Coalbrookdale Co, and Mr Palmer for the Bank, should be the three Inspectors. I had an arrangement with Mr Saunders & others of the GWR that they would amalgamate their line with the Bristol & S.Wales Union, and then I should get all my money back in full. We were then making a good trade profit, and all went on smoothly and the first 5s/0 in the pound [i.e. 25%] was soon paid to all.

Sometime after this one of Goldney's friends came with a contract for drainage work at Receife in Brazil (now Pernambuco, on the coast, near the tip of the bulge towards Africa). As Rowland would have nothing to do with it, the man went to Goldney who was still a Director of the bank. The upshot was that he would ensure that the bank would finance the necessary debentures if Rowland would:

'again get him returned at the coming Election'. This Rowland did, taking the chair at a large meeting of electors which was reported in the *Devizes & Wilts Gazette* of 20 August 1868. Mr Goldney referred to the proposed contract in Brazil 'hoping and trusting however that long before the election is over the contract will be in full force, and I shall then be glad to claim some share of credit for having brought to the town what I believe to be of benefit not to Mr Brotherhood alone, but to the inhabitants generally. (Cheers)'. Goldney was duly elected, and sent Rowland a letter of thanks on 17 November 1868 'I cannot sleep tonight without first offering to you, my thanks for kind and unremitting exertions during the Contest, which has ended so happily for me, to your kind efforts and exertions I am indebted for a very considerable portion of the results'.

The drainage contract was soon arranged and Rowland sent out his sons Fred and Ernest to Receife, followed by son Rowland who joined them to carry out the works. Tools and material to the value of £6,747 had been sent out by January 1869. Meanwhile the works in Chippenham had been busy with bridge work for Ceylon, India and elsewhere, and following Goldney's advice the Bank and other Inspectors released Rowland 'to carry on the works again himself'. Rowland arranged to go to Receife but in early March, just as Rowland was leaving for Southampton, he received a message from the Bank saying that he must stay in the country and they would not finance his debentures.

I then saw that I had allowed Mr GG. to deceive me, I had served his purpose, and sold myself ... So as the Bank and those connected with it, had then got nearly all I had. I was compelled to Stop the works. A meeting was called. There were only Nine Trade creditors, and they were all ready and willing to forgo there [sic] amounts, to keep me going. But the Bank and party, were determined to realize, although at a very bad time, so on the 31st of March 1869 I made an assignment of nearly everything I then possessed for the benefit of my Creditors & the Bank.

Rowland was justifiably furious, not only at the loss of his business but at the great financial loss incurred by the forced sale of shares at an unfavourable time:

To know that some persons who took my [B&SWUR] shares each four at on for £16 sold them at £138 and my £43,500 which had been credited to me by the Bank at £6,960, were then worth then in the market £60,230, with such a loss and the sacrifice of the Railway works, Plant, Stock in Trade, and including the Land and House property at Chippenham which had been valued just before at £119,255 was to me at the time most appalling.

The closing sale was conducted by Messrs Fuller, Horsey, Son & Co. of London on Monday 15th November, 1869 'and 9 following days (Saturdays excepted)'. Notable items listed on the cover of the catalogue included six locomotives, over 60 wagons, and a 'Contractors' sewage pump and engine combined, by Kittoe and [Peter] Brotherhood with vertical boiler' (*see page 4*).

The Railway Works then remained empty for about 10 years, when Gabriel Goldney let part of it to H.Dowding, a local brewer. One hopes that the electorate had already shown their opinion of his action in closing down the town's largest employer, particularly as a slogan at the election had been 'Vote Tory/Goldney and see/keep the smoke coming out of Brotherhood's chimney'. A store built by Brotherhood in the 1850s and later known as the Malthouse was demolished in 1986. Other parts of the works site were later occupied by the Wiltshire Bacon Curing Company and a cheese factory.

Aerial view of Chippenham station and its surroundings. The former Railway Works occupied the triangular site in the centre foreground, the engine shed having been beside the main line near the gas holder (*top right*), opposite the point of divergence of the Calne branch, bearing away to the right.   *Courtesy Chippenham Museum*

Later still, the Westinghouse Brake & Signal Company occupied part of the site and progressively purchased the remainder until by 1972 they owned all of it, as well as other premises nearly. When parts of the Westinghouse Company's factory in the brake engineering and development shops at New Road, on the site of the Railway Works, were being renovated in 1975, the work included removing the casing around some cast-iron pillars. These were found to have different diameters, ranging from a more than a foot to only a few inches and tapered gently from top to bottom. At least one had 'Brotherhood, Chippenham cast' on it. Close examination showed that together they would produce a set of iron masts if stood one on top of another. Possibly they were a relic of the *Great Eastern* project. The whole site was sold in 1987 and cleared for redevelopment.

According to the sale catalogue, Mr Brotherhood's office contained models of a railway wheel with patent tyre fastenings, a capstan for screwing piles into hard ground, a railway bridge pier, and a 'highly finished' lattice-girder bridge. There are numerous references to bridges and permanent way materials in his autobiography, see Appendix One.

Wagons

Details of around 1500 wagons known to have been built by Brotherhood for the Bristol & Exeter, Great Western and South Devon railways are given in Appendix Two.

The sale catalogue for 17th November, 1869 shows an assortment of other wagons and related items.

Lot 582: A NEW 8-TON HIGH-SIDED OAK-FRAMED COAL WAGGON 4 feet 8½ inches gauge, 14 feet by 7 feet 6, 3 feet 3 deep, fitted with flap doors on each side with wrought iron hinges, wrought iron draw bars, coupling chains, double breaks and lever on 4 solid wrought iron wheels 3 feet diameter, 2-inch tyres, wrought axles 4½ inches diameter, cast iron axle boxes and springs fitted with frames, guards and breaks. [Lots 583-601 were 'A DITTO', i.e. 19 similar wagons, the buyer of one to have the option of taking five at the same price.]

Lot 602: A 6-TON 4-WHEEL LOW-SIDED BROAD GAUGE RAIL TRUCK 22 feet by 9 feet fitted with draw bars, coupling chains, *Brown's* patent buffers, axle boxes fitted with brasses and springs. [Lots 603-609 were 'A DITTO', i.e. 7 similar wagons.]

Lot 610: A 10-TON COAL TRUCK 17 feet by 10 feet by 3 feet deep, (oak framed) draw bars, coupling chains, *Brown's* patent buffers, on 4 solid wrought iron wheels 3 feet 6 diameter, 2-inch tyres, guards, axle boxes and breaks. [Lot 611 was 'A DITTO' on *Mansell's* patent wheels with wooden centres.]

Lot 612: A 10-TON WROUGHT IRON TILT TRUCK with semicircular ends, wrought iron draw bars, coupling chains, *Brown's* patent buffers, solid wrought iron wheels 3 feet diameter, and wrought axles. [The tilt was a waterproof sheet on a frame, covering the wagon; it was not a type of tipping wagon.]

Lot 613: A 6-TON LOW-SIDED BALLAST TRUCK with flap on either side, draw bars, coupling chains, *Brown's* patent buffers, on 4 wheels, cast axle boxes fitted with brasses, wrought axles, and springs. [Lots 614-622 were 9 similar wagons. Lot 683 was a broad gauge ballast truck with end flap running on 2ft 6in. wheels.]

Lot 623: A 6-WHEEL HIGH-SIDED HAY TRUCK with wrought draw bars, coupling chain, spring buffers, 3-feet-3 wrought wheels, wrought axles, and cast boxes. [Maybe used to collect produce from his 'farm'.]

Lot 624: A NEW NARROW [standard] GAUGE END TIP CONTRACTOR'S EARTH WAGON, on four 2-feet-6 wrought iron wheels and axles, oak frames, elm-sided. [Lots 625-633 were 9 similar wagons, while Lots 634-644 were 11 similar wagons, 10 new and one old, but having 2-feet wrought iron wheels and axles.]

Lot 645: A NEW ELM-FRAME FOR BROAD GAUGE EARTH WAGGON on for 2-feet-6 new wrought iron wheels and axles. [Lots 646-653 were 8 similar frames.]

While many of the rails in the following lots were 'Great Western section' there were over 12 tons of '$1\frac{1}{2}$ inch square wrought iron tram rails', some in 15 feet lengths, which had probably been used for the earth wagons on contracts.

There were several platelayers' trolleys, both broad and narrow gauge. Lot 677 was 'A timber framed broad gauge velocipede on 3-feet wrought wheels and axles and driving motion' and Lot 678 was 'A ditto on 18-inch cast iron wheels and wrought axles, and an extra hand motion.' These were probably inspection trolleys, propelled by one or

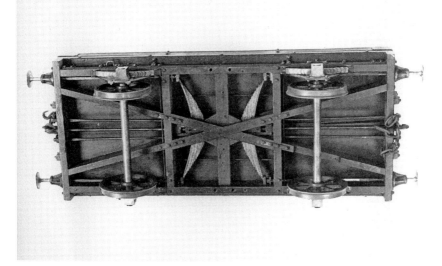

One eighth full size model of a standard gauge GWR wagon still preserved in Peter Brotherhood Ltd offices at Werrington, probably one of 400 such wagons built in 1865. It is painted dark brown with yellow lettering. The bright engraved plate has three lines, reading: BROTHERHOOD BUILDER CHIPPENHAM. Note the diagonal timbers in the frame to give rigidity and avoid distortion by buffing or coupling shocks, and also the way the drawbar is attached to the centre of a large leaf spring while the buffer rods bear against its ends, so one spring serves both purposes, and also the safety chains. See drawing page 276.   *Collection S.A.Leleux*

two men operating a rocking beam connected to a crank on one axle. There were also assorted components including wheels with 'Lowmoor and Blaenavon Weldless tyres'.

Locomotives

In view of Rowland's enterprise in establishing and repeatedly expanding the Railway Works, it is surprising locomotive construction had not begun earlier. Probably he was just too busy with existing work, but once Peter had completed most of his training he was available to take charge of this new development. Information about Brotherhood locomotives is scanty and conflicting, and this account collects known references. Although some locomotives seem to appear several times, it should not be forgotten that there is some surmise, and that other locomotives may not have been recorded.

In the context of 1858, Rowland wrote in his autobiography:

> I bought a strip of land by the side of the works fronting the Station at Chippenham, and built a new shop for Peter to make his small Loco Engines in he had made the broad gauge Moloch in an old shop outside.

This building later became part of the cheese factory (c.1896 – c.1920), and was demolished around 1988. *Moloch* could have been built for work on construction or maintenance contracts, ballasting for example, or for use as the works shunter as there must have been a lot of rail traffic bringing in raw materials and coal and taking out finished products. Any locomotive used for this purpose would have been broad gauge, as standard gauge did not reach Chippenham until June 1874. It could well have been the broad gauge 0-6-0T locomotive advertised as Lot 580 at the closing down sale in November 1869. This was

> A 6-WHEEL INSIDE CYLINDER LOCOMOTIVE ENGINE, 7 FEET 8[sic] INCHES GAUGE, six wheels coupled, with cylinders $16\frac{1}{2}$ inches diameter, $21\frac{1}{2}$ inches stroke, link reversing motion, inside frames, saddle tank, wrought iron multitubular boiler with wrought iron firebox 4 feet 5 by 3 feet 7 by 4 feet 6, 111 wrought iron tubes 2 inches diameter 11 feet 6 long, 4 feet 8 solid wrought iron wheels with $2\frac{1}{2}$ inch Bowling tyres, *Giffard's* 10 m / m injector, and breaks [sic] to all the wheels.

Maybe it was not sold, and Rowland contrived to take it with him to the Bute Ironworks at Cardiff, for use as the works shunter, as *Locomotives of the GWR – Part 2, Broad Gauge* (RCTS, 1952) records that the Bristol & Exeter Railway (B&ER) 'purchased two nondescript tank engines from Brotherhoods in March 1874'. One was an 0-6-0 tank, 4ft $8^1/_2$ in. wheels, $16^3/_4$ x 24in. cylinders, carrying a Brotherhood plate dated 1874 although the RCTS considered it 'improbable that this firm actually built the engine.' In 1874 definitely not, but 15 years earlier probably yes. Later it became GWR 2091 (not 2096), and was withdrawn in December 1876, soon after the GWR bought the B&ER, suggesting it was pretty well worn out when sold. The other was *Glyncorrwg*, an 0-4-2 tank made by Manning Wardle, number 116 of 1864, which had been bought by Brotherhood from the South Wales Mineral Railway (SWMR) in 1872 when it was converted to standard gauge. The SWMR ran from Briton Ferry near Neath to serve collieries at Glyncorrwg. The B&ER numbered it 110; later it became GWR 2058 and was withdrawn in January 1881.

Peter's notebook *(see Appendix Four)* recorded a lot of manufacturing details for three sets of materials for 'New Coupled Engines 1858

Typical page from Peter's notebook *(contents listed in Appendix Four)*. This page relates to sundry components required for three 0-6-0 locomotives built in 1858.(N.C.E. stands for 'New Coupled Engines' written in full on another page.) Note timber cleading (lagging/covering) for the boiler and the leather buffers.

Swale as rebuilt as an 0-6-0ST   *Courtesy National Railway Museum*

Engines No 1, 2, 3'. They were 0-6-0 goods engines with 5ft wheels, and had cylinders with 24in. stroke. The boilers contained 249 tubes and complete weighed 8 tons 7 cwt. A surprising item to modern eyes, in the list of materials, was 'Saddlers: Leather buffers 6@$^1/_3$ ea', so obviously tenders were fitted (otherwise 12 buffers would have been required), and as none were mentioned perhaps second-hand ones were to be used. Leather buffers were in fact little used after 1854, and probably the tenders had sprung ones. Erection of each locomotive cost £100. Unfortunately no gauge is mentioned. They may have been broad gauge, as standard ('narrow' in contemporary GWR-speak) gauge did not reach Chippenham for another 16 years; although standard gauge is possible bearing in mind their possible later history, the known construction of standard gauge Brotherhood locomotives before 1869, and possibly from 1862, and the larger potential market for standard gauge. It is unlikely they were built for construction contracts, except perhaps for the last stages, but they could have been used for maintenance, for example hauling the trains of ballast from Foxes Wood or Maidenhead, assuming the GWR allowed privately owned locomotives to haul trains over its main line. Maybe they were just a speculation which failed to interest any of the main line railways. If Peter was thinking along these lines, it lends some credibility to the suggestion that the model *Pearl* (*see later*) was built to encourage sales of main line locomotives.

One of these 0-6-0s may have become *Swale*, which 'was obtained second or third hand from Brotherhood ... in June 1860.' (*Locomotives of London Chatham & Dover Railway* – RCTS, 1960.) *Swale* was the first 0-6-0 goods locomotive owned by the London Chatham & Dover Railway (LCDR), and was named after the stretch of water between Sheppey and the Kentish mainland. It had 12in. x 18in. cylinders, a domeless boiler, 4ft 0in. wheels and worked at 90psi. The iron firebox and tubes tended to contract whenever cold air entered through the fire door, causing leakage. *Swale* was partially rebuilt in early 1860, which could have been its conversion from one of Peter's 0-6-0s, including a set of smaller wheels. (The original builder is not known.) It was displaced from main line work and, rebuilt as an 0-6-0ST, relegated to shunting in 1865. *Swale* was withdrawn as 141A in September 1881, having run 254,444 miles on the LCDR.

For some reason, the locomotive summary on the cover of the 1869 sale catalogue did not include Lot 581, which may have been another of Peter's 0-6-0s. Inside it was described as

A 6-WHEEL INSIDE CYLINDER LOCOMOTIVE ENGINE, 4 FEET 8¹/₂ INCHES GAUGE, with 6 wheels coupled, 12-inch cylinders, 20 inches stroke, link reversing motion, inside frames, multitubular boiler with ninety-one 2-inch wrought iron tubes 9 feet 6 long, LOWMOOR FIREBOX 3 feet 2 by 3 feet 3 by 3 feet 8 high, 6 solid wrought iron wheels with Bowling tyres 1³/₄ inch. Tender with Wrought Iron Tank containing 900 gallons, outside frames, set of 3-feet-6 wrought iron wheels and break.

Another interesting item in the sale catalogue was Lot 1004 '*A strong timber framed locomotive bogie* 17 feet long by 5 feet 9 wide on four 12-inch cast iron wheels 3 feet high, 4¹/₂-inch wrought iron axles, wrought iron rails, break apparatus, 2 pairs shafts' which had obviously been used to carry locomotives to and from contract sites.

On the main staircase in King's College, Strand, London, stands a 15in. gauge (approximately quarter full size) model 2-2-2WT named *Pearl*. Plates over the leading wheels read 'P.BROTHERHOOD CHIPPENHAM' but give no date. The model *Pearl* is nothing like a contemporary GWR locomotive of the same name, which was one of Gooch's Standard Goods class, a broad gauge 0-6-0, built in May 1852 and withdrawn in February 1878. J.N.Maskelyne, an engineering student at King's 1910-14 and a respected authority on railway matters, carefully examined the model in 1958:

I came to the conclusion that it represents no particular prototype, and that the proportions of its details are not altogether satisfactory. The handrails along each side strongly suggest GWR broad gauge influence, and in a very general way, the main proportions appear to be governed by broad gauge practice. But the frame arrangement and shape are in no way similar to Swindon practice for the broad gauge, and there is no precise similarity to the practice of any of the locomotive manufacturers. The outside frames are strongly reminiscent of Matthew Kirtley's early 2-2-2 engines for the Midland Railway.

Against all this is the fact that the model must have been very beautifully made originally, and I am strongly inclined to believe that it was built to an enthusiast's design about 100-110 years ago [i.e. 1850-60]. In E.L.Ahron's book *British Steam Railway Locomotives, 1825-1925*, Fig 102, page 93, is a drawing that is as near to Pearl as I have ever found one.

This drawing shows the six locomotives supplied by Robert Stephenson & Co. to the Midland Railway in 1852. They had driving wheels of 6ft 8 $^1/_2$ in. diameter and wheelbase 15ft 6in. The corresponding figures for *Pearl* scale at 6ft 8in. and 15ft 6in. Shrewsbury & Birmingham Railway No 22, built by W.Fairbairn & Sons in 1849, is also very similar.

Engraved on *Pearl's* buffers are the words 'J.Brown's Patent, Atlas Steelworks, Sheffield'. This patent was taken out in 1859, although the buffers fitted do not match the description in the patent. *Pearl's* are brass with wooden heads. *Pearl* could have been used to test Peter's patent boilers (he had one at the Society of Arts Exhibition in April 1859) but its boiler is of simple construction and bears no resemblance to any of his patent designs. A report in *The North Wilts Herald* of 25th January, 1862 stated:

A most interesting and instructive lecture... was delivered by Mr P.Brotherhood to a large and highly respectable audience.... the lecture was remarkable not only for its explicit character, accompanied as it was by most beautiful diagrams and various illustrations with a model engine made by the lecturer himself.

This model could well have been *Pearl*. If this was its first public appearance (and why should the local paper comment on the model if it was well known?) *Pearl* was probably completed in 1861. Construction would have presented few difficulties, bearing in mind Peter's training and the resources available in his father's works.

A website about 15 inch gauge railways (gn15.info) suggests *Pearl* was built in the 1850s as a sample of the locomotives then being built by Brotherhoods. It also suggests that it could have been used on a very early miniature railway in a village near Southampton, where the 'parson ... was later to become Arthur Heywood's father-in-law'.

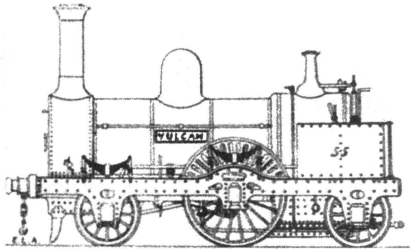

Shrewsbury & Birmingham Railway 2-2-2 No. 22 Vulcan

The nearest prototypes found to *Pearl*.
Upper: Midland Railway 130-135 made by R.Stephenson & Co. 1852.
Lower: Shrewsbury & Birmingham Railway No. 22 Vulcan, built by W.Fairbairn & Sons in 1849, as GWR No. 55.

Bearing in mind the dates and types of locomotive actually built at Chippenham, the first suggestion is improbable, although maybe Peter hoped also to construct passenger locomotives. The second suggestion, but placed in the 1860s, is plausible. Peter could well have known the area from visiting relatives, as his mother came from that village, and might have been asked to build a locomotive for it. As for Arthur Heywood, the champion of 15 inch gauge estate railways, he was born in 1849 but did not marry the daughter of the Rector of Alresford near Winchester until 1872. Although he would have been in his teens if *Pearl* had been used on such a railway, it could have spurred him to do something similar at his home near Uttoxeter on the Derbyshire Staffordshire border.

It appears that the model locomotive *Pearl* had accompanied Peter to his own works at Compton Street in 1867 and was then found to be an encumbrance. In February 1980 the King's College Archivist sent me copies of two letters from Peter Brotherhood which had been discovered in the College archives. As they correct erroneous information in the First Edition of this book, and which has also appeared in at least two publications in recent years, this is the opportunity to put the record straight. The letters are reproduced in full below.

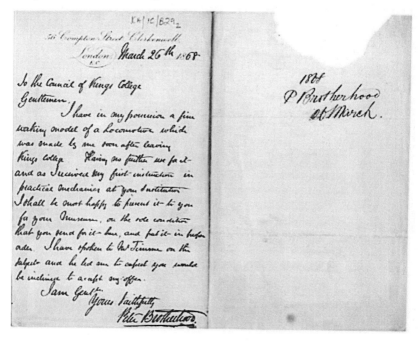

56 Compton Street, Clerkenwell,
London E.C. March 26th 1868

To the Council of Kings College
Gentlemen,
    I have in my possession a fine working model of a locomotive which
was made by me soon after leaving Kings College. Having no further
use for it and as I received my first instruction in practical mechanics at
your Institution I shall be most happy to present it to you for your
Museum, on the sole condition that you send for it here, and put it in
proper order. I have spoken to Mr Jimme on the subject and he led me
to expect you would be inclined to accept my offer.
I am Gentm.
Yours Faithfully
Peter Brotherhood

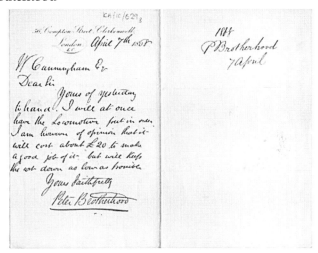

56 Compton Street, Clerkenwell,
London E.C. April 7th 1868

W. Cunningham Eq.
Dear Sir,
Yours of yesterday to hand. I will at once have the Locomotive put in
order. I am however of opinion that it will cost about £20 to make a good
job of it, but will keep the cost down as low as possible.
Yours Faithfully
Peter Brotherhood

Peter Brotherhood left King's College School in 1856-7 (although he was last listed as a student in 1854) so the letters confirm the building date for *Pearl* to around 1860. The letters also show that the College acquired *Pearl* in 1868, some 50 years earlier than my estimate in 1965. The Archivist thought that it 'could possibly have been in the engineering workshops in the sub-basement where 'Joseph Henry's tram languished for many years'. The sub-basement was certainly a warren of rooms and passages when I was a student at King's, so this could well have been her home, but even so it is still very strange that Maskelyne missed her when he was a student at King's from 1910 to 1914.

The Archivist also mentioned an oral tradition in the College. R.W.K.Edwards who lectured in mathematics 1895-1923 sometimes brought his son and daughter to College on Saturday mornings. They amused themselves by stuffing burning rags into *Pearl's* funnel and watching the smoke come out! The son is well known as Jimmy Edwards, and it is a nice story. However, it could well be apocryphal as Jimmy was only three when his father left.

15in. gauge model locomotive *Pearl* in King's College, Strand, London, in 1919. In 1958 it stood on the intermediate landing just off the left of the picture.

A.Cory, collection S.A.Leleux

Being built around 1860, *Pearl* is the oldest large scale model locomotive in existence and probably only the second one made (the Norris Locomotive Works in Philadelphia had made a 15in. gauge model of unknown type in 1854). Provision of a water tank under the footplate with no inlet for a supply from a tender indicates that one was never provided, although a small truck would have been required for a driver and fuel, so *Pearl* is a 2-2-2WT although it looks like a contemporary 2-2-2 passenger tender engine. Quantities of scale in the boiler shows that it has been used, although no packing was found in any of the piston or pump glands when *Pearl* was dismantled for restoration around 1960, details of which, and a description of the locomotive, being given in Appendix Six.

Peter's notebook (*see Appendix Four*) gave details, dated 10th June, 1862, of weights and costs, for a 'Small Locomotive Engine', a 2-4-0ST with inside cylinders and 'skeleton wheels' 3ft $2\frac{1}{2}$ in. and 2ft 3in. diameter i.e. about 3ft 6in. and 2ft 6in. allowing for the tyres. The locomotive weighed $11\frac{1}{2}$ tons, of which the boiler and chimney was 2 tons 4cwt. Materials cost £301-3-10, and wages about £300-0-0. This appears to have been the prototype for the firm's 2-4-0ST, and could have been the 9in. 2-4-0ST Brotherhood locomotive *Nellie* at Fox Walker's Bristol works when they closed in 1879/80.

The usual way of transporting locomotives to and from contracts having no rail connection was by road on a horse-drawn trolley, such as Lot 1004 at the closing sale, described above. It must have been both laborious and slow to use, and Peter designed an alternative, described in the report of the *Trowbridge & North Wilts Advertiser* for 1st November, 1862:

A LOCOMOTIVE ON THE HIGHWAY In the different works he has in progress, Mr Brotherhood the eminent contractor of Chippenham, requires the use of several locomotives, which have hitherto been very cumbersome articles to move from one locality to another. To meet this difficulty, Mr Brotherhood has brought out an engine, designed by his son, which is capable of travelling both on common roads and railways... [On a recent journey the engine, weighing about eleven tons and drawing a cart of fuel, travelled from Chippenham to the B&SWUR contract] a distance of about thirty miles in less than eight hours, deducting the time taken up by stoppages for water, &c., being a mean speed of six miles per hour, over very hilly country.

No other details were given, but I suspect that this locomotive was very similar to a traction engine, with extensions bolted to its wheels to spread the load when on a road, and means to lock the steering when on

Traction engine constructed by Brown & May of Devizes in 1863. Peter's road-rail locomotive could have been of very similar design. Note the steersman at the front, a common feature on contemporary road engines.
'*Development of the English Traction Engine*' by R.H.Clarke, Goose, 1960

rails. The steersman could well have stood on a platform at the front, with a 'ships wheel' connected to the pivoted axle, as was used on contemporary road locomotives built by the local Devizes firm of Brown & May. While a 2-2-0 may seem an improbable design for an industrial or contractor's locomotive, in fact Aveling & Porter supplied well over a dozen to the Kent cement industry in the 1880s. Nothing more is heard of this ingenious locomotive.

Peter was in the drawing office at Maudslay, Sons & Field, Lambeth, for 1863 but appears to have returned to Chippenham and locomotive manufacture in 1864. The sale catalogue listed several locomotives and a quantity of rolling stock to be sold on third day, Wednesday 17th November, 1869:

Lot 576 A NEW 6-WHEEL INSIDE CYLINDER LOCOMOTIVE ENGINE, 4 FEET 8 1/2 INCHES GAUGE, 4 WHEELS COUPLED with cylinders 10 inches diameter, 1 foot 6 stroke, link reversing motion, inside frame, saddle tank, wrought iron multitubular boiler WITH COPPER FIREBOX, 3 feet by 2 feet 6 by 3 feet 1 high, sixty-six 2-inch wrought iron tubes 8 feet 6 long, 4 wrought iron coupled wheels 4 feet diameter, with 2 1/2 inch Lowmoor tyres, pair of 2 feet 6 leading wheels, wrought iron axle 4 1/2-in diameter, journals 4 1/2 by 5 inches, wheelbase 11 feet, *Brown's* buffers and breaks [sic]. [Lots 577 & 578 were] A

DITTO [and Lot 579 was] AN OUTSIDE CYLINDER 4-COUPLED 4-WHEEL
DITTO WITH LOWMOOR IRON FIRE BOX.

The three 2-4-0ST (not four, as listed on the front of the catalogue) and
the 0-4-0ST could well have been the three Brotherhood locomotives
advertised for sale at Orpington and Sevenoaks on the completion of the
Tonbridge Direct Railway contract (*The Builder* 1st June, 1872 and *The
Engineer* 5th July, 1872), particularly as the sale catalogue gave the buyer
of one lot the option of buying others at the same price. One of them
may have been sold from the Tonbridge Direct contract to the Frenze
Estate, or Scole Railway, near Diss, Norfolk. This railway was
constructed by the local landowner in 1869, and was dismantled
following his death in 1885. Earlier the locomotive had been recorded as
an 0-6-0, but it now seems probable that it was a 2-4-0ST, although one
source gives it the Brotherhood 0-4-0ST from the Bishop's Castle
Railway (*see below*). When the railway at Frenze was dismantled
following the owner's death, the locomotive was sold by auction and
then offered for sale by J.T.Williams, Bermondsey station, London from
July 1887 until January 1889. (*Industrial Locomotives of East Anglia*, IRS)

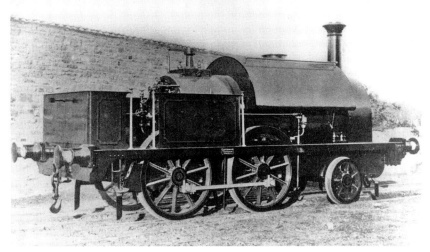

Brotherhood standard gauge 2-4-0ST, No. 12 of 1846 (according to the plate on the original
print) but more likely dating from 1864 or 1866 (*see text*). The original photograph from
which I made this copy hung for many years in the Bristol offices of Crossley Bros where
Charles Brotherhood worked. A similar photograph is an illustration in the *Chronicles of
Boulton's Siding* by A.R.Bennett (Locomotive Publishing Co, 1927).   *Collection S.A.Leleux*

The Bishop's Castle Railway in Shropshire (Act obtained 1861) had a Brotherhood 0-4-0ST *Bee*, used during construction and subsequently taken over when the line opened in October 1865. From the dates it must be an earlier locomotive than the 0-4-0ST advertised at the 1869 closing down sale. However, *Bee* was too light for regular work on the finished railway and was disposed of in 1870. It could have gone to the Scole Railway (*see above*) or to the Duston iron ore quarries, on the western outskirts of Northampton. By 1863 these quarries had a long standard gauge tramway, and the locomotives there eventually included a Brotherhood 0-4-0ST with 9in. cylinders from an unknown source, which was scrapped in 1909 when the quarries closed (*Ironstone Quarries of the Midlands, Part III*, E.S.Tonks, 1989). If it was not *Bee*, this locomotive could have been the 0-4-0ST advertised at the sale in 1869.

In addition to the quarries at Duston, *Industrial Locomotives of Buckinghamshire Bedfordshire & Northamptonshire* by the Industrial Railway Society also states that the Northampton engineering firm, Allchin, Linnell & Co. Ltd, advertised a 'six wheels four coupled standard gauge saddle tank locomotive, with 10 x 14 inch cylinders', in several trade papers in March 1889, and then what could well be the same locomotive was advertised in the July 1889 *Machinery Market*. Details are the same, with the addition of 4ft 6in. wheels, by Brotherhood, £300. Maybe there was a misprint, as other Brotherhood 2-4-0ST had 3ft 6in. or 4ft wheels.

A.R.Bennett wrote a series of articles, published in *The Locomotive* in 1924, about the locomotive dealer I.W.Boulton of Ashton-under-Lyne, who operated from the 1850s to 1890s. These articles were later collected and published as *The Chronicles of Boulton's Siding*. Among the last locomotives described by Bennett (in the issue of 15th September, 1924) were two which were said to have been 'some of the last built by Brotherhood's of Chippenham'. Accompanying the article were photographs of a 2-4-0ST and an 0-4-0ST standing on mixed gauge track, obviously taken at the same place, allegedly at Bath although more likely the photographer came from Bath. No further information was given. Maybe these were the prototypes and had been photographed for advertising purposes, and this is why Boulton had the pictures.

The maker's plate on the original photograph of the 2-4-0ST carried the number 12 and date 1846. The number is reasonable for 'some of the last built', but the date is impossible, because *Moloch*, apparently the first locomotive, was not constructed until 1857/58. If the mould for the works plate had been damaged when the pattern was withdrawn 1866 could have become 1846, at least in the eyes of the painter who picked out the lettering. Peter left Chippenham and set up his own business in March 1867 so locomotive manufacture could well have ceased by then and these would be 'some of the last built'. On the other hand, Rowland may have continued locomotive building after Peter's departure, as amongst the large amount of raw material and components for sale in 1869 were 10 'new solid wrought iron skeleton engine wheels 3 feet 8 diameter' (presumably for 4 ft diameter driving wheels), 'one set new engine skeleton wheels 2 feet 7 diameter with crank pin bosses' (presumably for 3 ft diameter driving wheels) and 'two ditto 2 feet 2 diameter' (presumably for 2ft 6in. leading wheels). Alternatively, the figures for the date could have been put into the pattern in the wrong order, so it should have been 1864. This could be the date if they were prototypes, built soon after Peter's return to Chippenham from Lambeth.

It is interesting to note that at the time of closing the Railway Works, Rowland had three 2-4-0ST described as 'new' and the 0-4-0ST (although that was not so described) on his hands, in other words about a quarter of his estimated total production. Perhaps this is an example of his lack of care in managing his resources. Many locomotive manufacturers built for stock from time to time, but not to such an extent. On the other hand maybe locomotives were in constant production, as the sale catalogue listed a number of new wheels (*see above*).

Brown & May of Devizes supplied two locomotives built by Chaplin of Glasgow to Brotherhood. These had vertical boilers and geared drive, and were used on the B&SWUR. Brotherhood supplied another Chaplin locomotive to the Southampton Dock Co. in November 1865.

There were several other possible Brotherhood locomotives. *Phoenix*, a broad gauge six-wheel four-coupled tank (i.e. 0-4-2 or 2-4-0) with 12 x 22in. cylinders, built around 1863, was used by William West & Sons, of St. Blazey, when building the Newquay & Cornwall Junction Railway (a three mile long branch from Burngullow, 10 miles east of Truro, to china clay works, opened 1869). Some sources say it was built by Brotherhood although J.W.Lowe in *British Steam Locomotive Builders* suggests West may have built it themselves. In October 1877 the Waterford & Limerick Railway (W&L) bought a second-hand 0-6-0ST, having cylinders 15 x 18in. and 4ft 0in. wheels from the Avonside Engine Co. It needed alterations and was not delivered until June 1878. It became W&L 34, and as it needed a new boiler in 1888 this suggests the original was fitted 1860-65. According to R.N.Clements, tradition states it was originally 7ft gauge, possibly from a South Wales colliery. Its link with Brotherhood is doubtful, although it could have been rebuilt from one of Peter's 'New Coupled Engines' (like *Swale*, see above).

Summary of Locomotives Built by Brotherhood

ID	Name /Number	Type	Date	Gauge	Cylinders	Driving Wheels	Notes
A	*Moloch*		1858	Broad			In Rowland's MS
B		0-6-0T		Broad	$16^1/_2$ x $21^1/_2$		Closing sale 1869
C	B&ER 111	0-6-0T		Broad	$16^3/_4$ x 24	4ft $8^1/_2$in.	GWR 2096 withdrawn 1876
D	3 locos	0-6-0	1858	?	x 24	5ft	Peter's notebook
E	*Swale*	0-6-0		Std	12 x 18	4ft	Purch LCDR 1860, rebuilt as 0-6-0ST, withdrawn 1881
F		0-6-0		Std	12 x 20		Closing sale 1869
G	*Pearl*	2-2-2WT	1860	15in.	4 x $5^1/_2$	1ft 8in.	King's Coll., London
H		2-4-0ST	1862	Std?		3ft 6in.	Peter's nbk, $11^1/_2$ tons
I		2-4-0ST		Std	9 x		At closure of Fox Walker, Bristol 1879
J		2-2-0T geared	1862	Broad?			Local paper, 11 tons
K	*Bee*	0-4-0ST	1865	Std			Bishop's Castle Rly 1865-70
L		0-4-0ST		Std	9 x		Duston Iron Co., (production began 1855) scraped 1909
M	No. 12	2-4-0ST	1864/66	Std			Photograph
N	3 locos	2-4-0ST	New	Std	10 x 18		Closing sale 1869
O	3 locos	2-4-0ST		Std			Tonbridge Direct Rly sale 1872
P		2-4-0ST		Std			Frenze Est *c*.1865-85
Q		2-4-0ST		Std			For sale Bermondsey 1887-89
R		2-4-0ST		Std			For sale Northampton 1889
S		0-4-0ST		Std	10 x 18?		Closing sale 1869
T	W&LR 34	0-6-0ST		5ft 3in.	15 x 18	4ft	Reputed ex-broad gauge
U	*Phoenix*	2-4-0/0-4-2T	1863?	Broad	12 x 22		Built by West of St Blazey?

Notes:

A, B, C may be the same

E, F may be rebuilds of locos D – variations in sizes due to wear or the actual rebuild

H, I may be the same

K, L may be the same

M may be one of locos N or loco P

O may be locos N

One of locos O may be P

P, Q probably the same

R could be L as 'four wheels coupled' could be either 0-4-0ST or 2-4-0ST

S could be K

Doubtful whether T, U were built by Brotherhood.

Although I.W.Boulton had photographs of a 2-4-0ST, the same photograph as M, and an 0-4-0ST (S?) he probably did not actually own these locomotives.

Total, allowing for assumed duplicates, about 12 so probable production was about 15.

CHAPTER FOUR

ROWLAND BROTHERHOOD
LATER LIFE 1869-1883

After the enforced closure of the Railway Works in March 1869 Rowland left Chippenham. The *Wiltshire Times* suggested that he should be given a testimonial but nothing seems to have come of this. At the end of 1869 he made an agreement with Messrs Herbert & Charles Maudslay to be General Manager of the Bute Ironworks, Cardiff, for a period of 10 years.

Herbert Charles Maudslay had resigned from the Lambeth engineering firm (where Peter had been an apprentice) and joined with his brother Charles Edmund to take over the shipyard formerly occupied by Norman Scott Russell, on the left bank of the Taff. The business was mainly with dock gates, including the Cumberland Basin at Bristol in 1878, but business declined and the partnership was dissolved in 1879. The firm made the gates at the junction lock, between the East Dock and a new basin, at Cardiff. At this time Rowland lived at 9 Charles Street, Cardiff. His sons Fred, Harry and Charles also came to Cardiff.

The Old Dock gates at Newport had become so heavy due to repeated strengthening that they could hardly be moved. Rowland undertook to

Brotherhood standard gauge 0-4-0ST, illustration from *Chronicles of Boulton's Siding*, taken at the same place as 2-4-0ST (*see page 45*).   *Collection S.A.Leleux*

make new wrought-iron gates, having water-tight compartments which conferred some buoyancy and so relieved some of the load on the pivot. The gates were floated round by sea from Cardiff and worked so well that another pair was ordered; altogether the four gates cost £8,200.

This work led to other orders. Out of 20 gates required for new docks constructed on the Bristol Channel at this time, Brotherhood at the Bute Ironworks made 16: Bristol 6, New Bute Dock Cardiff 4, Alexandra Dock Newport 2, Old Dock Newport (above) 4. Most of these gates were over 40ft deep due to the considerable rise and fall of the tide in the Bristol Channel.

The company made an iron pontoon landing stage 225ft long for the Bristol docks at Hotwells. Steam hopper dredge barges and £5,000 worth of iron roofs and bridges for Brazil were also made at this time, in addition to other work. However, the Maudslay Brothers did not want to enter for the large foreign railway and bridge contracts that were available so they gave Rowland his notice and £500 compensation, and at the end of 1874 he moved to Bristol.

Whilst he was at Cardiff Rowland wrote a letter entitled 'Sewage & Water Supply' which was published in *The Builder*:

> Having suffered when young with fever, and since lost several friends ... I venture to pen these lines. During 45 years, constantly having something to do with well sinking, drainage, sewering, waterworks, etc my experience has shown me that as gunpowder is dangerous when put in contact with fire, so is night soil when in contact with water, where old wells, drains, cesspools, and inferior traps, and badly fitted water closets, are allowed to remain in use.
>
> Knowing the danger ... I endevoured, with other persons, to obtain a public water supply for the town; but not succeeding, I sank a private well for the use of ourselves and workmen, procuring most excellent water from the deeper springs, and from this well most of the inhabitants of the town are now supplied. As to rivers, I well remember seeing fine salmon taken from the Thames between Isleworth Ferry and Richmond Bridge, and often watched the gradual pollution of its waters since with regret.

He suggested sinking deep wells so as to avoid impure surface water. Mentioning his father's work he said that it was a waste to send sewage into the sea; instead it should be used as manure and so enable many areas of waste land, commons, downs, etc. to be brought into cultivation.

Rowland had a little capital left with which he bought equipment, and early the next year (1875) he obtained the contract for the construction of a new goods shed for the GWR at Bristol. The old dock he had made nearly 40 years before was filled in and replaced by new jetties with steam and hydraulic cranes. The whole surface of the goods yard was raised by 3ft 6in. and the layout rearranged. Around the same time he lengthened the down platform at Corsham and erected a crane in the new goods shed at Bath. The GWR accepted Brotherhood's tender of £15,000 for a new grain store at Bristol, but this was cancelled following the amalgamation with the Bristol & Exeter Railway. However, Rowland was compensated by being given the contracts for sundry small jobs. He completed his work in Bristol, total value over £30,000 in 1876, and this was the last work he did for the GWR.

The Severn Tunnel Railway Act was passed in 1872 for a line leaving the B&SWUR near Pilning then passing under the river to rejoin the main line near Rogiet (Severn Tunnel Junction), thus eliminating the ferry crossing or the detour via Gloucester. The GWR began work on the tunnel early in 1873, but progress was slow and by 1877 only one shaft and 1,600 yards of heading (pilot tunnel) had been dug from it under the river.

The GWR then invited tenders for carrying out the whole work. As the contract was for cash, with payment assured, some of Rowland's friends suggested that he should tender. His estimate, sent in August, was for £987,372-10-0 and was the cheapest by £3,000. Other tenders

Severn Tunnel construction shaft and pumps near Portskewett. Rowland Brotherhood assisted his son Rowland with this contract 1877-79. *Courtesy National Railway Museum*

were from Webster (of London drainage) and T.A.Walker. However, Brotherhood required five years against Walker's four, and the extra year's interest made Walker's bid the lower. The Directors then announced that they could not accept any of the tenders and continued the work themselves. They did let two small contracts, to Rowland Brotherhood (Rowland's third son) and Oliver Norris of New Passage. Rowland (son) undertook to sink two shafts, Marsh and Hill shafts, on the Monmouthshire bank and to drive headings east and west from them. Norris had similar work on the Gloucestershire bank and the GWR continued at Old Shaft.

Rowland (senior) helped his son with the work, which proceeded apace. By the middle of October 1879 the headings under the river were within 130 yards of each other, when the heading west from the Old Shaft struck the Great Spring, which flooded the workings. Brotherhood's headings from Marsh and Hill shafts were unaffected but all work was stopped. Subsequently a fresh contract for the whole tunnel was let to T.A.Walker and all the works in hand were given to him on 18th December, 1879, after which the Brotherhoods had no further part in the project. The tunnel was eventually opened at the end of 1886.

Soon after Rowland (senior) was taken ill and his condition gradually deteriorated. Writing in February 1882,

> In December 1880 Peter boldly advised me not to undertake more work. Stating that not only would he assist me then but continue to do so, which promise I am most thankful to say he has most nobly kept up to the present hour.

Rowland Brotherhood died at his home, Everton Villa, Chertsey Road, Redland, Bristol, on 4th March, 1883, aged 70. He was buried high up the side of the hill in Arnos Vale Cemetery, Bristol, under a heavy sheet of polished red granite in plot Q156. Also buried there are his wife Priscilla (died December 1888 aged 65) and children Maud (died November 1923 aged 67) and James (died October 1930 aged 86).

CHAPTER FIVE

PETER BROTHERHOOD
ENGINEER 1838-1902

Peter Brotherhood was the second son of Rowland Brotherhood. He was born at Maidenhead 'in the Parish of Bray' (a village on the southern edge of the town) on 22nd April, 1838 and was registered by his mother Priscilla on 21st May. Whether she could not read very well to check the entry, or the registrar could not understand her Hampshire accent, but for some reason Peter's birth certificate gives his father's name as Robert and the surname of both his parents as Brotherwood. In addition, his father's occupation is given as 'Castrator'!

With his elder brother William he entered King's College School, London, on 29th January, 1852, and left in 1855 aged 17 (King's College records listed him as a pupil 'in the last academical year' in the 1855-56 Calendar), or possibly in 1856 (*Dictionary of National Biography*). He was never a student in the Senior (university) department of the College. Whilst at school the brothers lived at 40 Bloomsbury Square. (Their younger brother Rowland was listed as a pupil at King's College School in the 1857-58 and 1858-59 Calendars, so presumably he was there 1856-58.)

On leaving school Peter served in his father's Railway Works for a short time (presumed from 1855-56 until at least March or even October 1857) and then went to the GWR locomotive works at Swindon where he spent two years (presumed 1857 to 1858). According to his obituary, he also had considerable experience in civil engineering work on the GWR, probably as an assistant on his father's contracts. On his return to Chippenham in 1859 he supervised the design and construction of locomotives and other railway equipment. Rowland wrote, referring to 1858 or 1859,

Peter Brotherhood as young man, probably taken around 1862 (when he would have been 24).
Collection S.A.Leleux

53

I bought a strip of land by the side of the works fronting the station at Chippenham and built a new shop for Peter to make his small loco engines in. He had made the broad gauge *Moloch* in an old shop outside.

Peter seems to have been generally busy with projects for his father until 1862, including going to Canada for a possible contract for a railway from Halifax to Quebec, and work on the *Great Eastern*, as well as building his small locomotives (*see Chapter Three*), and the 15in. gauge (quarter full size) model *Pearl*. He then studied marine engineering in the drawing office of Messrs Maudslay Sons & Field, in Lambeth, south London, the premier engineering firm in the country at that time and where many famous engineers received their training. This took place from late 1862/early 1863 until 1864, when he returned to Chippenham. Peter married Eliza Pinniger Hunt at Clapham Parish Church, Surrey (now Greater London) on 19th April, 1866; he was then a few days short of his 28th birthday, and Eliza was five months younger. Neither had been married before. Peter's income then was £500pa. Following their marriage, Peter and Eliza took a house at Calne, the terminus of a short branch line from Chippenham.

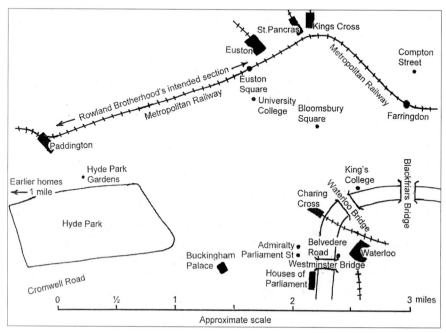

Outline map of central London, showing Peter's works and his homes

Eliza was the eldest daughter of James Hunt of Kensington and Brighton, a contractor building sections of the East India Railway from 1850 to the mid-1860s (some details are given in *Appendix Five*). Her mother had died in the Mutiny (1857) so Eliza went out to Mirzapur to keep house for her father. She had met Peter before she left for India and had waited for him.

Rowland's finances were beginning to cause concern in 1865, so it is perhaps not surprising that Peter, now married, left to set up in business on his own account in 1867. On 'Lady Day' (25th March) 1867, in partnership with George D.Kittoe, the firm of Kittoe & Brotherhood commenced business at 53-56 Compton Street, London EC1 (halfway between King's Cross and Liverpool Street stations, about half a mile north-east of the Underground station at Farringdon). The partners were engineers and millwrights specialising in brewery machinery. It seems likely that Kittoe was an older man, seeking to retire, as in 1871 his place was taken by George Gatton Melhuish Hardingham, a young man probably only recently having completed his apprenticeship. Peter's brother-in-law, Sir Frederick Seager-Hunt, then Chairman of the Seager Evans Distillery, Millbank, London SW put up the necessary capital which enabled Peter to become the sole proprietor of his firm early in 1878. Hardingham left, to become the London Manager for a Danish railway rolling stock company, and eventually practised as a Consulting Engineer, dying in 1940.

At first Peter and Eliza lived at 15 Elgin Road (later renamed Elgin Crescent), Notting Hill, but in 1874 he moved to 25 Ladbroke Gardens, still in Notting Hill, where they lived until 1884. By this time they had five children: Arthur born 1867, Mary (1870), Montague (1874), Stanley (1876) and Edith (1878). In 1884 the family moved to 94 Cromwell Road, Kensington, and again in 1889 to 15 Hyde Park Gardens, Bayswater, halfway along the northern side of Hyde Park.

What must have been one of the first products of Kittoe & Brotherhood, a beam engine built 1867, survives in preservation. It was ordered by Mann, Crossman & Paulin Ltd for Albion Brewery, Whitechapel – later part of Watney Mann – and was in regular use until 1934 when put out of action by a cracked bedplate. However, a Robert Morton horizontal engine had been attached to the same crankshaft and flywheel in 1872, quite a common practice at the time to obtain additional power, so following the fracture the connecting rod of the Kittoe & Brotherhood engine was detached from its crank and the Morton engine continued to run until 1946. The beam, 13ft 6in. long, was supported by four cast-iron columns 10in. in diameter and 8ft 6in. high.

Kittoe & Brotherhood beam engine, now preserved at Cold Harbour Mill, Devon. Note the massive beam transmitting power to the connecting rod (*right foreground*), the wood lagging on the cylinder (*right*), and the makers' plate.

S.A.Leleux, 20th August, 2010

The single vertical double-acting cylinder was 27in. bore x 60in. stroke, driving a flywheel 16ft in diameter. The valves were operated by Watt's parallel motion. Overall, the engine weighs 10 tons (the bedplate 3 tons). It was moved from store in April 1992 to Coldharbour Mill, Working Wool Museum at Uffculme near Cullompton, Devon, where it was slowly reassembled in a contemporary engine house, completed by July 1997. The restored engine was officially commissioned by the then Managing Director of Brotherhoods, Ian Arbon, on 24th February, 1998. This historic engine is run from time to time.

Another early product, advertised in 1868, was a refrigerator for cooling wort, a solution of malt in water, an early stage in the brewing process. The wort was circulated by a Kittoe patent steam driven vertical 'Paragon' pump, a type also supplied in large numbers for pumping water, and was made in sizes ranging from 50 to 7,350 gallons per hour.

The catalogue cover for the sale of the Railway Works in 1869 mentioned a Kittoe & Brotherhood combined sewage pump and engine, which would 'throw 12,000 gallons per hour to a height of 50 feet'. It had a wrought-iron vertical boiler of 4 feet 6 diameter, 7 feet 6 high, with a Kittoe & Brotherhood patent donkey feed pump. It must have been almost new, this firm having been formed only in March 1867.

Kittoe & Brotherhood made 'Apparatus for sinking screw piles by steam power'. A sturdy 4-wheel rail-mounted iron frame forming the water tank carried a vertical boiler at one end. This supplied steam to an engine driving a pair of vertical augers through reduction gearing, one on each side.

Contractor's hole boring machine, for posts of all kinds, by Kittoe & Brotherhood. Until the mid-20th century contractors' plant was often mounted on rails for convenience in moving.

Around 1870 it was stated in *The Engineer* that if a really high speed steam engine was to be a success it would have to be single-acting (i.e. only one power stroke per piston for every revolution of the crankshaft). This was because the connecting rod bearing brasses in the early high speed vertical double-acting engines soon began to wear due to the constant reversal of pressure (i.e. as every stroke of the piston was a power stroke, the bearings were subjected to alternate pushes and pulls) so the engines knocked badly and had excessive maintenance costs. The later invention of forced lubrication solved this problem. Peter invented his famous 3-cylinder radial engine, the first successful high speed steam engine, in 1872. The first one made was used at Woolwich for driving a fan. Subsequently he developed and improved upon his original designs.

The following description of the Brotherhood radial engine is from the specification of Patent No.287 of 24th January, 1873 *Applying steam power to centrifugal and other machines.*

This invention relates to means whereby steam power can be directly applied to the working of rapidly revolving machines, such as centrifugal machines, circular saws, threshing machines, rotary pumps and propellers or the like, without the intervention of bands, gearing or other connection for increasing the speed of rotation. For this purpose I have placed three cylinders, having each the one end closed, and the other end open, with their axes intersecting at angles of 120° or thereabouts, so that their open ends all communicate with one central cavity which is supplied with steam. Within this cavity is a crank on a shaft which projects through the side of the cavity and each cylinder is fitted with a piston connected by a connecting rod to the other crank. (The pistons were long and so self-guiding, like those in a car engine.) On the shaft is fixed a disc fitted with openings and passages for steam, and this disc bears against the side of the cavity in which are formed ports for the passage of steam to the outer ends of the three cylinders, and also to an outer cavity, from which an exhaust pipe conveys the waste steam.

The position of the openings and passages in the disc is so related to that of the steam ports that each of the three cylinders is successively filled with steam, or is made to communicate with the exhaust cavity as the crank and disc revolves, and thus by the unbalanced pressure acting successively on the several pistons they are caused to reciprocate in turn and impart rotary motion to the crankshaft. As the side of each piston presented towards the central cavity is always subjected to the pressure of steam in the cavity, it acts for moving the crank only on the outward stroke, the inward stroke being performed whilst there is pressure on both sides of the piston. The strain in each connecting rod is thus always in the direction of tension and its joints may be loosened by the action of wear or otherwise without causing noise or blows in the apparatus.

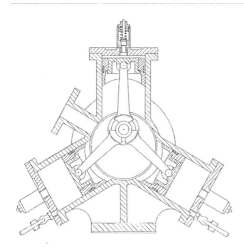

Cross section of typical 3-cylinder engine. Steam, compressed air or water entered the outer ends of the cylinders (inlets not shown). The long, self-guiding pistons were attached directly to the connecting rods which all drove the same crank. The cylinders exhausted into the crankcase – the exhaust pipe is clearly shown. This particular engine is fitted with spring loaded pressure relief valves.

The plate or disc which forms a rotating slide is provided with a passage through it, and a cavity in it successively covering and uncovering as it revolves with the crank ports leading respectively to the outer end of the three cylinders and openings communicating from them alternately to the central cavity and the exhaust cavity.

The engine was first exhibited at the Agricultural Hall, and then the Vienna Exhibition of 1873 where it created considerable interest. It came into extensive use, starting instantly from any position and running at high speed with no vibration. Well over 7,500 of these engines were made in the next 20 years. They were used as steam engines, providing power for ships' auxiliaries (fans, steering gear, winches etc.), force pumps, centrifuges, blowing engines, air compressors, exhausters, etc. and even as water engines (for hydraulic capstans etc.),. The design was very versatile. It is said that some 3-cylinder engines were used to blow organs in London churches. Locally, a 3-cylinder engine, thought to have been constructed in the 1930s, was used from 1955 until the 1980s to power a crane in a limestone quarry at Ancaster, about 30 miles north of Peterborough. It used air at 100psi, presumably from the same source which supplied rock drills in the quarry. The last reciprocating steam engine supplied to British industry was a 3-cylinder engine supplied to Ravenscraig Steelworks, Motherwell, in March 1987.

The *Transactions* of the Institution of Mechanical Engineers in 1875 include an article by F.W.Webb, the Chief Mechanical Engineer of the London & North Western Railway (LNWR) describing the use of a Brotherhood 3-cylinder engine to drive a 7ft diameter saw cutting hot

3-cylinder engine driving a circular saw for cutting metal, 1874. Note the patent flexible coupling between the two units.

steel ingots in their works at Crewe. An ingot 10in. square could be cut in 25 seconds, using steam at 50psi to drive the engine and saw at about 600rpm. The saw enabled steel ingots to be cut to size for forgings, saving time, material and reheating. It was also used to rough out crank axles from steel slabs. Further applications of the saw were contemplated. The previous saw had been driven by locomotive type cylinders through 1:6 step-up gearing but this was dangerous, 'the gearing having been sent through the roof twice, and the engine house knocked down'.

Brotherhood's patent No. 3989 of 1887 related to 'Improvements to 3-cylinder engines'. There were three improvements: hollow connecting rods to reduce weight and increase stiffness, piston slide valves, and a hollow trunnion and crank to carry oil to the bearing surfaces while the engine was running (but this was not pressure lubrication). Early engines had poppet valves (like a car engine), later ones just a simple slide valve in a rotating disc. A number of versions of the 3-cylinder engine were made, depending on the customers' requirements, and the above improvements were not applied to every engine.

The 3-cylinder engine found particular application in three very different areas: electricity generation, hydraulic machinery, and

Whitehead torpedoes. Before treating these areas and others in more detail, it is worth noting that a Brotherhood & Hardingham catalogue dated January 1876 listed the following products:

1. 3-cylinder stationery steam engines in four sizes developing 7 to 35ihp at a piston speed of 300ft per minute and mean steam pressure 40psi. These engines were used to drive all the other products listed except for the Paragon pumps.
2. 'Helical' centrifugal pumps (axial flow)
3. Direct acting and traversing sawing machines
4. Ship steering apparatus
5. Direct acting fans
6. Grabs and hoists
7. 'Dynamo-electric' machines direct coupled to engines running at 500 to 950rpm
8. 3-cylinder compressors direct coupled to engines
9. Centrifugal separators direct coupled to engines at 1,500rpm (sugar refining)
10. Paragon vertical steam pumps in five sizes with capacities from 950 to 4,500 gallons per minute.

Brotherhood & Hardingham advertisement

Electricity generation requires the rotor of the generator to spin at high speed, obtained with the existing slow speed steam engines by a step-up belt drive between the engine and generator. This added to the space required and the cost, and reduced efficiency. The first direct-driven dynamo powered by a Brotherhood engine was on the French ironclad *Richelieu* in 1875. (On this vessel 3-cylinder engines were also used for driving centrifugal pumps direct.) A French chocolate manufacturer, M.Menier, mounted a Brotherhood engine and a Gramme (electricity generating) machine in his yacht to supply power to an arc light that enabled him to travel along the tortuous channels of the Seine and Marne between Paris and his works at Noisiel. Brotherhood electric generating sets were installed in many British and foreign ships for supplying current to carbon arc lamps, which were mainly used for searchlights (incandescent lamps were not invented until 1879, so arc lamps were universal for electric light). According to R.H.Parsons in *Early Days of the Power Station Industry* (CUP, 1939), a Brotherhood engine directly driving a dynamo was used for the experimental lighting of the terminus of the PLM Railway in Paris by means of Lontin arc lamps on 7th September, 1877. According to an 1879 advertisement, dynamos by Wilde, Siemens and Gramme had all been driven directly by Brotherhood engines. Direct drive applications often incorporated a Brotherhood flexible coupling in the shaft, to overcome any minor misalignment of the engine and generator shafts.

3-cylinder engine driving a pair of Siemens dynamos, 1879.

In 1877, Colonel Mangin designed a special form of mirror for use in searchlight projectors. Mangin's projector was mounted on one carriage and a second carried a small vertical boiler, a 3-cylinder Brotherhood steam engine and a dynamo. This second carriage weighed nearly five tons at first, but much smaller equipment of lesser power were shortly afterwards made for field use. A large Mangin projector was used on board the warship *La Surveillante* to light the coast of the island of Tabarka in Tunis to facilitate the landing of French troops in 1880. Smaller mobile ones could, it was said, be drawn by one horse, and it was even suggested that the smaller equipment might be taken to pieces and carried on mule-back in mountainous countries. A carrying power of up to 6 km was claimed for the larger projectors and up to 3 km for the smallest field type.

French mobile searchlight unit (Mangin projector), powered by a Brotherhood 3-cylinder engine, c.1878.
Courtesy Science Museum, London

During the autumn of 1881 there was an international engineering exhibition in Paris. Later, the exhibits were described at length in *Engineering*. The issue of 21st October, 1881 referred to

> the excellent exhibit of Mr. Peter Brotherhood, who shows a number of 3-cylinder engines coupled to different types of dynamo machines ... (including) a Gramme machine coupled to a Brotherhood engine and running at 1500 revolutions, furnishing a 200 Carcel light. This is especially adapted for torpedo boats, and with a Mangin projector, objects are rendered visible for nearly 3000 yards.

Other Brotherhood powered generating sets supplied searchlights of 20,000 and 45,000 'candles'. The issues of 2nd & 30th December contained descriptions and illustrations of searchlights built by M.M.Sautter & Lemonnier, Avenue de Suffren, Paris, for the French Government. Both designs incorporated Brotherhood 3-cylinder engines with direct drive to a dynamo. The first was a horse-drawn unit, having the engine and Gramme generator transversely mounted in front of a vertical boiler. The front of the unit carried a Mangin projector and reel of cable. The type was 'recently adopted by the French Government for military service, and is especially intended for use in fortifications and other defences'. The second unit was self-propelled, and could haul 'guns or stores, while at the same time it carried an electric light apparatus'. The Brotherhood engine and dynamo were mounted on top of the traction engine's boiler, with a clutch and gears between them so that the drive could be taken to the front road wheels; steering used the rear wheels. No searchlight was mounted on the unit.

The Suez Canal opened in 1873, and traffic built up rapidly to 30 or more vessels each day. Initially navigation was only by day, but by providing every ship with suitable lights capacity was virtually doubled. Ships without their own electric light could, on entering the canal, hire a suitable plant, comprising a Mangin reflector, dynamo and motor, and return it on leaving. The first ship to navigate the canal by night was the P&O RMS *Carthage* in June 1886. The *Carthage* brought the experimental apparatus from London, and it was unshipped at Suez for use by the next northbound P&O vessel. 'The dynamo is one of Gramme's patent, and is worked by one of Brotherhood's three-cylinder engines. The latter is driven by steam supplied by the main engines on board.' The electric navigation light was used for nine hours and the remaining seven hours of the passage were by daylight. 'The whole apparatus is portable, and packed in one large tank, the whole being about two tons and a-half in weight.' *Electric Lighting for Marine Engineers* by S.F.Walker (published 1892) carried an advertisement for 'Suez Canal Plant', comprising the 'regulation projector forward' (15,000 candle power nominal), an arc masthead lamp, and all necessary switchgear etc., for £150, with a suitable generating plant driven by a Brotherhood 3-cylinder engine running at 700rpm for an additional £134.

The third edition of *L'Eclairage Electrique* by Le Comte Th. Du Moncel, published in Paris in 1883, around page 310, describes military uses, including Mangin and other searchlights with dynamos driven by Brotherhood 3-cylinder engines. Then on pages 316-320 it covers lighting for railway trains. A powerful electric headlight mounted on top of the locomotive's smokebox would announce the presence of the approaching train. During 1882 a Schuckert dynamo driven by a Brotherhood engine had been mounted on the front footplate of Chemin de Fer du Nord 4-4-0 No. 2873, which was one of a series built between

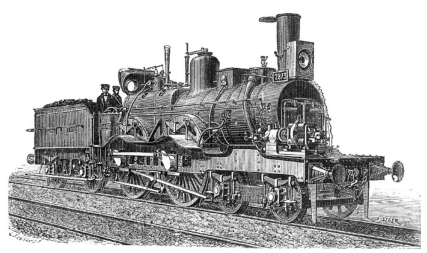

'Locomotive equipped with its electric light appliances'. Chemin de Fer du Nord 4-4-0 No. 2873, with its 3-cylinder engine and dynamo on the front footplate for a powerful headlight at the base of the chimney, 1882. Illustration from *L'Eclairage Electrique* (3rd edition) by Le Comte Th du Morcel, published by Librairie Hachette et Cie, Paris, 1883, page 317.

1877 and 1879, known as 'Les Outrances' because of their formidable performance, and the powerful headlight was fitted at the base of the chimney. It seems that similar experiments had been undertaken in Germany, with the dynamo and engine mounted on a small platform on top of the boiler, between firebox and dome. The Chemin de Fer de l'Est had experimented with train lighting supplied by axle-driven dynamos, supplemented by accumulators for when the train was stationary or running slowly. However, the author thought that it would be better to adapt the system to be powered by a Brotherhood engine and thus avoid the dead weight of the accumulators on every carriage, although in fact it was the axle-driven generator and accumulator backup which became the standard.

In the winter of 1881/82, a dynamo driven by a small Brotherhood engine mounted on the locomotive provided current for an experimental electrically-lit train operated on the Glasgow City & Direct Railway by the North British Railway, which lasted until 1886 when a third rail supply for the train from a stationary plant was substituted.

Train lighting is covered in *Electricity in the Service of Man* by R.Wormwell (Cassell & Co, 1893), page 593. It mentions a 4,000 candle power locomotive headlight, with current supplied by a Schuckert flat-ring machine, which is set in motion by a Brotherhood steam-engine, which receives steam from the boiler of the engine. The dynamo on the steam engine was generally mounted in front of the boiler.

This is presumably the application described above. The author continued by considering electric lighting in carriages, used by the

'Midland and London Brighton & South Coast Railways for many years, noting that while axle driven dynamos served, auxiliary batteries had to be provided and automatically switched on when the train is stationary. However, yet again a small Brotherhood or other engine, supplied with steam from the locomotive boiler, has been used to drive the dynamo, the engine and dynamo being placed either on the locomotive itself, or in a guard's van or special truck immediately behind the locomotive.

In the latter case it was presumably supplied with steam by flexible pipes similar to those later used for steam heating.

Although Peter Willans' high speed steam engine, patented in October 1882, is commonly regarded as the power plant which first enabled engine and dynamo to be directly coupled, the foregoing shows that Brotherhood engines had been driving dynamos direct for at least

3-cylinder engine with piston valves driving a dynamo, 1882. Note the flexible coupling in the main shaft.

five years before. In order to meet customers' requirements, the Brotherhood 3-cylinder engine developed many variations, including units with piston valves instead of rotating slide valves, and even tandem compound engines.

Brotherhood's 3-cylinder engine proved ideal for operating hydraulic machinery. It had no dead centre so it always started from any position of the crank, and pressure was always on the outer end of pistons so the connecting rods were always in compression and hence automatically took up wear. During an Institute of Mechanical Engineers lecture on hydraulic machinery in 1874, a member noted that he had seen a Brotherhood hydraulic capstan working at the LNWR Broad Street goods station, London. Stripping the engine to examine the valve and reassembly took only 17 minutes, showing the machine's simplicity of construction. Peter Brotherhood said that hard phosphor-bronze was used for the valve, and for crank pin bearings. The length of the exhaust port in the valve was exactly same as that in the cylinder face:

> The cast-iron connecting rods or struts for the three cylinders of the hydraulic capstan were made in a very simple manner by casting the three together as one piece, boring them for the crank pin, then breaking them apart, after which the ends only required rounding with a file, without any expensive fitting.

A paper on Portable Hydraulic Drills presented to the Institution in February 1887 noted that the hydraulic motors used in Toulon Dockyard were 'Brotherhood's three-cylinder engines'. In 1874 Peter sold the patent for the application of his engine to drive hydraulic machinery and capstans to the Hydraulic Engine Co. Ltd, Chester, who made some 1,200 of these engines before discontinuing their manufacture in 1955. The running instructions for these engines stated 'it was essential that tallow or best lard oil be alone used for lubrication and on no account may any vegetable or mineral oil be admitted to the internal working parts'. A Brotherhood 3-cylinder hydraulic engine with cylinder 4in. x 4in. stroke was used to open and close the Wellington Street swing bridge at Hull, the operation taking $1\frac{1}{2}$ minutes.

The earliest known reference to a Brotherhood air compressor was published in *The Practical Magazine* during 1874, which describes a low pressure machine suitable for blowing furnaces or ventilating purposes. A 3-cylinder engine running at 400rpm was mounted on one side of an air chamber or receiver and another 3-cylinder unit acting as a compressor was mounted on the other side of the air chamber. The driving shaft passed through the chamber and carried a heavy flywheel.

The balance of the 3-cylinder machines, plus the effect of the flywheel, must have made the unit almost vibration free. It was reported during a meeting of Institution of Mechanical Engineers on Compressed-Air Machinery in 1874 that a Brotherhood 3-cylinder engine using air at 45psi was driving a drill for coal cutting at Blanzy Colliery, near St Etienne, France.

In 1864 Robert Whitehead invented the self-propelled torpedo, driven by a horizontal 2-cylinder compressed air engine. There were several trials and demonstrations – in Austria in 1867 and 1868 and Sheerness in 1870. Following the Vienna Exhibition in 1873, the Superintendent of the Royal Laboratory at Woolwich Arsenal had been very impressed by the suitability of Brotherhood's new type of engine for driving torpedoes, due to its compactness and symmetry, with the crankshaft on its centre line. The Brotherhood engine was introduced into Whitehead's own torpedoes in 1876, and into British ones in 1877. It was used extensively thereafter, and it was still in use in the older types of torpedo in the 1960s, although its high noise level necessitated

Motor driven high pressure air compressor for the torpedo service on board ship. The maker's plate reads: 'P.Brotherhood Patent London' with 'Belvedere Road Westminster SE 1898' in the central three lines.

its replacement by more silent means of propulsion in modern torpedoes. As the power required increased so engines with four cylinders at 90° were introduced; these functioned in the same way as the 3-cylinder version. In 1874, presumably for trial purposes, Brotherhood had used air stored at 450psi, then reduced to 90psi, in a small engine weighing 7lb for a Whitehead torpedo, having cylinders 1 $\frac{1}{8}$ in. x 1$\frac{1}{2}$ in. stroke, producing 2.5hp. In 1876 he devised and submitted to the authorities at Woolwich (which at that time had responsibility for naval weapons as well as for the army) a servo motor for use in torpedoes.

Torpedo engines had three (later four) cylinders and powered 14, 18 or 21in. diameter weapons. The torpedo tubes were either submerged or deck mounted. Submerged tubes were fixed, so that they had to be aimed by pointing the whole vessel towards the target. These tubes were hinged along their centre line and the torpedo was loaded by opening the tube and lowering it in. After closing the tube a valve was opened to fill it with sea water. A door at the outer end of the tube could then be opened, and the weapon was ready to fire. The deck mountings comprised one, two or three tubes fitted on a revolving platform, giving a wide field of fire. These tubes were loaded by inserting the torpedo in the breech end, like a shell in a gun.

Few inventions can have had such an effect on warfare as the torpedo. It gave a small ship the potential ability to cause major – even fatal – damage to much larger vessels, and thereby upset existing concepts of naval power. For best effect, a torpedo needed to be launched near its target, hence the development of small fast torpedo boats. Even motor boats could be used, like the British MTBs and corresponding German boats in the Second World War. For protection against torpedo boats the fast, well- armed, torpedo boat destroyer was developed. It was not long before it was realised that the torpedo boat and torpedo boat destroyer could be combined into the same vessel, armed with torpedoes and guns, and so the modern destroyer was born. For a time the threat of torpedo attack even put the future of the big ship in doubt. However, from around 1884, protection for major ships at anchor was provided by fitting them with anti-torpedo nets hung from booms, later replaced by having permanent nets around the ships' anchorages. From around the same date the first proposals for under water armour were made. Furthermore, around 1900 the fighting range of battleships was only about 3,000 yards, although trials since 1899 had shown that ranges could be doubled. The threat of long range torpedo attack by the opponent (major ships of the period were usually fitted with torpedo

Torpedo being launched during the Turko-Russian War at Batum harbour.

tubes) was one spur to increase the fighting range, and with that came the need to develop more powerful guns and means of accurately laying them.

The Whitehead torpedo was first used in actual war on 29th May, 1877, when two unarmoured British ships, *Shah* and *Amethyst*, engaged the Peruvian ironclad *Huascar*. It had been seized by the leader of the defeated party in a Peruvian revolution and had molested a number of British ships, besides threatening to bombard coastal towns unless a ransom was paid. As the Peruvian Government disclaimed all responsibility for this piratical behaviour, 'Rear Admiral de Horsey, in command on the Station, decided to compel her surrender'. After two hours of inconclusive firing, *Shah* launched a torpedo, but 'the range was too great and its speed too low to reach the target.' The first victim of the new weapon was a Turkish guardship at the entrance of Batum harbour during the Turko-Russian War of 1878. This torpedo was propelled by a Brotherhood engine using air at 1,000psi.

The potential of a new weapon system, a submarine armed with torpedoes, was vividly demonstrated on 22nd September, 1914, in the very early days of the First World War. Three old cruisers, completed in 1901/02, HMS *Aboukir*, *Hogue* and *Cressy*, were cruising off Sheerness and the Hook when they were spotted by the commander of U9, Lieutenant Otto Weddigen. First he torpedoed the *Aboukir*, then the *Hogue* which had lowered its boats to pick up survivors, and finally the *Cressy*, which was attempting to help the other two cruisers. Some

1,400 sailors died. Later in the war, unrestricted submarine warfare with torpedo attacks on merchant shipping nearly caused a crisis in Britain due to the loss of imported food and materials. History then repeated itself in the first half of the Second World War, when submarines armed with torpedoes again caused such huge losses in the Atlantic that Britain was close to being forced out of the war.

The 3-cylinder Brotherhood torpedo engine was progressively developed to produce 50hp and the pressure inside the air vessel increased to 1,400psi. In 1893 a 53hp torpedo engine weighed 52lb, and fitted into 14in. diameter torpedo. A 4-cylinder radial unit was introduced by the company in 1899 which boosted the power output to 56hp, and a nickel-steel air vessel, fitted into the 18in. Mk V RGF (Royal Gun Factory) torpedo allowed air pressures to climb to 2,200psi. Torpedoes were driven by compressed air, which cooled on expansion. Improved performance was obtained by incorporating heaters to warm the air, and later engines became semi-diesel when warm fuel was injected into the cylinder where it was burned. Peter took out patents for the launching of torpedoes in 1880 and 1881.

As the service air pressure for torpedoes was raised progressively from 700 to 3,500psi, it led to a demand for light weight high efficiency high pressure air compressors. In 1876 Peter patented a 4-stage 2-crank

$^1/_8$ full size model torpedo (29in. long, $2^1/_2$in. diameter) and its launching ramp made by C.W.Bryant.

compressor with water-cooled cylinders giving output at 700 to 1,000psi. Existing compressors used four cylinders of decreasing size, driven from a single crankshaft, but the result was a large machine, and space was at a premium in warships. Peter devised an improved design while returning by train from an Institute of Mechanical Engineers meeting in Birmingham. The number of cylinders was reduced to two, but he obtained

> the advantages of four stages of compression by a combined piston and plunger, to which motion was imparted by a crosshead worked by a pair of double-acting steam-cylinders, the valves of which again were actuated from a crankshaft fitted with a flywheel.

There was also an ingenious cooling system. The first such compressor was fitted to the first British torpedo boat, HMS *Lightning*. Modified, it subsequently became the standard compressor in the French Navy, and 'was adopted in almost every navy'. Peter Brotherhood developed other types of compressor from this engine, especially his 3-stage pump worked from a single rod which further saved space and weight, described by *Engineering* in its issue of 18th May, 1883.

Compressors for torpedoes became an important part of his work. By 1895 a total of 225 sets had been supplied to the Admiralty for use in torpedo boats etc. and a further 380 sets delivered to various foreign powers. In 1893 compressors were made in sizes, from 10 to 40 cubic feet of air per hour at 1,500psi, and for torpedo boats they had an output of 10 cubic feet per hour, running at 350rpm, weighing 5cwt.

Around 1895 one of the difficulties experienced with torpedoes by the Royal Navy was 'failure to start' and 'hang up' of engines. The difficulty was overcome by adopting 'starting positions' for propellers in 1897; when consulted Peter Brotherhood had admitted that there were three positions at which 'hang up' could occur. Until 1902 the design of torpedo engines had been left very much to the firm, but in view of the experience gained at the Royal Torpedo Factory with engines incorporating heaters to give increased speed and range it became necessary for new engines to be designed at that factory, but Brotherhood continued to manufacture them.

Peter discovered the principle of intercooling in compressors by accident. He was attending the trials of one of his first multistage compressors, in which the compressed gas from one stage forms the input for the next stage of compression, when he happened to touch the pipe leading from one cylinder to the next. He burnt himself, and ordered a water jacket to be fitted. Subsequent trials showed that the modified compressor was far more efficient, and thereafter it became standard practice to cool the gas between each stage of compression.

Peter Brotherhood was elected an Associate of the Institute of Civil Engineers on 5th May, 1868, and transferred to Member on 4th February, 1879, but he took little active part in its proceedings. He applied for membership of the Institution of Mechanical Engineers in April 1874 and was elected the following August, his application being proposed by Mr F.W.Webb, Chief Mechanical Engineer of the LNWR, and seconded by H.Chapman. He was also a Membre de la Societe des Ingenieurs Civils (France), and was elected a member of the Iron & Steel Institute in 1877.

LOCOMOTIVES FOR THE 18-IN. RAILWAY AT CREWE.
CONSTRUCTED FROM THE DESIGNS OF MR. F. W. WEBB, LOCOMOTIVE SUPERINTENDENT.
(For Description, see Page 174.)

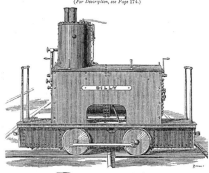

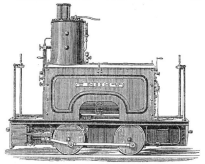

Crewe Works 18in. gauge locomotive *Billy*, as built 1875, powered by a Brotherhood 3-cylinder engine between the frames. When rebuilt, in a similar design to conventional companion *Dickie*, outside cylinders driving the leading axle were fitted below the dome/triple chimney unit.

Courtesy Engineering September 1, 1876.

Probably in the nature of an experiment, to see whether his friend's revolutionary new engine could be applied to rail traction, Webb designed two additional locomotives for the 18in. gauge railway system used to move materials within Crewe Locomotive Works. (Ramsbottom, his predecessor, had laid down this railway in 1861 and designed some small 0-4-0ST locomotives to work on it; one is preserved at York.) Webb's first locomotive for this railway, *Billy*, was completed in July 1875, and had a Brotherhood 3-cylinder engine between the frames, geared to the front axle. The other locomotive, *Dickie*, completed in May 1876, had a pair of conventional outside cylinders, but was otherwise similar to *Billy*. From subsequent events it appears that *Dickie* was the better engine, and probably in late 1877 *Billy* was rebuilt to a similar design, surviving until 1931.

MR. PETER BROTHERHOOD'S WORKS, LONDON.

(For Description, see Page 390).

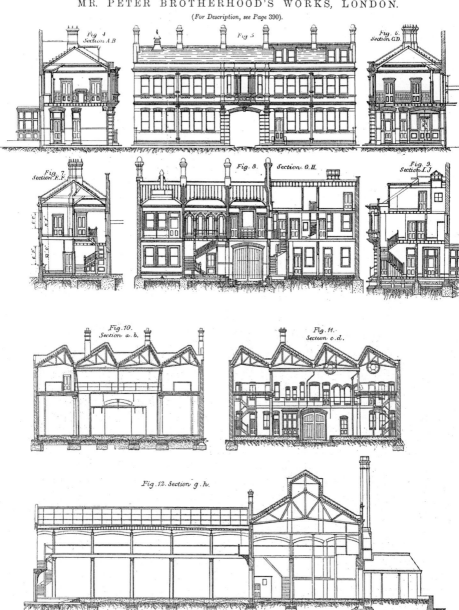

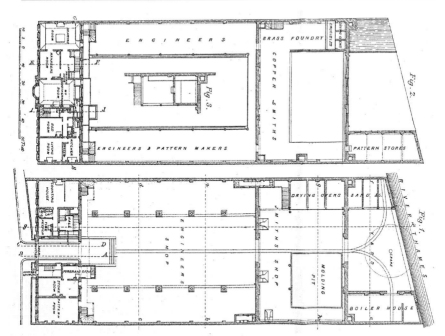

Peter Brotherhood's purpose-built works at Belvedere Road, Lambeth.

Courtesy Engineering April 27, 1883

George Blake Oughterson, formerly manager of an engineering works at Rouen, joined Peter Brotherhood as general manager in 1878, filling the gap left by Hardingham, and he held this position until 1897. By 1878 the Compton Street Works had become too small due to the increasing demand for Brotherhood products. Peter used to sit in the St Stevens Club beside Westminster Bridge, look south across the River Thames, and say 'That is where I shall have my works!' This ambition was realized in 1881, and Peter Brotherhood, Engineer, took possession of a new factory laid out on the most modern lines at 15-17 Belvedere Road, Westminster Bridge, London SE1, roughly where the London Eye now stands. Eventually the works frontage on the west (river) side of Belvedere Road ran south for about 65 yards from opposite the end of Chicheley Street (which still exists). One advantage of the site was its closeness to the Admiralty, just across nearby Westminster Bridge. A full description of the new two-storey purpose-built premises was published in *Engineering* of 27th April, 1883. Behind the factory itself was a small yard fronting the Thames, with a crane to unload goods from the river on to a hand-worked tramway (of about 18in. gauge) which ran the full length of the building. A branch served the boiler house on the east side of the yard. Such tramways to carry materials were once common in engineering works.

Engineering noted, in passing, that steel had almost completely replaced wrought iron in the firm's products, and all bearings were made from phosphor-bronze cast on the premises. Several 3-cylinder engines were used in the works: the two line shafts running down the pillars at either side of the shop each had its own engine, geared down 4:1, the electric generator, and the cupola fan also had these engines. 'The building is warmed by hot water pipes arranged on Perkin's system, and situated some 9ft or 10ft above the floor' and enabled the temperature to be carefully controlled, thus preventing moisture being deposited on the work. 'Altogether the establishment is a model one.' Such was the pressure of business that the works was considerably enlarged on the western side of the site in 1896-7, roughly doubling its size.

Erecting Shop, Belvedere Road, with many 3-cylinder engine castings visible. Note the two sets of line shafts, one supplying power to machines on the ground floor and the other driving machines on the gallery.

Interior of Belvedere Road works, with vertical steam engines under construction *c*.1905. Note the lights, overhead crane, and narrow gauge railway the length of the shop.

Around this time Peter Brotherhood was awarded medals at a number of exhibitions. Ones he is known to have received – there may well have been others – were:

1. World Exhibition 1873 Wien (Vienna) For Merit. On reverse, head of Franz Joseph I, Kaiser (Emperor/King) of Austria, Bohemia,Hungary etc.
2. For Progress World Exhibition 1873 Wien. On reverse, head of Franz Joseph I as above.
3. International Exhibition Paris MDCCCLXXVIII (1878). The central figure is Marianne. On reverse, around the rim French Republic Plans for Buildings for the Universal Exhibition of Champs de (Field of) Mars (later site of Eifel Tower) and Trocadero (Gardens).
4. Universal International Exhibition 1878 Paris with Marianne and the name Brotherhood on the banner carried by the small figure.
5. International Electricity Exhibition Paris 1881 with Brotherhood across the centre. On reverse, French Republic and head of Marianne.

6. Universal Exhibition 1889 having the Eiffel Tower, constructed from 1887–89 as the entrance to this exhibition. On reverse, French Republic and Peter Brotherhood displayed below Marianne.

The advent of fast torpedo boats meant that there was the need for a high power but low weight boiler plant to power them. The British Navy carried out tests in 1886 which showed conclusively that ships having a forced draught to their boilers greatly increased their combustion rate, and hence steam production, in comparison with ships having natural draught boilers. Thereafter warships had forced draught, provided by steam driven fans, one to every boiler. Excellent business for Brotherhood, as a ship like HMS *Tiger* (1913) with 39 boilers required 39 fans.

Around 1890 Peter began to manufacture open vertical high speed engines (i.e. the crankshaft and connecting rods were visible), relying on drip feeds for lubrication like most contemporary open engines. They were suitable for fans, centrifugal pumps, dynamos etc. His first ordinary double-acting engines were fitted to the royal yacht *Victoria & Albert* (not the ship launched May 1899 but its predecessor with this name). Two engines taking steam at 20psi drove dynamos at 250rpm giving 200amps at 80 volts (16kW). They were designed, completed and under steam within 27 working days of the order being received!

The 1895 catalogue survives and makes interesting reading. It is full of the first person 'In all my experience I do … etc'. It lists 61 ships in British Navy with 3-cylinder engines driving generating sets, 52 with

PETER BROTHERHOOD,

LIST OF H.M. SHIPS SUPPLIED WITH PATENT
3-CYLINDER FAN ENGINES.

ANSON,	IRON DUKE.	SANSPAREIL,
ARCHER,	LATONA,	SAPPHO,
AUSTRALIA,	MACICIENNE,	SCOUT,
BLENHEIM,	MARATHON,	SCYLLA,
BRISK,	MEDEA,	SEVERN,
CANADA,	MEDUSA,	SPARROW,
CHAMPION,	MELAMPUS,	SUPERB,
CLIVE,	MELPOMENE,	TARTAR,
COLLINGWOOD,	MERSEY,	TERPSICHORE,
COLOSSUS,	MOHAWK,	THETIS,
CORDELIA,	NAIAD,	THRUSH,
COSSACK,	PHŒNIX,	THUNDERER,

Part of a page from 1895 catalogue, listing Royal Naval ships with 3-cylinder fan engines, to provide forced draught for boiler rooms and general ventilating purposes.

Left: 3-cylinder fan engine. Note the long 'snout' to support the extended crankshaft and the bracket to bolt the unit to the bulkhead.

Patent compound double-acting open high speed engines, as described in the Company's 1895 catalogue. Steam at 100psi was used first in the high pressure cylinder and then passed to the larger diameter low pressure cylinder to extract more energy, before being sent to exhaust.

3-cylinder fan engines (for ventilation and to pressurize boiler rooms to assist combustion), 38 ships totalling 74 sets double-acting engines driving dynamos, 54 with HP air compressors for torpedoes. In addition, 641 compressors had been supplied to ships of foreign navies. Over 7,500 3-cylinder engines had been constructed. Besides the Royal Navy, Brotherhood engines and compressors had been fitted in naval ships of: Argentine, Austria, Belgium, Brazil, Denmark, France, Germany, Greece, Italy, Japan, Norway, Portugal, Russia, Sweden, Turkey, USA – 16 countries. Some passenger and mail steamers also carried Brotherhood machinery.

Peter and Eliza had five children. The eldest, Arthur Maudslay Brotherhood, was born on 11th July, 1867. Details of his secondary education are not known, except that unlike his brothers he did not go to Charterhouse. In October 1883, aged 16, he entered his father's new works in Belvedere Road, leaving at Easter 1885 to follow the

Engineering Course at University College, London, in the sessions 1885-86 and 1886-87. Arthur then served his time as an engineering pupil of F.W.Webb at the LNWR Crewe works from August 1887 to August 1890. He spent a year in the drawing office, and he had some time in the locomotive out-door department. At the end of his training, Peter engaged him as a draughtsman, and then made him assistant manager from 1st January, 1891. His application to join the Institution of Mechanical Engineers, dated 11th May, 1891, was proposed by Peter and seconded by Henry Chapman, the firm's overseas representative. Unfortunately Arthur died of typhoid fever at the family home on 6th December 1893, aged 26, and was buried in Kensal Green cemetery. One of Peter's obituaries stated that Arthur 'gave promise, when assistant general manager of the works, of being a distinguished engineer'. Probably as a result of Arthur's death, James Lester Clark was appointed assistant manager to Peter Brotherhood in 1894.

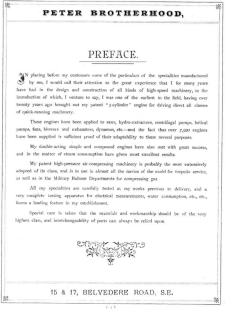

Preface to 1895 catalogue. Note the extensive use of the first person – 'I' and 'my'.

The next child was a daughter, Mary, born on 21st April, 1870. On 28th May, 1896 she married George Crawley, and died in April 1964, a few days short of her 94th birthday. Her husband was an architect who built on Long Island and in London. His father had built railways in Mexico in the 1850s.

Montague was born on 23rd January, 1874. Aged 13, he went to Charterhouse, Weekites House, starting in the Oration Quarter (Autumn Term) of September 1887, and left at the end of Cricket Quarter (Summer Term) 1892, age 18. For his first three terms he was a member of the choir, and became a house monitor (prefect) for his last two terms. He reached the Vth Form but was not an exceptional scholar, and moved to the 'C' forms in 1891, where instead of the traditional Classical based curriculum it was 'a bit closer to the kind of curriculum in use today'. The 'C' forms had evolved from the old Army Classes set up for boys intending to sit the entrance exams for Sandhurst or Woolwich, but had become open to any boy wanting to study a broader, 'more useful', curriculum. He played cricket for the 'Harpies' club, and was recorded as a successful bowler. (The Harpies club sides were formed from the 11 boarding houses combined into four groups.) According to a report in *The Carthusian*, on 1st June, 1891 he bowled nine overs (out of 66), with two maidens, gave 15 runs, took two wickets, and scored a duck. Another report stated that he was missed at the match on 27th June, 1892, where 'Weekites were without the assistance of M.Brotherhood', and his younger brother Stanley scored nothing in the first innings and four in the second. He wanted a career in the Army, thereby greatly disappointing his father. Montague gained admission to Sandhurst, entering in February 1893, and passed out with honours in the summer of 1894. Commissioned as 2nd Lieutenant in 1892, he joined 18th Hussars in October 1894, reaching their base at Umballa, in the Punjab, India, (where the regiment formed part of the normal British Army-in-India) in December. They moved to Lucknow early in 1897 where Montague died of cholera on 21st October, 1897, aged 23. His obituary in *The Carthusian* said 'He made an unusually large number of friends among Carthusians' and 'He was most popular with his regiment, as he had been at school and Sandhurst.' He is commemorated on his parents' grave at Kensal Green.

Peter and Eliza's youngest child was a daughter, Edith, born 22nd December, 1878. She married Jack Rudd, the second son of a partner of Cecil Rhodes in De Beers diamond mines, on 22nd April, 1899, by whom she had two daughters, Frances later Mrs Strachey, and Katherine. Later she married Mr Legros. She died on 8th May, 1936. Her ashes are interred in her parents' grave at Kensal Green.

Between Montague and Eliza was Stanley, born 10th January, 1876. He, too, went to Charterhouse, Weekites House, at 13, starting in the Oration Quarter 1889 until the end of Long Quarter (Spring Term) 1894, age 18. He was a member of the school's rifle corps from Long Quarter 1893 until he left, becoming corporal towards end of 1893. He played football (half-back), cricket and fives for his house, was in the 4th XI for football, and played football for the Harpies club side. His obituary in *The Carthusian* noted that in 1893 he won the House Swimming Cup in record time, covering 300 yards (275m) in five minutes, and he 'was a great sportsman'. On 7th April, 1894, shortly before he left school, he took part in 'Light Dumb-bell Exercises' in an 'Assault at Arms'. Stanley was not outstanding academically. He reached the Under Vth form (progress up the school was by ability, not age). He always wanted a career in the Navy, but Arthur's unexpected death in December 1893 and Montague's decision around the same time to be a soldier meant that Stanley became involved with his father's business.

Stanley was registered as an Engineering student at University College, Gower Street, London, in 1894-5 and 1895-6 where he studied Mechanical Engineering under Professor T.Hudson Beare. Presumably he then went as Peter's assistant at Belvedere Road, becoming General Manager in 1899. Amazingly, Stanley's diary for 1899 survives and extracts are in Appendix Seven.

A typical entry in the order book for April 1899 shows items for HMS *Leviathan*, then under construction by Clydebank Engineering & Shipbuilding Co., comprised:

Two Air Compressors 30 cubic ft to 1700 psi in 70 mins. Revs per min 350. Steam Pressure 200psi. Hydraulic tests – Cylinders 400psi – Air Pump and parts subjected to full press – 2550psi. Other parts as may be directed. Compressor fitted with Condenser and Separator Column. [Pressure vessels of all kinds are routinely given hydraulic pressure tests. Put crudely, if the vessel fails under hydraulic test there is a sudden flood, while a failure using compressed gas would result in an explosion – on numerous occasions exploding boilers or similar have blasted components weighing over 100lb distances of over 100 yards!] Four Reservoirs 6ft long, 11.25 cubic ft capacity and sundry pipework solid drawn, galvanised. [A very similar installation was ordered in December 1899 for HMS *Kent*, then being built by Hawthorn Leslie on the Tyne.] Four Electric-Light Machines, Brotherhood-Silvertown [one of the firm's regular suppliers of electrical generators at that time] combination at 400 revs, output 600 amps, 80 volts, Cylinder test pressure – HP 450psi, LP 250psi, Steam Press 100psi, Back Pressure in Exhaust Pipe 25psi, Consumption (of steam) Per IHP – 34lb. [While Brotherhoods would supply skilled labour for installation on board ship] all other labour and lifting gear to be supplied by the Clydebank Co.

In June 1902 plans were made to illuminate the Belvedere Road factory for the coronation of King Edward VII, scheduled for 26th June, but postponed at the last minute due to the King's appendicitis. It was eventually held on 9th August. Crosse & Blackwell Ltd, food manufacturers also of Belvedere Road, had obviously been impressed by Peter's earlier illuminations, and in August placed an order for 'connecting up and supplying current for the illumination of their premises on the occasion of the King's Coronation'.

An unusual order in 1902 was from Trinity House, who required a small 3-cylinder engine with cylinders only $2^{1}/_{2}$ in. bore by 2in. stroke to power an experimental siren at Pendeen lighthouse near Land's End. Orders for other installations followed.

Peter was a popular employer, popular that is with his employees although not with his fellow employers – he paid a farthing ($^{1}/_{4}$ d., £1/960) an hour more than the approved rate! He was always well dressed, arriving at work in a frock coat and top hat, changing into a similar outfit immediately on arrival. First thing in the morning he would make a tour of the factory, asking after the men's families and inspecting the work. If he found a casting which did not look up to standard he would ask for a hammer and hit it. His judgement was rarely wrong, and a poor casting would shatter under the blow. The hammer would then be returned to its owner and Peter would wipe his hands by running them up and down the back of his coat, which as a result was characterized by two long greasy marks. His sister Kate used to call him 'Peter the Great'. For all his ability he did not like speaking in public.

For some time Peter had suffered from indifferent health, but 'the end came somewhat suddenly' on 13th October, 1902, due to internal haemorrhage. He died at his home in Hyde Park Gardens, aged 64, and was buried in Kensal Green Cemetery, North London (grave number 34455, in square 164 which is just south of West Centre Avenue and west of Oxford Avenue). The grave has a large stone cross mounted on a triple plinth. The plot had been purchased by Peter on 6th December, 1893 for his son Arthur Maudslay, who is commemorated on the top layer of the plinth. On the second layer is a memorial to his brother Montague, who had died at Lucknow. The lowest plinth commemorates Peter Brotherhood and Eliza Pinniger Brotherhood (born 27th November, 1839, died 30th December, 1926) 'beloved parents of above'. At the foot of the plot is a memorial to Edith Katharine Legros, second daughter of Peter and Eliza, whose cremated remains are here.

Over a period of 45 years, Peter had taken out no less than 39 patents, mainly covering air compressors, engines, and valves or pistons. *Engineering* and *The Engineer*, both of 17th October, 1902, as well as professional journals, carried impressive obituary notices. *Engineering* wrote:

> He was by intuition a thorough mechanic, and contributed in no inconsiderable degree to the evolution of the modern high-speed engine, while to him were also due many improvements of importance in connection with air-compressors for high pressures, and hydraulic motors.

Mr Brotherhood had what might be termed a mechanical instinct. He could evolve from his experience, even in the earlier days, sizes and capacities without any formulas or calculations, and he was seldom, if ever, wrong in his results. He had a great penchant for experimental work, which he was fortunately able to gratify. While never professing intimate knowledge or great capacity for the commercial department of an engineering business, he was ever ready to give freedom of control to his manager. His one order was that 'first-rate material and first-rate workmanship' must be ensured at all costs, and to this and his designs can be attributed the continuous success of his business.

Peter desired a 'modest and inexpensive' funeral. His will made provision for his widow and a few relatives, including his sister Kate, confirmed marriage settlements for his two daughters and then the remainder of his estate went to Stanley, who was to continue to receive his present salary of £1,500pa, plus profits from the business.

Peter Brotherhood

CHAPTER SIX

STANLEY BROTHERHOOD 1902-1920

The 1901 Census gave Stanley Brotherhood's occupation as 'Mechanical Engineer's Manager'. His household at Windlesham, Surrey, about three miles south-west of Sunningdale, comprised Stanley, aged 25, wife Vera aged 24, sister Mary Crawley, and six servants, five females (cook aged 25, parlourmaid 45, lady's maid 24, a general servant 16, and housemaid 27) and a 15-year old pantry boy. Stanley inherited the works following Peter's death in 1902.

In the years which immediately followed Stanley took out a number of patents for internal combustion engines and their ignition. These could well have been connected with the delivery of the Peter Brotherhood 4-cylinder petrol engines developing 35hp which were fitted to nine double-deck buses supplied in 1904/05 by Milnes-Daimler to the Birmingham & Midland Motor Omnibus Company (Midland Red), numbers 01270-8, or with the car (*see below*). At this time a number of firms were attempting to provide engines, chassis and bodies for the

4-cylinder 35hp petrol engine for Birmingham & Midland Motor Omnibus Co. (later Midland Red), 1904-5. Note how each cylinder is separate from the others and individually bolted to the crankcase.

Enclosed 2-crank compound engine driving a dynamo, 1903, with hinged doors giving access to the moving parts when required. Available in 11 sizes, with low pressure (LP) cylinder from 12in. to 32in. diameter, outputs 95 to 720hp. A triple expansion version was also manufactured, in 4 sizes, with LP cylinder from 24in. to 40in. diameter and output 280 to 970hp.

new but potentially huge motor bus market. For example, London had only 13 mechanically propelled buses at the beginning of 1904 but by the summer of 1905 there were 73 and about 800 by 1907. Brotherhood's quoted to supply 30 to 40hp engines to several firms but the Midland Red order was the only one received.

Most early vertical steam engines were of the open type, lubricated by drip feeds that kept speeds low. Brotherhood totally enclosed, force lubricated, vertical steam engines were introduced in 1903. Channels bored along the crankshaft conveyed oil under pressure to every bearing, which permitted higher speeds. The totally enclosed crank case contained the oil and prevented its loss. Both simple and compound versions were made, in a range of sizes, production continuing to 1962. An early use for these engines was to drive electricity generating sets, two of the first being on the cruisers HMS *Amethyst* (40kW) and *Duke of Edinburgh* (105kW). A corresponding range of totally enclosed compressors with forced lubrication was also introduced, and was still manufactured in limited numbers in 1979. These single and 2-stage double-acting compressors were to meet the increasing use of compressed air for pneumatic tools, tunnelling, air lift pumps, blowing submarine tanks, etc.

A compressor catalogue for 1904 stated that an important feature was the standardization of parts 'made to gauges'. Methods adopted to improve their efficiency included: very thorough water-jacketing of all cylinders and valves, several stages of compression, with thorough cooling between each, light valves and direct air passages, perfect lubrication to all moving parts by the supply of oil under pressure, by enclosing the mechanism in a dustproof casing, and reduction to a minimum of the number of moving parts.

For pressures up to 80psi single stage compressors were used, with the double-acting steam cylinder mounted above the compressor cylinder. Compressors were always double acting except for the 2-stage single crank machines, in which the second stage was compressed beneath the trunk piston. If the compressor had two or three cranks the steam cylinders were compounded, but the air cylinders were all the same size if it was a single stage compressor. The air valves were light discs held in place by light spiral springs, and were easy to inspect or change. The pistons were cast iron, the piston rods annealed forged steel, and the crankshaft was made of the highest quality acid open-hearth forged steel, thoroughly annealed after rough machining. The bearings were large, and those under the main crankshaft were semi-circular, to permit removal without having to lift the crankshaft. The crosshead brasses were phosphor bronze and the main bearings, together with the crank brasses, were gun metal lined with white metal. The cast-iron crank case was strongly ribbed and fitted with large inspection doors. The interior was given several coats of white enamel 'to prevent the escape of any particle of sand or grit which may remain in the castings and also facilitates inspection of moving parts by improving the lighting'. Intercoolers were fitted in the base of the casing, and comprised many parallel tubes (for the gas) surrounded by a contra flow of water.

The single-stage compressors had outputs in the range 200 to 2,160 cubic feet free air per minute at 50psi when running at speeds of 300 to 450rpm. At the other end of the scale was a compound 5-stage steam driven air compressor with a capacity of 10,000 cubic feet free air per hour compressed to 3,000psi. The machine ran at 120rpm and, in common with other high pressure compressors of the time, retained the common drive previously described.

The law requiring a motorized vehicle to be preceded by a man on foot carrying a red flag had been repealed as recently as 1896. Despite the repeal of the 'Red Flag Act', social acceptance of the car by the upper classes was slow until it was learned that King Edward VII was an enthusiast, having taken delivery of his first car in 1901 while still Prince of Wales. Stanley obviously saw potential in manufacturing cars, and so Brotherhood-Crocker Motors Ltd was formed in 1905 to manufacture 'Brotherhood Motor Carriages'. The partners were: Stanley Brotherhood, Mr Crocker, and Percy Richardson, a former employee of the Daimler Motor Company and considered one of the leading designers of the day. The company's works were at 158A Norwood Road, West Norwood, London SE27, about five miles from Belvedere Road where engines, gearboxes, and some other important items were manufactured.

The car was of advanced design, but was made as simple as possible without sacrificing performance. The 4-cylinder 3.9 litre engine developed 20hp at 900rpm, and drove the rear wheels through a 4-speed gearbox and chains. Modern features were the automatic advance/retard mechanism for the ignition (as the fuel/air mixture burns at a fixed rate, it is necessary to advance the ignition as engine speed increases to ensure that the fuel is completely burnt on each

Brotherhood Crocker Motors stand at the 1905 Motor Show. Countess Amherst's car is on the left.

Brotherhood cars being constructed in the Company's works at West Norwood, about five miles south of Belvedere Road.

stroke; most early petrol engines had a quadrant control for the ignition which the driver adjusted by experience, listening to the sound of the engine), and placing the bulb of the horn in the centre of the steering wheel. The basic chassis cost £675. The car was fully described in the *Automotor Journal* between 4th February and 25th March, 1905, and made a considerable impression at the 1905 Motor Show. A 40hp model was introduced in 1906.

Surviving records show that 10 cars were built. Percy Richardson had the prototype and toured the country, completing 9,000 miles 'without any trouble'. Countess Amherst's car was a double landaulette (a convertible car on which only the rear seats can be uncovered), seating 7-8 people, with Mulliner bodywork. The Honourable Charles Weld Forester covered 7,000 trouble free miles and stated 'I undertake long trips without a mechanic'! Mr Fred Kelly spoke of similar reliability, and continued:

> The second coachman who drives speaks of the simplicity of the car. Just near here we have a hill 1 in 6, three quarters of a mile long, a regular brute, we have never failed to get up the same in second gear. I have ridden in nearly every car running, but never want to ride in a better.

Earl Fitzwilliam had a double phaeton car with brougham top. It cost 1,000 guineas (£1,050). He was a champion for cars, and set up the Fitzwilliam Works in Sheffield to make them. The Earl of Mar and Kellie

Four examples of Brotherhood cars. Clockwise from top left: Percy Richardson driving the prototype. Landaulette built for Countess Amhurst. Mr Fred Kelly on his 20hp car. Hon. Charles Weld Forester on his 20hp car.

Advertisement for the Brotherhood car. Note the reference to control by only two pedals, leaving the hands free for steering.

had a limousine, the body being built by Hooper & Company. The remaining cars were owned by Sir Max Waechester (whose laundaulette was driven by his head coachman), Mr Percy Barlow, MP for Bedford, and Mr R.H.Fowler, head of the Leeds engineering firm Fowler & Company, owned the remaining two.

Despite this apparent success, Stanley disposed of his interest in the venture in January 1906. Possibly the impending move gave little time for other ventures. Little is known of the subsequent history of Brotherhood-Crocker Motors Ltd. In 1905 the 7th Earl Fitzwilliam, a Director, set up a new factory at Tinsley, Sheffield, equipped with the latest machinery to manufacture engines, gearboxes, chains etc. The name was changed in November 1907 to the Sheffield Simplex Motor Company Ltd. Its first car bearing the combined double 'S' badge was a 45hp model introduced in 1908. The company continued production until 1914. During the First World War a few 6-cylinder chassis were built for armoured cars. A 6-cylinder 40/50hp car was exhibited at the 1920 and 1921 Motor Shows, and then the company faded away. One of the last cars built is on display at the Kelham Island Museum, Sheffield. Perhaps the company became the Shefflex Motor Company of Tinsley which constructed several small petrol railcars for minor British railways in the late 1920s.

Years later, in 1919, Stanley wrote: 'For many years before the War we had been mainly employed on Admiralty work; over 90% of our output being for the Naval Service.' Brotherhoods supplied equipment such as high pressure compressors, torpedo engines, generating sets, pumps, and fans to various navies. 'Despite the fact that the firm was mainly engaged in work for the British and foreign Governments, the industrial and commercial side was not overlooked. It was gradually developed and proved of great value in later years.' The continued rise in demand for Brotherhood products caused congestion in the works and a move to a larger site was urgent.

London County Council (LCC) had been formed in 1889, and was looking for a site for London County Hall. In 1903 Stanley had offered the lease of the Belvedere Road Works site (from the Ecclesiastical Commissioners, with 70 years to run) to the LCC, but later withdrew the offer. Valuers acting for Brotherhoods in November 1905 described the location as approximately 150 yards from Westminster Bridge Road, with frontage of 155 feet along the River Thames – the London Eye now stands on part of the site. Extensions had almost doubled the size of the original Belvedere Road factory. The valuers reported that this 'unusually valuable waterside site of about 33,500 sq. feet 'had buildings made of stock bricks with red brick and stone dressings and consist of lofty Workshops spanned by glazed roofs, paved with blue Staffordshire bricks, laid with tram lines through the various departments.' It had an unrivalled situation for the City, West End, and all of south London, besides being close to Waterloo station and Nine Elms goods depot. They suggested £85,000 compensation, but after protracted negotiations the land was sold to the LCC for £50,000. Later, when construction of the new building began, the Thames was dredged along the bank. All manner of old tools, faulty castings, and other scrap was found. Since one of the doors of the old machine shop had opened on to the river it was obvious that if anything had gone wrong it had been dropped in when no-one was looking!

Surveys of a number of centres resulted in the decision to purchase 100 acres of land at Walton, on the northern outskirts of Peterborough, 76 miles north of London. The city was well served by rail and road, there was ample space, and a large potential labour force in the railway works at New England and other local engineering works. The similarity of the city and company names was fortuitous.

The main site comprised 20 acres along the Lincoln Road, on the east side of the Great Northern Railway (GNR) (East Coast) main line from

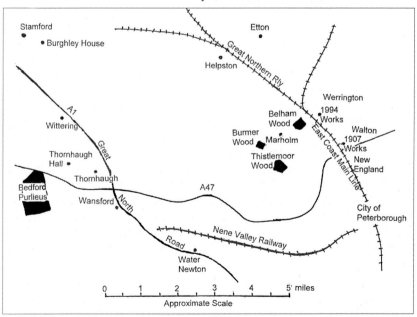

Map of area north-west of Peterborough showing places mentioned in the text

Plaque on wall of Peterborough offices. Note the lettering is central if 'LTD' and the 'S' of Engineers are omitted, suggesting this was originally on one of the works in London, probably Compton Street when Peter was first independent. *S.A.Leleux*

Bust of Peter Brotherhood in the entrance to the 1907 offices at Peterborough. *S.A.Leleux*

King's Cross to Scotland, with a further 80 acres on the other (west) side of the railway. The larger area was never used, due to difficulties in bridging the railway, and for many years it was rented to a local farmer. Construction began in mid-October 1906. Handysides of Derby supplied the steelwork. They had difficulties due to the great demand for steel for rebuilding San Francisco, destroyed by earthquake the previous April.

It had been hoped to open the works in March 1907, but delays to the steelwork caused postponement, probably to May, and the first job was turned out at the new premises on 15th July, 1907. Appropriately, it was a brass casting for a high pressure air compressor for the Admiralty. Over 40 high pressure air compressors were made for the Admiralty in the six months following the move.

Production was progressively transferred to Peterborough without any loss of output. The majority of machine tools from Belvedere Road were taken to Peterborough and many new machines were purchased. Many of the employees came too, moving to new houses that the Company had built in New England. *The Citizen* of 13th February, 1907 reported that there was the prospect of 290 new houses being built on former allotments in New England:

> The first sod has already been cut for three new streets through the property, and these thoroughfares will give access to 290 plots, each 120ft deep, on which substantial houses for Messrs Brotherhood's artisans and New England mechanics generally will be built. They will probably be such houses as will let

at an inclusive rental of £20 a year each [now over £1,100 – or sell at around £130,000 in 2006!]

The developer, Mr Rowe, was an enthusiastic sportsman and he named the streets concerned 'after three woods in the Fitzwilliam [Hunt] country which never drew blank – Thistlemore Road, Belham Road and Burmer Road.' (These woods are all close to the village of Marholm.)

As the time for the move from Belvedere Road approached a list was displayed in the works, inviting those who were willing to go to Peterborough to sign. Many had no idea where it was – St Petersburg in Russia was one suggestion! An undated newspaper article, presumed early June 1907, reported that Brotherhood's works was to open in three or four weeks. 'It is estimated that upwards of 300 men will be employed at the Works, but it is not intended to bring that number of old employees from the London works.' As a result, the firm was inundated with applications from 'all over the country'. It was thought that housing might be a problem but 'there are about 20 in readiness for the men at Walton and a similar number at New England (the next suburb towards the City Centre).

Most of the actual moving was done by the South London Pantechnicon Company, whose bills were paid in October (£144-16-2), November (£36-2-7 & £34-17-6). This suggests that the greater part of the move was in the autumn, confirmed by the Wages Summary Book for July 1906 to June 1910, which survives. The weekly wages in 1906 were:

Draughtsmen	51/-
Pattern makers	43/9
Smiths	41/-
Moulders, Fitters, Turners	40/-
Labourers	24/-
Boys	8/-

The London labour force averaged 244 men and 31 boys, with a weekly wages bill of £508. From 5th September to 31st October, 1907 inclusive there are dated but blank pages in the wages book, and then it is filled in weekly again. This probably marks the closure of the London works and full transfer to Peterborough. By July 1908 241 men and 54 boys were employed, but at lower rates than in London as the weekly wages bill was £469. Numbers remained at about this level until October 1909. From then until June 1910, when the book finished, there was a steady growth in the numbers employed to 330 men and 57 boys.

The Company provided Bridge House, about 250 yards south of the works beside the Midland & Great Northern Railway line to Wisbech, for the works manager. Mr Johnson from London lived there until he retired in 1915. He was succeeded by Osland Jones who was the last manager to use it.

Stanley lived at the Haycock, Wansford, until his new home was built in the village of Thornhaugh, about eight miles west of Peterborough close to the Great North Road (A1). The large house was designed by his architect brother-in-law George Crawley, and built in 1911 by the Peterborough firm John Cracknell Ltd who had previously built the firm's new offices. It was 'in the Tudor style', made of local stone. One quarry was later partially filled in and converted into ornamental ponds in the gardens, and there was another quarry in Bedford Purlieus, a large wood nearby. Originally the house had three storeys but the upper one was removed following a major fire in November 1937. Since Stanley's death the house has had several owners, including being at one time a guest house for the Peterborough firm Perkins Engines Ltd.

The new works had a frontage of about quarter of a mile along Lincoln Road, with the offices facing the road. Inside the main entrance was a circular hall with a glass-domed roof. Two white busts were placed in niches in the hall. The one on the left was of Peter 'so realistic you would expect him to speak to you', said a 'London' man. The other was of his father-in-law, Sir Frederick Seager-Hunt, whose capital had enabled Peter to become independent. Outside, the guttering was initialled 'PB' and dated 1907. Over the entrance was a brick representation of the Company's symbol, a radial engine, and on each side of the entrance was a slate plaque, gilded, with engraved lettering 'Peter Brotherhood Ltd Engineers'. These plaques were probably from Crompton Street, as the writing was central only if 'Ltd' and the 's' of 'Engineers' were omitted.

An internal road separated the offices from the noise of the works, which covered 7.5 acres in 1926 after expansion during the war. About 60 per cent of the roof was glass. The works had a siding from the Great Northern Railway (later LNER) main line. Branches served the coal bunkers (monthly consumption in October 1911 was 245 tons), oil tanks and foundries, and one went into the packing shop. Shunting was mainly carried out by hand or tractor, although in the 1920s the Company used a 35hp paraffin locomotive of their own design and manufacture. This was based around the firm's tractor (*see next chapter*) with the addition of flanged wheels. The main shops were connected by a narrow gauge railway, of about 18in. gauge, with turntables instead of

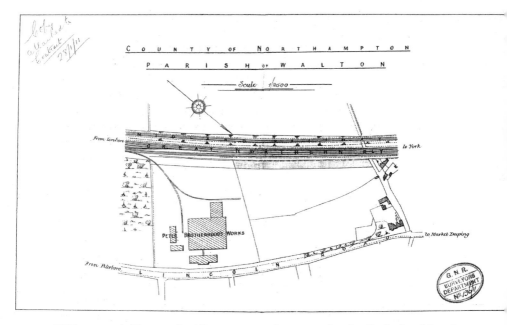

GNR map, probably part of a siding agreement document, showing Brotherhoods' works, with the offices in front, and two sidings connecting with the main line for receipt and dispatch of goods. Behind the four tracks of the Great Northern main line is the double track Midland Railway line from Stamford to Peterborough. Dated 28th January, 1911.

Collection S.A.Leleux

points, which was used to carry components in small trucks from one department to another.

Two long serving members of staff joined in 1907, and their 50 years of service was duly reported in the 2nd August, 1957 issue of the *Peterborough Standard*. Mr William Thomas Law had joined as an apprentice fitter on 29th April, 1907, but soon became a turner, and was still, in 1957, employed in the heavy turning shop. A future Works Manager and Company Vice-Chairman, Mr W.T. Freestone had joined in October 1907, coming from the firm of Blackstone, engine manufacturers, at nearby Stamford. Initially he operated a vertical boring machine, and his brother was a striker in the forge.

For some years it had been observed that torpedoes had slightly increased speed and/or range when fired in warm water. In 1907 the Hardcastle torpedo was invented which included a device for heating the air used for propulsion. This roughly doubled the power available, so either the range could be doubled or the speed increased by about 10 knots. Thus, for example, at 1,000 yards range the speed rose from 35 to 43 knots, and at 4,000 yards 20 knots rose to 30. It is believed that eventually Hardcastle became a Brotherhood employee.

The production of impulse steam turbines was commenced in 1907. For many years they were an important part of the Company's output, being manufactured in sizes up to 10,000hp. By 2000 Peter Brotherhood Ltd was the only remaining British steam turbine builder.

Stanley converted the firm to a private limited company, Peter Brotherhood Ltd, registered on 16th December, 1907 with Registered Offices at 53 Parliament St, Westminster. Mr Bryant was Manager and Mr Carnt Assistant Manager.

On 27th May, 1908 the contract for an electricity generating set for 'London University Building South Kensington' was signed. Oxygen and hydrogen compressors, with four stages reaching 1,800psi, were first made in 1910 and supplied to the Balloon Section of the War Office. Demand for the 3-cylinder radial engine declined but orders for other products steadily increased over the years to 1914. Up to the outbreak of war the output mainly comprised: high and low pressure compressors, 'electric light' engines (single crank simple and 2-crank compound types), single crank tandem compound steam engines, centrifugal pumps (up to 700 gallons per minute against a head of 40ft), steam turbines, torpedo engines, compressed air fittings, vacuum and pressure gauge testing apparatus, and fluid friction dynometers.

Most of the dynamos for 'electric light engines' and the motors for driving compressors were supplied by Laurence, Scott & Co., but electrical gear was purchased from other companies too, including British Thompson Houston, British Westinghouse, Dick, Kerr, Phoenix Dynamo, and Siemens Brothers. On several occasions over the years the Company considered manufacturing its own electrical equipment but it never did so. One of the first turbines built was coupled to a Dick, Kerr DC generator and early in the First World War was installed on the test bed to supply current for the lighting load. It ran continuously for four years until the commutator disintegrated, throwing molten copper around the erecting shop, fortunately without injuring anyone. Another of the first turbines drove a generator in Islington Corporation power station.

On 9th January, 1912, with the international situation becoming increasingly tense (following the Agadir Crisis of 1911), the Board minuted:

It was decided to commence a night shift at the earliest possible moment in order to cope with the Torpedo Engine work at present in hand, and the

Torpedo parts likely to be secured to the order of Messrs Whitehead & Co.
[And] In response to Messrs Whitehead's enquiry, it was decided that we
should quote them for all the Torpedo parts which they desire us to make.

Soon there were also domestic problems. On 12th March the Board
resolved to continue normal work during the Coal Strike, unless
prevented by a lack of foundry coke. A week later it was decided to keep
going until Easter, and if necessary prolong the Easter holidays. Despite
this, on 28th March it was agreed that due to shortage of coal, it was
necessary to close the works from Thursday 4th April until Monday 15th
April.

In June 1912 the Directors decided to make several extensions to the
works. The question of giving fortnight's leave to Territorials (part-time
volunteer soldiers) was discussed, and it was agreed that as the period
of training did not coincide with the week in August when the works
was closed, only one week's leave should be given. In October there was
a report of inconclusive discussions between Mr Arthur Evans and Mr
Bryant 'for the manufacture and sale of Semi-Deussal [sic] type of oil
engines'. In December it was decided to order another Babcock & Wilcox
boiler (price about £1,000) and underfeed stoker gear (so the coal fuel
would no longer have to be manually shovelled on to the fire) costing
£250 from the Underfeed Stoker Co. The following December it was
agreed to fit stokers to the other two boilers.

As 1912 moved into 1913 the works were very busy. The Board noted
that

> at the present time, when additional satisfactory workmen are not easily
> obtained, every opportunity should be taken to advance deserving improvers,
> apprentices and youths to more responsible work. So far as this has been done
> recently, the results have been satisfactory.

The May 1913 Board meeting considered an incident involving an
employee, Mr Stallard, who had sent a circular letter offering details of
an air compressor he had invented during his employment at
Brotherhoods. It was decided that

> Mr Brotherhood should interview Mr Stallard and if he has no satisfactory
> explanation that his services should be dispensed with. Furthermore, it was
> decided to draw up 'a formal agreement to be signed by those who had special
> opportunities of gaining knowledge of the firm's manufactures, ensuring that
> all inventions and discoveries made by such a person during his employment
> by the Company should be deemed to be made by him for and on behalf of the
> Company.

A future key figure joined early in 1913, and in July the Board minuted

> Mr Neal having been promised his salary should be £4.0.0 per week (i.e.
> £225pa), or £1200pa if he should prove satisfactory after a 6 months trial, it was
> decided to give him this amount as promised.

Alexander Marcus Neal had lectured on motors at nearby Oundle School since 1905. He had been a lieutenant in the Officers Training Corps, had played fives, and had organized geological expeditions. He was working on Brotherhood's test bed in 1915 when he was made personal assistant to Capt A.J.Carnt, one of the Directors. When Carnt retired Neal became a Director in his place, and was Chairman for over 20 years following Stanley's death in 1938. Carnt used to accept and acknowledge an order, examine the price, and then call in the shop foreman to tell him the maximum cost he could incur.

Orders in 1913 included: 155 high pressure and 48 low pressure compressors, 179 steam engines ranging from 7 to 250kW, 45 steam turbines, 51 centrifugal pumps, 18 3-cylinder air engines, 177 hydraulic

motors, and unspecified numbers of torpedo engines. The hydraulic motors were small Pelton wheels, driven by water at 1,000psi, for generating current, up to 25amp at a constant 20 volts, for firing guns in ships' turrets. This volume of work kept the works very busy, so that when war broke out it was in an excellent position to supply increasing numbers of the machinery listed, as well as many other items.

Vertical engine and centrifugal pump for *HMS Warspite* 1913.One of four 15$^1/_2$ & 24 x 9in. 2-crank compound engines arranged for direct coupling to a 28in. centrifugal pump capable of delivering 18,700 gallons per minute against a head of 34ft.

The Peter Brotherhood Sports Club opened in 1908 with 20 members who played football and cricket at a ground off Marholm Road. In 1911 it moved to a playing field behind the Paul Pride Inn, and 1918 to a site at New England. In early Peterborough days there was an annual works outing to Skegness, although latterly this was restricted to foremen and above.

As soon as war was declared in August 1914 the works became a restricted area and a military guard was provided. The guard room stood on the site of the later fire station. No-one was allowed into the works without a pass, and all employees were issued with a buttonhole badge having the inscription 'On War Service'. Between August and the end of 1914 the Admiralty and other shipyards increased their orders to a total of: 87 low pressure air compressors (for submarines), 217 high pressure air compressors, 187 steam engines, 120 fans, 1,226 torpedo engines, 74 torpedo tubes, and 63 submarine bilge pumps.

The vertically enclosed steam engines were known as electric light, pump, or fan engines, depending on their use, and differed in details.

```
                    NOTICE.


        These works will be closed for the Christmas
    Holidays from 5.30.p.m. on Thursday the 24th inst.,
    until 9.a.m. on Monday 28th.

                    _____


        In view of the requirements of the Admiralty at
    the present time it is quite impossible to grant any
    extra leave beyond the time stated and we feel sure
    that all will recognise this fact, and by returning to
    work at the proper time, show that the necessity of
    their services here at the present time is understood
    and that the appreciation which the Admiralty has
    expressed if their services to King and Country has not
    been undeserved.
```

Works notice about Christmas Holidays, December 1914. Typed in purple ink, with the two underlines in red.

Electric light engines had a heavy flywheel and were coupled to their generators. Pump engines needed no flywheel as the pump impellor acted as a flywheel. These engines had brackets which bolted on to the pump casing. Engine and pump crankshafts had solid half-couplings which were bolted together. Fan engines, used to provide the forced draught for stokeholds, did not have flywheels either, but had a long 'snout' to support the extended crankshaft. The fans were of the overhung type. The fans themselves were handmade by a couple of specialists who toiled in a corner of the works.

High pressure compressors for were of four main types: for submarines, patrol vessels, destroyers, and cruisers. Brotherhoods supplied a lot of ancillary equipment too, so that the installation for a typical destroyer included:

2 Y6 steam driven compressors
1 set spare gear
1 separator column (to removed moisture)
2 20ft metallic hoses
6 charging columns
6 reducing valves
2 reservoirs each of six bottles, 6ft 7in. by
   8.5in. outside diameter, air service piping,
   bulkhead and deck fittings, etc.

The spares were strapped to a piece of $^3/_{16}$ in. steel plate which was mounted on a convenient bulkhead near the compressors. The compressors had solid bronze cylinder blocks surrounded by copper cooling coils, which were enclosed within a bronze 'bonnet' the full diameter of the cylinder block. The plungers were bronze or monel metal and had fibre piston rings. As the rings had a life of only eight hours the design allowed for quick and easy replacement.

For years, Brotherhoods had manufactured small numbers of a very simple pressure gauge testing apparatus. During the war many more were supplied as the gauge gave quick but accurate readings. Similarly, hydraulic test pumps, which could easily reach 5,000psi with hand operated gear, designed for use within the works, were supplied in quantity to test compressors on board ship. All these were standard lines, only the demand had changed, but soon new products were being designed and made to meet the needs of the armed forces.

On 17th November, 1914, in order 'to accelerate the delivery of Torpedo tubes and other engines', the Board decided to order about 50 machine tools, total cost £10,800. The Christmas holiday was to be as normal, from 5:30pm on Thursday 24th December until 9am on Monday 28th December. By the February 1915 Board Meeting the Directors noted 'owing to war conditions ... necessitating the maximum overtime should be worked, in addition to night shift and Sunday work ...' The pressure continued, and in May the Board decided:

> In view of the urgency of the work at the present time, it was decided to curtail the usual Whitsuntide holiday, but on condition that the men returned to work on Tuesday it was resolved to grant them a holiday on Whit Monday and if the number of men returned to work on Tuesday was satisfactory to grant a holiday on the last Sunday of every month.

In June 1915 'it was decided to increase the lavatory accommodation for the Torpedo engine shops', which was probably to accommodate women workers.

As a result of urgent requests made 'at several conferences between Mr Bryant and the Naval Ordnance Authorities' it was agreed in July 1915 to manufacture 4in. gun mountings, the necessary machinery being ordered at the August meeting. A minute of 21st August reflects the fact

450hp 18-cylinder Green petrol engine for coastal motor boats, with three banks of 6 cylinders. The levers operate the clutch and reversing gear.

that Japan was one of the Allies in the First World War, authorizing an agreement between the Company and the Koba Steel Works of Koba, Japan, as licensees for their manufacture of air compressors and accessories to the Japanese Government.

After the Navy came the Army! A minute dated 4th September, 1915 noted an urgent request from the Director General of Munitions

> that we should undertake the manufacture of howitzer sights was discussed, and it was decided to endeavour to meet the case by putting up entirely new shops for the purpose.

A large new shop, later called the old gun shop, was opened to manufacture mountings and sights for 12 pounder and 4in. naval guns. Gun sights were produced in a new low shop on the north side of the offices which became the general stores. The Government Inspector here was Dick 'Howitzer' Jones. He did not get on very well with W.T.Freestone, who had been, promoted turret shop foreman early in 1915, and soon after to sight shop manager. In this, 'Howitzer' Jones was probably among the first in a long line of sufferers! Freestone's promotion to the sight shop left the turret shop foreman's post empty so it was filled by William Thompson, a turner in the heavy turnery. His promotions closely followed Freestone's, but he actually became Chairman from 1961 to 1965. New shops totalling 2.25 acres were erected during the war.

Towards the end of the war the iron foundry was moved out of a bay in the main works (later used by the fitters) to a new building on nearby Fox Covert. A large pond had to be drained when the site was cleared. The new foundry was equipped with an 11 ton ladle, made by Brotherhoods themselves from rivetted steel plates.

A new shop was built on the south side of the works for the manufacture of 450hp Green engines, which had three banks of six cylinders in line and were used to power coastal motor boats.

James Blades (1901-1999), who later became a professor at the Royal Academy of Music, joined the Company as an apprentice in September 1915, leaving in 1919. He is probably best known for playing the signature on J.Arthur Rank films, three drum beats on a 30-inch Chinese tam-tam, synchronized with the film of the heavyweight boxing champion Bombadier Billy Wells miming at a huge gold-painted papier mache disc. In his autobiography, *Drum Roll* (Faber Books, 1977), he describes his first days at the works. He was collected at the works entrance by George Snow, who took him to the drawings store, via the time office where he was given 'a number (722), my time card, and a pass which not only allowed me to enter and leave the works, but testified to my doing my bit for my 'King and Country". James became the assistant to a couple of clerks both over 70. He had to issue drawings on request and to scour the works looking for any that had gone astray. His basic hours were 6am to 5.50pm, Monday to Friday, and 6am to noon on Saturday: 54 hours after allowing for 45 minutes breakfast (8.15 to 9.00am), and one hour dinner break each day, for which an apprentice was paid 5/-. Due to overtime he actually earned over 7/- in his first week, and thereafter worked almost the same hours as other day workers.

Double shift hours were 6am to 6pm, and 6pm to 6am, with Saturday night off and one free Sunday per month. Day workers doing one shift worked 6am to 8.30pm on Monday, Tuesday and Thursday, finished at 5.30pm on Wednesday but 'worked through' from 6am Friday to 12 noon Saturday, and on three Sundays each month they worked 9am to 5.30pm. Arriving more than three minutes late cost a man quarter of an hour's pay. Summer Time was introduced for the first time in May 1916. It started one Sunday but many men had forgotten to change their clocks and so they arrived an hour early for the 9am shift!

Some of the men James met in the various shops had tales to tell about going to sea in battleships to test the firm's equipment (this was one reason why he had chosen Brotherhoods in the first place), and there were various pranks. They ranged from sending a new lad to the stores to obtain a handful of half inch holes, to holding a man in conversation while a confederate painted the heel of his shoe white:

> To say that life at Brotherhood's was pleasant is much of an understatement. Parodies of well-known songs were used as the occasion demanded. As a man was explaining something to an apprentice a wag would begin 'Tell me the old, old story' or 'He knows all about it'.

James began his apprenticeship as a fitter working with a very tall chargehand, Bill Churchyard, whose vice was raised on blocks, and next to him was Billy Conyers who was so small that he had to stand on a block to reach his vice. After a couple of days' trial, Big Bill and Little Bill initiated him according to the ancient custom of the bench. This included an explanation of the tools of his trade, a lecture on the conduct expected, and smearing oil on a private part before ornamenting it with a piece of cotton waste. His obituary in *The Times* (25th May, 1999) noted that

> His boyhood training as a turner and fitter stood him in good stead throughout his career, for he was always able to improvise fittings and instruments and to

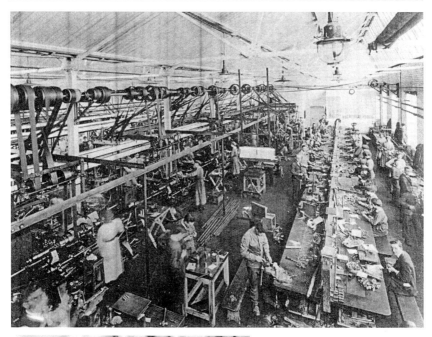

Above: Men and women fitters in the First World War. Note the line shaft supplying power by leather belts to the machines below. At a convenient place in the power transmission belts to every machine there was a pair of pulleys, one fixed to the shaft and one loose on it. A lever enabled the machine operator to move the belt from the free pulley to the fixed one, or vice versa, so the machine could be started or stopped at will. In addition, many machines (such as in the bottom left corner) had a stepped drive pulley having 3 or 4 different diameters, so the machine's speed could be altered by changing the step used.

Woman wearing a PB overall working at a vice in the First World War.

Some Brotherhood female employees. Unfortunately the occasion justifying table cloths, flowers and possibly cakes is not recorded. Women wearing pale overalls could have worked in cleaner areas than those wearing dark overalls.

Workshop in 1919, with a gun suspended from the overhead crane and a larger gun standing near the far wall.

make all the gadgets necessary to replace the third and fourth hands with
which so many composers seem to think all drummers are blessed.

An annual event after dinner on Christmas Eve, watched by men and
management, was the Bun and Lemon Competition. A boy from each
department competed to eat the flesh of a lemon (but not the peel) and
then a currant bun, for a prize of one shilling. The boys stood on a long
bench and a man held a newspaper beneath each to catch any crumbs.
Everything had to be eaten! The key to success appears to have been 'to
eat slowly and swallow every morsel before taking another bite'. The
winner had to sing a song of his own choice before receiving his prize.
Despite being the smallest boy in the contest, James was urged on by
cheers from the audience, so he won and 'beat a boy from the Light
Turnery by about three mouthfuls'. He was 'cheered, and two of the
chaps from our bench carried me shoulder high round the shop'. The
foreman gave him an extra sixpence and 'took off his bowler hat which
all foremen wore in those days and placed it as a crown on my head'.

Family connections have already been mentioned. The father of one
employee, Rue Hardy, was a Brotherhood fitter and had taught his son
how to use tools before he joined the firm. His first job in November
1915 was filing burrs off mine covers in the torpedo fitting shop under
foreman Stokes. Stokes wore a lounge suit and bowler hat, with a watch
chain across his waistcoat. On his first day Kemp-Welch, the head of
department, passed by and spoke to the lad. 'How long have you been
here?' 'I started this morning, Sir.' 'You know how to use the tools then.'
Rue adds that he never looked back from that day, and retired in 1966 as
Deputy Manager of the Beer Department.

The works toilets were the responsibility of 'Dan, Dan, the lavatory
man'. Dan demanded 'Number and Department!' from all who visited
his establishment. These were noted, together with time of arrival, and
you were allowed 'Ten minutes only!' Attempts to stay longer brought
Dan back: 'Number ***, Out!' Dan's squares of newspaper were cut as
true as a die, but were unsatisfactory reading as they rarely contained a
whole article!

The first orders for buoys, naval mine firing mechanisms, depth
charges and their firing pistols were placed in 1915. In the following year
one of the Sandford brothers (who later distinguished themselves in the
Zeebrugge Raid in April 1918) was in the works, supervising the
construction of Sandford Generators, a type of un-moored oscillating
naval mine. The mine was kept at a fairly constant depth after laying by
a mechanism which adjusted its bouyancy, using a charge of

compressed ammonia gas controlled by a hydrostatic valve. The use of drifting mines was long the subject of discussion and it seems that the only occasion they were laid was in January 1918 in the Heligoland Bight. Their limited application coupled with manufacturing difficulties caused further production to be cancelled.

The Ministry of Munitions (MoM) ordered 25 200bhp aero engines in 1915. Stanley's brother-in-law Jack Kemp-Welch designed the engines which had two banks of six water-cooled cylinders in V disposition. It is thought that this was the first time water cooling had been used in an aero engine. When the contract had been given the firm had explained that no delivery date could be promised due to pressure of other work. Design and experimental work took a long time, and although by then the engines met the required specification they were not equal to the best available, although at the Ministry's request power had been increased by 10 per cent. The first engine had been completed and was under test, but work on the others was suspended. Instead, the Company concentrated on engines for tanks. As a result, in July 1917 the uncompleted contract was taken over by another firm. The development with Ricardo of a 600hp supercharged aero engine, begun in February 1916, was abandoned. It would have had four times the power of his

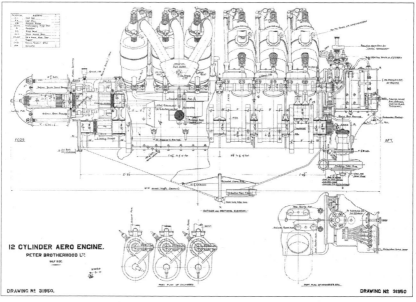

Drawing of 12-cylinder aeroplane engine, dated 31st May, 1917. Note the draughtman's skill drawing the inclined cylinders as ellipses when seen from above.

150hp tank engine, a huge increase. Both the water cooled vee-12 225hp aero engine and 300hp petrol tank engine featured in a 1920s catalogue. Kemp-Welch also designed hoisting gear for torpedo ranges. The double winch drums were driven by reversible 3-cylinder air engines.

Plans to extend the firm's private main line sidings were sealed in November 1915. By then the increase in shop capacity was overloading the works power house, where three steam engines and a single turbine were running flat out for $5^{1}/_{2}$ days per week, so it was also agreed to advertise for new or secondhand gas engines and dynamos up to 400kW as standby in case of breakdown, and to ease the overloading to the existing electrical plant caused by wartime extensions to shop capacity.

Within a few days there was an offer of a 200kW gas plant, and the Board agreed to 'purchase the plant complete in view of the fact that it was immediately available for meeting the present emergency'. It comprised two Westinghouse gas engines and their gas producers. Each engine drove a 100kW generator. The engines and generators were housed in a large corrugated iron shed. The gas producers (making carbon monoxide) were outside, adjacent to the coal yard and thus convenient for their source of fuel. Towards the end of the war two large Blackstone twin-cylinder hot bulb oil engines, driving generators through wide leather belts, were installed. (Hot bulb: The fuel was vapourized in a chamber connected to but outside the cylinder, the chamber having to be heated by a blowlamp before starting, although once running the engine generated sufficient heat to maintain the hot bulb's temperature. The attraction of later 'cold start' engines is obvious.) These two twin cylinder Blackstone engines were used until the beginning of the Second World War, when they were sold to an Egyptian firm. The gas engines, and another Blackstone engine installed in the sight shop, had been replaced between the wars by big Brotherhood-Ricardo sleeve valve diesel engines. The diesel engines were retained as standby and were run weekly, and last used in the 1973 coal strike. The firm generated most of its own power until the late 1950s, requiring a weekly trainload of coal for the boiler house (latterly shunted by tractor).

It was agreed to order more machine tools (over 50 altogether) for howitzer sights in January 1916. The Board also considered a letter from Mr Ricardo (the first time he had been recorded in the Minutes)

stating the terms under which he was prepared to assist and advise in the design of a 600 B.H.P. Aero Engine embodying his ideas on supercharging ...

and in view of the importance of the matter and the expressed wishes of the Admiralty, it was decided that Mr Ricardo's terms be agreed.

Ricardo visited Brotherhoods around the end of January 1916 and it was hoped that serious work on the design of the new 600hp aviation engines would now be proceeded with. Over the following years Ricardo sold a number of ideas to Brotherhoods for commercial development.

Tanks were first used in action on 15th September, 1916. Built by Fosters of Lincoln, they were driven by 105hp Daimler engines. However, experience showed them to be under powered, and the engine was unreliable as it relied on splash lubrication, with consequent overheating and failure of big end bearings. Engine lubrication failed completely if the tank tilted significantly, for example when climbing over a parapet. Furthermore, the engine burnt a lot of oil, leaving prominent smoke trails which made tanks easy targets for artillery. The tank concept, though, had obvious potential and was worth developing.

Colonel Stern, Chairman of the Tank Supply Committee, agreed that a more powerful, specially designed engine was essential, and specifically recommended that Ricardo should design it. In early

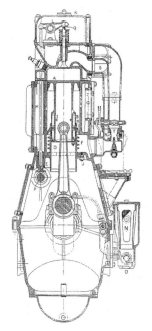

October 1916 there was a meeting with a number of would-be constructors of the engine, including Brotherhoods. It was decided the new engine should be 150hp, capable of continuous running when tilted at 45 degrees from horizontal, and under no circumstances should it emit any smoke. Its bearings had to be easily accessible for

Section of Ricardo tank engine. Fuel was burnt in the space above the piston A. Any unburnt fuel could trickle down the cylinder wall and escape through the aperture H. The piston had a cylindrical extension of smaller diameter than the cylinder bore, which was guided by the guide cylinder F. Any lubricating oil which escaped from above the guide would also trickle out of the aperture H. Thus there was little opportunity for fuel to dilute cylinder lubricating oil, or for cylinder oil to enter the combustion chamber and burn, causing smoke. The later tractor engine was very similar.

6-cylinder 150hp engine for MkV tank, 1918

maintenance, it had to be able to run for 100 hours without major adjustment or overhaul, had to weigh no more than the existing Daimler engine (25cwt) and to be exactly the same size to permit existing tanks to be upgraded easily. Harry Ricardo then designed a 150hp engine of the same external dimensions as the original.

Peter Brotherhood Ltd had constructed the first hand-made prototype 150hp engine some nine weeks after receiving Riccardo's working drawings, prepared by Mirrlees, Bickerton and Day who also acted as the parent company for the construction of these engines. It gave almost 50 per cent more power from the same 18 litres swept volume. Brotherhoods went on to manufacture 300 engines in 1916-17, alongside Brewett Lindley & Co., Crossley Bros, L.Gardner & Son, and Mirrlees. The engines had six cylinders 5.625in. in diameter by 7.5in. stroke, and developed 150hp at 1,200rpm. A full description was published in *Automobile Engineer* of April and May 1919. Some were fitted into Mk IV tanks but most went into the Mk V, first produced in June 1917. These tank engines were the first mass-produced internal combustion engines manufactured in Britain.

Trials of a tank fitted with the new engine were held in Fox Covert, a piece of rough ground beside the works, later occupied by the foundries, power house and car park. These five acres, plus 93 acres on the other side of the GNR, had been purchased in November 1916. The site was visible from the road, and local interest in the new weapon was such that one conductor on the tram route past the works used to chalk 'ITS OUT AGAIN' on the side of his tramcar! Thomas Sewell, then a senior apprentice, remembered being offered a ride on the tank, and sliding off the incomplete body when it lurched. Capt Carnt's son, Alan, was a tank officer and was impressed by the improved performance, especially the increase in speed.

Just before the war Austin Hopkinson developed a coal cutting machine, driven by a modified 3-cylinder air engine, and during the war a total of 66 engines were supplied. The standard 3-cylinder engine was falling out of use, only 12 being manufactured in the same period.

The increased demand for Brotherhood equipment had its effect on the works. The labour force increased to over 3,000, including 500 women, divided between day and night shifts. Although exempted from military service some men joined up, and in some cases were later recalled to the works, as for example Bert Hutchins who returned to supervise gun sight manufacture. When called out of the ranks and told he was going home he 'blooming near kissed the sergeant major'. During the war period four men were employed to repair the leather belts which transmitted power from the overhead line shafts to the individual machines.

As already noted, apprentices worked long hours too. R.J.'Rue' Hardy had a basic wage of 5/- per week in 1916, but overtime brought his first week's wages to 13/3. He received seven coins: a golden half sovereign (10/-), three silver shillings (3/-), and three copper pennies (3d.), in a tin which had his clock number painted on it. The empty tin (often without its lid!) was dropped into the box provided outside the pay office. With these wages he bought a good made-to-measure suit.

Peter Brotherhood Ltd was the co-ordinator for Peterborough Engineering Employers and 'acted on behalf of various other Peterborough engineering firms' in matters of common interest. A letter of 24th May, 1916 contained proposals, jointly with other Peterborough engineering employers, for an agreed rate of compensation to employees for stoppage of work due to 'Hostile Air Raids'. A reminder had to be sent on 2nd August:

> In consequence of disturbance by Zeppelin (airship) raids on Friday night and Monday night last the men are pressing us to hasten the arbitration decision re compensation for lost time.

In July the Admiralty made enquiries for new type of catapult to launch aircraft, and details of the proposed design using energy in a flywheel to haul the launching trolley were sent in August.

Chlorine gas had first been deployed by the Germans on the morning of 22nd April, 1915 with devastating effect, but after gas masks were issued it was little used, other gases having taken its place. In September 1916 Brotherhoods asked the Castner Kelner Alkali Co., Runcorn, for any special information in connection with chlorine compression, material used (bronze or copper), and whether oil could be used for internal lubrication, because 'We are asked to make compressors for compressing and liquifying chlorine (made by electrolysis of salt) into bottles for Government work'.

The 'Agreement with H.R.Ricardo & Engine Patents Ltd relating to the manufacture of internal combustion engines was sealed and signed' on 16th January, 1917, and a month later five additional patents relating to 'Improvements in Internal Combustion Engines' (probably heaters in torpedoes) were signed and sealed. Before 1914, less than 10 per cent output was commercial orders, but by July 1917 the firm was almost solely engaged on Admiralty work. In August there was discussion of increased capacity for gun manufacture for the Admiralty, at a cost of £100,000:

> In order to secure the full output from the new plant, we should require about 200 more mechanics, but for these we should train as many female workers and discharged soldiers as possible.

One of Brotherhood's employees, 18 year old Robert Lake, had a narrow escape in January 1917. A large submarine, K13, had just been completed at Fairfield's yard, Glasgow, and was undergoing trials. The K class were driven by oil-fired steam turbines, as existing diesel engines were insufficiently powerful to give the required surface speed of at least 21 knots. According to Brotherhood's representative in Glasgow, Robert Henderson, there had been 'serious trouble' with the compressors and on the Saturday Fairfield had asked for an expert to go aboard and discuss the problem with their outside manager, Mr Steel. On the Sunday the two Brotherhood fitters, Bean and Lake, identified the problems and repaired the aft machine but had not finished repairing the forward one by the time they left. They had agreed to go down the River Clyde with the submarine on the Monday, 29th January, but only on condition they were put ashore before it dived, as had been the arrangement on a previous occasion.

Submarine K22 (formerly K13) lowering its funnels.   *Courtesy RN Submarine Museum*

Henderson's long letter of 31st January said that the first that senior shipyard staff knew that anything was amiss was when Lake did not turn up for work on Tuesday morning, and it was discovered he had not been in his lodgings overnight. Enquiries showed that the submarine had made two successful dives and had made a third at about 4pm Monday afternoon but had not resurfaced. Between 80 and 90 men had been aboard. It was known that the aft part was full of water with heavy loss of life and divers had made contact with survivors in the fore part of the vessel. The survivors had communicated their names to the divers, and they included 'Brotherhood's man'. The next day Henderson was able to telegraph that Lake was safe and well, following it up with a letter. Lake and 47 others, about half Naval personnel and half Fairfields' men or other contractors, had been rescued and brought ashore late evening. The letter continued,

> it seems he was taken down unintentionally and his presence proved to be a
> very fortunate circumstance as ... it was largely due to the admirable working
> of the forward bilge pumps and air compressor and to his own skilful handling
> of them that so many lives were saved.

A later letter explained the circumstances. The ship was on its acceptance trials in the Gareloch (a stretch of water off the north side of the Clyde estuary) and everything up to the time of the accident had gone well. Lake had run the aft compressor and pumped the aft air bottles. Before the diving trials he and several others, including men

ALL BUSINESS COMMUNICATIONS TO BE ADDRESSED TO THE COMPANY

The Fairfield Shipbuilding & Engineering Co Limited

Govan

Glasgow

TELEGRAMS. "FAIRFIELD,GLASGOW."
TELEPHONES, GOVAN 393 (6 LINES).

LONDON OFFICES. 8 Victoria St Westminster, S.W.
TELEGRAMS. "KENTIGERN,VIC.LONDON."
TELEPHONES, VICTORIA 7644.

12th March 1917.

CONFIDENTIAL

Dear Mr. Brotherhood,

I am sorry that absence from home has delayed a reply to your letter of the 3rd instant on the subject of the unfortunate mishap to Vessel No. 522.

It was an extremely anxious time for everybody concerned and a particularly trying experience for those on board whose lives were saved.

I am pleased to be able to confirm all that you have heard about your representative (R. Lake) and for your information I give you the following copy of the report made about him by our Shipyard Representative on board the vessel :-

" I would like to draw your attention to the conduct of a young man
" named Lake representing Messrs Brotherhood who was on board K.13
" on behalf of our Engine Department when she sank in the Gareloch.
" During all the time we were submerged this young man stood by and
" ran the forward H.P. compressor when required; often when scarcely
" able to stand and by his conduct set a good example to others.   I
" would suggest that you write Messrs Brotherhood thanking him for
" the services he rendered to us during that trying time."

and the reason why we did not write you as suggested is that we had Admiralty instructions to keep quiet at any rate until the ship is raised.   I am sorry to say she is not yet up.

I do not think anything can be done in respect to Lake's conduct being brought forward for recognition - I presume you mean recognition by the Admiralty - and where all that "could" certainly "did" their bit it would be invidious to make any selection.

With kindest regards,

Yours very truly,

Alex Lauie

Stanley Brotherhood, Esq.,
    53 Parliament Street,
        Westminster, London, S.W.

Letter from Fairfield Shipbuilding & Engineering Co. about the conduct of Robert Lake on board K13.

Letter from the Admiralty
commending Robert Lake for
his services following the
foundering of K13.

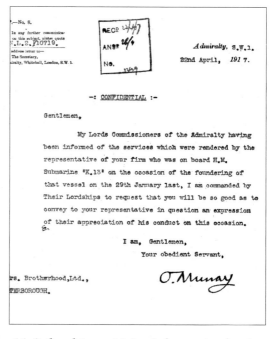

*—No. 8.

In any further communica-
on this subject please quote
.I. C. 70719.

address letter to—
The Secretary,
iralty, Whitehall, London, S.W. 1.

RECD 24/4/7
ANSD 24/4
No.

Admiralty, S.W.1.
22nd April, 191 7.

—: CONFIDENTIAL :—

Gentlemen,

My Lords Commissioners of the Admiralty having
been informed of the services which were rendered by the
representative of your firm who was on board H.M.
Submarine "K.13" on the occasion of the foundering of
that vessel on the 29th January last, I am commanded by
Their Lordships to request that you will be so good as to
convey to your representative in question an expression
of their appreciation of his conduct on this occasion.

I am, Gentlemen,
Your obedient Servant,

O. Murray

rs. Brotherhood,Ltd.,
TERBOROUGH.

from another contractor, had left the ship and joined the tender, having
dinner while the diving trials were carried out. Afterwards the tender
had joined the ship and Lake had seen Mr Steel, asking him about the
forward compressor. Informed that the diving trials were over, Lake
went aboard and had just reached the compressor department when the
ship 'went down like a stone'. There was an inrush of water, apparently
into the boiler and engine rooms, and the door leading forward from the
boiler room passage was only closed with difficulty. There were about 50
men gathered there. They soon had difficulty breathing and their ear
drums hurt. Lake suggested to the Captain, and obtained his
permission, to start the compressor and pump air into the bottles, to
reduce the pressure in the compartment, and subsequently slowly
released the air for breathing. The ship had sunk about 4pm on Monday
and air from the bottles was used until about 4pm on Wednesday, when
a ventilator was opened into the compartment. By this time the air was
very 'thick' as there had only been about 1,000psi in the bottles to begin
with. Lake also helped operate the bilge pumps as water was leaking in
badly where pipes and cables passed through the bulkhead. In the event
he ran the compressor and pumps for most of the time they were
submerged. There was no drinking water so he gave them the fresh

water out of the compressor's condenser and instead used salt water in the condenser.

On the Tuesday the Captain, and a friend, the Captain of K14 also under construction at Fairfields, had attempted to get help by escaping from hatches in the conning tower, which was accessible. Unfortunately the Captain of K14 became trapped and drowned but the Captain of K13 was successful, being blown to the surface in an air bubble and rescued. He was thus able to assist with the rescue efforts. When the ventilator was opened, water and some chocolate, their first food for 48 hours, were passed through. A hole was then cut in the bows and the men released at about midnight.

Later Mr Alexander Gracie, Chairman of Fairfield's, wrote to Stanley Brotherhood to

> draw their attention to a young man named Lake ... who was on board K13 ... when she sank in the Gareloch. During all the time we were submerged this young man stood by and ran the forward H.P. compressor when required; often when scarcely able to stand and by his conduct set a good example to others....

Later still the Admiralty formally acknowledged his help. At the end of April the *Peterborough Standard* reported that, at County Hall, Northampton, Earl Spencer, Lord Lieutenant of Northamptonshire, had presented Robert Lake of Helpston (a village about half-way between Peterborough and Stamford, five miles from the works) with the 'medal of the British Empire "for courage on board a submarine in dangerous circumstances"'. The firm had also recognised his courageous deed

> in a tangible way. In the presence of the staff he was presented with a handsome gold watch by Stanley Brotherhood, who referred to the feelings of pride and admiration they all felt at Mr Lake's achievement.

The official enquiry found that for some reason the ship had dived with the four 37in. diameter boiler room ventilators wide open, which would certainly account for the sudden influx of water.

An unusual order placed by the Air Ministry Supply Department in 1917 was for a portable liquid oxygen plant of 20lb per hour capacity. The Managing Director, C.W.Bryant, an expert in the liquifaction of gases, enjoyed designing the plant which comprised: liquifier, expansion engine of Brotherhood design and manufacture, four purifying towers, two driers, 4-stage vertical Brotherhood compressor of 4,000 cu. ft per hour capacity (chain driven by an aircraft engine supplied by the Ministry), radiators, make-up tanks, etc. The whole plant was mounted on a standard 5 ton petrol-driven army lorry. Drawings show that the timber bodywork was made by Barford & Perkins, perhaps because they could have had experience of constructing living vans for road roller crews. The acceptance test was a non-stop run lasting five days and nights, and was most satisfactory. However, the order was not repeated so possibly the project had been dropped in the meantime.

In January 1918 the company became involved with the 'fixation' of atmospheric nitrogen. Nitrogen comprises about 78 per cent of the Earth's atmosphere. It is a fundamental constituent of many explosives and fertilizers. While cheap and plentiful, atmospheric nitrogen is not very reactive and consequently, at that time, the usual source of nitrogen in a useful form was as nitrates, not least from the desert in Chile. Such a source was both limited and vulnerable in time of war. Bacteria in the roots of plants such as clover can 'fix' atmospheric nitrogen, converting it to nitrates, and various chemists attempted to find a chemical method which could be used commercially. The German Fritz Haber achieved this in 1905, being awarded the Nobel Prize for Chemistry in 1918 for his achievement. The Haber process takes hydrogen and nitrogen, under a pressure of 1,000 atmospheres and heated to 500°C, which combine in the presence of a catalyst to give ammonia. Although the initial yield was low, by removing the ammonia and recycling the gases through the reaction chamber it was commercially viable. Improvements over the past hundred years have increased the yields and reduced the pressures and temperatures required, but remember the early days when reading about Brotherhood's involvement.

On 7th May, 1918 the Ministry of Munitions placed an order for three 3-crank 4-stage compressors, and the steam engines to drive them, for its synthetic ammonia plant at Billingham and the subsequent manufacture of explosives and fertilizers. This order led to the Company's long association with Imperial Chemical Industries (ICI), which subsequently took over and expanded the Government's factory at Billingham. These compressors were the largest then built anywhere, and handled 1,000 cubic feet of mixed gases per minute which were compressed to 2,250psi. They were driven by 650hp 3-cylinder compound steam engines, taking steam at 150psi for the single 21.5in. diameter high pressure cylinder, which exhausted to two 25in. diameter low pressure cylinders. A very heavy flywheel between the engine and compressor enabled the unit to run steadily against full pressure even at very low speeds. The complete assembly, engine and compressor, was 34ft long, 20ft wide, and 17ft 8in. high. The compressors and the steam engines

Brotherhood liquid oxygen plant loaded on one of the Company's Sentinel steam lorries 1917.

3-cylinder vertical engine and compressor 1918. Note the symbolic 3-cylinder engine logo on all the inspection doors. The holes in the flywheel enable the engine to be rotated by hand during maintenance

Triple torpedo tube unit in the works.

that drove them at 200rpm were described in *Engineering* of 17th and 24th December 1920.

The cessation of hostilities in November 1918 saw many Government orders cancelled immediately, but one order which was not cancelled was for the Billingham compressors, and this eased the transition from war work. In addition, Brotherhoods developed existing products like compressors and explored new markets for them, or actively diversified and tried completely new lines. The firm worked hard to re-enter the civil market, which prior to 1914 had not been very important to the Company but was now vital.

The transition to peace time work was not easy. Stanley Brotherhood, as Governing Director, sent a long letter to the Secretary of the Admiralty on 14th May, 1919. It seems that, as many of their competitors had given publicity to their war work, Brotherhoods thought that they should do the same, 'in their own interests' and had published something, unspecified. The result had been a letter from the Admiralty saying that the Official Secrets Act was still in force and nothing should be published that 'might give information to a possible enemy nation'. Stanley pointed out that

On the outbreak of War we placed our Works and resources unreservedly at the service of the Admiralty, and expressed our willingness to undertake any work which the Admiralty considered necessary. This policy was continued throughout the whole period of the War. We undertook and carried out whatever we were asked to do, and although many opportunities arose for taking in hand classes of work which would have been useful for us for after-the-war purposes, as we had placed our Works at the Admiralty disposal, we did not take advantage of these opportunities. We have also made very large extensions to buildings and machinery to meet the Admiralty requirements. A large part of the costs remain to be paid by us, although the work for which the extensions were required has been cancelled. The cessation and cancellation of Admiralty orders and the probability that very little Naval material will be required for some considerable time, has placed us in a difficult position. Our Works at the outbreak of the War were already large, and it is unlikely that the extensions made for War purposes can be profitably used for many years for the commercial work we are likely to obtain, – meanwhile they have to be maintained and rates paid for them. We have been essentially an Admiralty armament firm. We now have to create a commercial business (which) ... will take some years..... In the manufacture of torpedo engines, we have, up to the end of the war period supplied these engines at the prices that were paid to us for many years before the war. This was done because we were particularly anxious to show that no advantage was taken by us of our position as principal makers of these engines, to the Admiralty. We also request this consideration may be given to us in order to preserve for the Nation the special experience

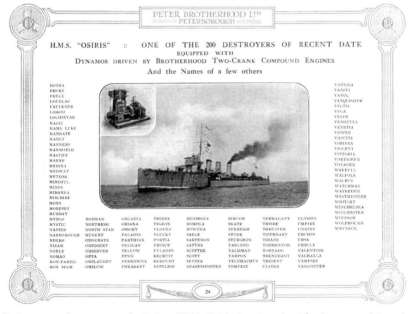

Post-war catalogue page depicting *HMS Osiris* 'equipped with dynamos driven by Brotherhood two-crank compound engines' and listing 'a few others'. *HMS Osiris* was one of 103 M class destroyers built in the First World War. She joined the Thirteenth Destroyer Flotilla in December 1916, was paid off in October 1919 and sold in 1921.

Courtesy Gloucestershire Archives, D5748/3/21 page 24

which, we believe, is a National Asset in the branches of work in connection with the Torpedo Service, in the successful development of which we have taken a prominent part since the commencement. No other firm in the country has similar knowledge or experience, which would be of great value should a National emergency again arise..... we should like to remind their Lordships that apart from machinery produced by us, including the organisation of plant and methods for rapid construction of torpedo tubes when sudden large requirements arose; we have done considerable experimental work in connection with:- Engines for aircraft, Mines, Paravanes [a device to protect ships from moored mines], Internal combustion engines without receipt of large orders for these articles. We have also, at the request of the Admiralty, supplied, without payment, designs for:- Range finders and range and height indicating gear, Gear for launching aeroplanes from warships, Means for discharging torpedoes without escape of air (splashless discharge). If their Lordships consider that our efforts on behalf of the Naval Service deserve recognition, we should be pleased to receive an expression of their Lordships' approval of our submissions [i.e. publication of list of products made].

Another source listed the following items made for Government orders (* indicates items mentioned in Stanley's submission):

Aero engines	25
Air compressors Low Pressure *	222
High Pressure *	943
Total	1165
Boat engines (Green)	21
Buoys	1630
Circulating engines & pumps *	
	230
Coal cutter engines	66
Depth charges	1636
Electric Generating Engines (reciprocating & turbine) *	462
Fan engines *	598
Gun mountings * 3 Pr, 12 Pr, 4in.	2142
Gun sights Naval *	1753
Not naval	2539
Total	4292
Hydraulic test pumps	131
Hydraulic motors	261
Mine firing mechanism *	55000
Mines	7500
total according to Stanley	25220

Mines (Sandford Generators) *	1000
Depth charge firing pistols *	73000
Pressure gauge testing gear	93
Sights for Naval Gun Mountings *	1753
Steam engines	1247
Steam turbines	24
Submarine bilge pumps	203
Submarine blower compressors	237
Tank engines	300
Three-cylinder engines	12
Torpedo engines * 18in.	5099
21in.	5554
Total	10653
Torpedo tubes, submerged & above water *	
	350
Torpedo warheads	305

'In addition (Stanley wrote) our men at each Port carried out a large amount of Repair work on vessels for the Fleet, beside innumerable small orders.' The matter does not appear to have reached a satisfactory conclusion with any speed, as four months later a Minute of the meeting on 18th September, 1919 read 'The question of cancellation and suspension of work on Admiralty orders was discussed, and it was resolved that a letter be written to the Admiralty pointing out the amount of upset caused.'

An indication of the effect of the Armistice on Brotherhoods is given by a letter written to the Director of Contracts at the Admiralty on 12th August, 1919:

We beg to inform you that the total value of the cancelled contracts by the Admiralty and the Ministry of Munitions amounted to the value of approximately one million pounds. The total value of orders received since the Armistice, a period of nine months, only amounted to one hundred and fifty seven thousand pounds...

However, the firm had not stood idly by, waiting, but had taken active steps to diversify. In March 1919 it had decided to commence the manufacture of small ammonia refrigerating sets. Subsequently, refrigerating plant, with compressors in a large range of sizes, absorbing from three to 500 horsepower, was installed in many parts of the world. Also in March the Board considered opening a Water Department in Manchester, where the design and construction of cooling towers

W 2 2 6

Cold start* single-cylinder oil (diesel) engine, based on Ambrose Shardlow design, producing 116hp at 210rpm. The flywheel weighed 5 ½ tons.(* Some early oil engines required part of the cylinder head to be heated red hot by a blowlamp before the engine could be started, hence the attraction of 'cold start'.) Note the shield over the crank to prevent oil being thrown out, and the horizontal shaft with a cam to operate one of the cylinder valves.

became a speciality. Many were supplied to Corporation power stations, for example: West Hartlepool and St Annes on Sea (both 11/19), Blackpool (10/22), Southport (4/23), St Helens (7/25), Bury (2/26), Barrow-in-Furness (5/28) and Maidstone (11/28).

Obviously sensing that steam was no longer the prime power source that it had been, in May 1919 the Board agreed to purchase the gas and oil engine business of Ambrose, Shardlow & Co. Ltd, Washford Road, Sheffield. Sixteen gas/oil engines with three gas producers were ordered, presumably for stock, in November. In the early 1920s Brotherhoods supplied two sets of producer gas plant, each with an electric lighting type gas engine, to the Eleveden Estate in Suffolk to power the estate's electricity generating plant. A member of staff remembers the engines had a rated output of 60hp, and had very heavy flywheels (4 tons) to ensure a stable output from the generators. The gas generator contained red hot anthracite, which made producer gas (primarily carbon monoxide) when air was drawn through it:

The engine would be started by hand pumping air through petrol soaked cotton waste into the engine's cylinder. The engine's low-tension magneto would then be tripped by hand to fire the charge in the cylinder. This single explosion would be sufficient to turn the engine over several revolutions drawing gas from the producer and running on this afterwards.

Having been involved with engines for aeroplanes and tanks during the war, Brotherhoods sought to use this expertise and plant. On 21st May, 1919 Humber Ltd, Coventry, was asked for information to enable Brotherhoods

> to tender for construction of the engines and gearboxes you require. We have excellent facilities for this work, which we are now being released from similar high class petrol engines and gears.

Stanley was a director of Humber Ltd. Six months later the Board noted a provisional order by Vulcan Motors for 2,000 engines at £95 each. It is a little surprising that the Company considered such a large order, as most products except for torpedo and tank engines had been made in small quantities, and the firm was not really geared for mass production, engines being made in batches of 20. Unfortunately, in May 1920 representatives from Messrs Humber pointed out to Mr Bryant various defects in the engines delivered, and the Vulcan contract ran into financial difficulties which took several years to resolve.

Cooling towers for Metropolitan Water Board, c.1919.

Steam wagon chassis, boiler in cab, underfloor engine, water tank at rear and coal bunker beside brake column.

Brotherhood steam wagon with tipping body, *c.*1920. The water tank has been repositioned behind the cab so it did not prevent the body tipping. Beneath it is the engine with shaft and gear transmission. The pipe into the smokebox door on the end of the boiler carried exhaust steam to a series of jets within the smokebox, where the steam was reheated by the flue gases and so was largely invisible by the time they emerged from the chimney.

CHAPTER SEVEN

1920s, UNDER AGRICULTURAL & GENERAL ENGINEERS LTD

Although Peter Brotherhood Ltd did not join Agricultural & General Engineers Ltd until September 1920, here is a convenient place to introduce this organization. Soon after the end of the First World War, Thomas Aveling, Chairman of Aveling & Porter Ltd, famous for steam traction engines and road rollers, and his friend Archibald Maconochie, who had made his fortune from jams and pickles and had supplied British forces in the recent conflict, suggested an amalgamation of various agricultural, transport and general engineering firms, mainly in East Anglia, so that together they would be better able to cope with the post-war decline in business by rationalizing their firms' production, and economies through centralized purchasing and sales. They would also be better able to meet American competition by being of comparable size to American firms. The idea was sound enough, but the execution was poor.

The list of companies eventually forming the Agricultural & General Engineers Ltd (AGE) combine is shown below, together with their major products.

Aveling & Porter Ltd	Rochester, Kent	Steam road rollers
Barford & Perkins Ltd	Peterborough, Northants	Motor road rollers, dairy equipment
E.H.Bentall & Co. Ltd	Heybridge, Maldon, Essex	Agricultural machinery
Blackstone & Co. Ltd	Stamford, Lincs	Oil engines
Peter Brotherhood Ltd	Peterborough, Northants	Turbines, compressors, torpedo engines, etc.
Charles Burrell & Sons Ltd	Thetford, Norfolk	Steam traction engines
Burrell's Hiring Co Ltd	Thetford, Norfolk	Hiring arm of Charles Burrell
Clark's Crank & Forge Co. Ltd	Lincoln	Crankshafts, assorted components for other firms
Davey, Paxman & Co. Ltd	Colchester, Essex	Fixed power plant, large oil engines, portable steam engines
Richard Garrett & Sons Ltd	Leiston, Suffolk	Steam wagons & traction engines, agricultural machinery
James & Fred.K.Howard Ltd	Bedford	Agricultural machinery
A.R.Knapp & Co. Ltd	Clanfield, Oxon	Hay loader
E.R.& F.Turner Ltd	Ipswich, Suffolk	Flour mill machinery
Bull Motors Ltd (Offshoot of Turners, later AGE Electric Motors Ltd)	Stowmarket, Suffolk	Electric motors

Not only are these companies quite assorted in their main lines of business but several large firms also in these lines of business, such as Fowler (Leeds), Marshall (Gainsborough), Ransome (Ipswich) were not members. They had either refused to join or had not been asked because their likely main product clashed with the aspirations of others within the group, so the hope of greatly reducing competition for home orders was not fulfilled.

Most of the details about AGE which follow have been taken from published histories of constituent companies: Blackstone (internet), Burrell (R.H.Clark), and Garrett (R.A.Whitehead), and particularly from *Reminiscences of a Lance-Corporal of Industry* (Hamish Hamilton, 1972), the autobiography of Edward Barford who joined AGE as the Chairman's personal assistant in 1923. He later salvaged two companies from the wreckage and became the Chairman of Aveling-Barford Ltd, manufacturers of diesel road rollers.

Agricultural & General Engineers Ltd was registered on 4th June, 1919, and by the end of the year most of the above companies had joined. They were mainly long-established family firms who were encountering difficulties in making the transition from war to peace, and who hoped that combination would help their firm to survive. Here was one source of weakness; the representative on the AGE Board of each constituent sought the survival of his firm, rather than thorough integration with the others, so economies through concentrating production on a few factories and closing the rest were never made, except for Burrells in 1929. It was also easy for the new Chairman, Gwilyn E.Rowland who replaced Maconochie in mid-1920, to have his own way by fostering mutual suspicion.

By May 1920 the authorized capital of AGE was £8,000,000 in £1 shares, making it one of the largest British firms of its kind. Its lack of success can be illustrated by the value of its shares. Between 1920 and 1931 the £1 Preference Shares fell from 20/6 to 1/1^1/$_2$. The only dividend ever paid on the Ordinary Shares was 4.86*d.* in March 1920, and since then these £1 shares fell to 3*d.*

Rowland had made his fortune as a tax expert, and seems to have been Maconochie's choice as successor. He had useful contacts in the City and with government officials, and to be fair worked very hard. Barford described him as a wily tactician, a dictator with a sadistic streak, who whipped his Directors into abject submission, and whose principle was to divide and rule. He also used every means possible to extract money from the constituent companies and have it paid to Head Office. But, as Whitehead said (*Garrett Wagons – Part 2*):

For all his faults, admittedly grievous, Rowland had the uncomfortable task of trying to coax a twelve-horse team to pull together when every inclination of the individuals was for each to go his own way.

Rowland also had delusions of grandeur. He thought AGE needed a prestigious London office, and in 1920 leased a site from London County Council (LCC) at Aldwych, opposite Australia House. Here, about half-way between Whitehall and the City, the new company headquarters Aldwych House was built at a cost of about £400,000 exclusive of interest. It was managed by a new company, Aldwych House Estates Ltd. There were five acres of office space over its nine floors. The central purchasing and home sales departments based here lasted only until 1920 and 1922 respectively, although overseas sales remained a Head Office function.

This, then, is the background to Peter Brotherhood Ltd throughout the 1920s. A Minute of 21st September, 1920 recorded 'The agreement between the Company and AGE re acquisition of shares was signed and sealed' and the transfer of the London office to Central House, Kingsway was confirmed. A week later a letter recorded the exchange of Brotherhoods' shares for a holding in AGE of 481,438 Ordinary shares, excluding 22,312 'which Mr Machonochie is entitled to' , and added 'PS Mr Brotherhood may wish to transfer some of his shares to members of his family.' Barford alleged that the spur which encouraged many of the firms to join was a 5 per cent commission paid to those concerned. This letter seems to confirm the allegation, except Maconochie received only 4.6 per cent.

In view of the problems facing Peter Brotherhood Ltd following cancellation of most wartime contracts, it is perhaps not surprising that the firm joined AGE, although quite how a naval armaments manufacturer and supplier of machinery for ships or power stations fitted in with the others is hard to see. Stanley was obviously not entirely convinced, since AGE only held 70 per cent of Brotherhoods shares, and it was an 'associated company', whereas AGE held all the shares in the other companies.

Going back to July 1919 the Brotherhood Board discussed and signed a proposed agreement with Mr G.H.Mann, who was to take charge of the Steam Motor Vehicle Branch of the business. In August Capt Carnt was to discuss the manufacture of the new tractor with a W.E.Martin.

First the steam wagon project, which regrettably was very short lived. Minutes record that Mann attended the Board meeting on 9th December, 1919 and reported on the progress of work in his Department. He next appeared 18 months later in May 1921 to report on progress with steam wagons, by which time at least one had been completed. However, in its

Prototype Peterbro tractor, with radial engine logo on the radiator, threshing, *c.*1920.

Minute of 7th June, 1921 'The Board noted with regret that it had been decided by the AGE not to exhibit the Steam Wagon at the Royal Show.' This was followed at the July meeting when

> Mr Mann's letter of resignation was read. Mr Mann attended the meeting & explained very fully the reasons which had prompted him to take this action. Mr Bryant promised to bring the points raised by Mr Mann before the next Committee Meeting of the AGE & it was decided that Mr Mann should be given an opportunity of reconsidering his decision.

At the meeting on 27th September, 1921 Mann's agreement was further discussed, and a further letter from him read, and it was decided to hold it over until after the meeting of the sub-committee at Head Office. (i.e. AGE). The result was evidently unfavourable, probably because Garretts were the 'approved' steam wagon builders within AGE. Although the author makes no comment, a sentence on page 28 in *Steam on the Farm* (Jonathan Brown, Crowood Press, 2008) reads: '... the firm of Aveling & Porter established a reputation for its agricultural engines. It produced traction and ploughing engines until 1921, when it pulled out of that business to concentrate mainly on road rollers.' As within AGE both Burrell and Garrett constructed traction and ploughing engines it seems to me, in view of the fate of Brotherhood's lorry, that AGE probably forced the decision on Aveling & Porter to concentrate on road rollers to remove one source of internal competition.

The meeting on 20th December, 1921 under 'Steam Wagons' minuted that Mann attended and the possibility of retaining his services for another six months was considered, but he said he had decided to terminate his engagement at the end of the year 'as arranged'. It was also suggested that he should act as Agent for the sale of steam wagons. He subsequently moved to Llandudno. The following July,

> It was decided to pay Mr Mann the sum of £250 being the amount of Royalty due to him to the 30th June 1922 under the terms of the Agreement. Mr Mann's patents held by us to be handed back to him. (Between 1920 & 1922 Brotherhood and Mann had taken out three patents· for improvements to boilers, improvements to tipping gear for road vehicles, and improvements relating to slide valves.)

At the same meeting 'It was decided to sell the [firm's] "Clayton" Wagon & run one of our own steam wagons' for works haulage.

Brotherhoods left the steam wagon market, probably under orders from AGE. An allegation of patent infringement by the Yorkshire Wagon

Peterbro tractor fitted with extension wheels in the shops. This one has 'Peterbro' across the radiator and' Peter Brotherhood Ltd Peterborough' on the front wheels' centres.

Company which also used Mann's design of boiler probably contributed to the decision, although by then the patent had expired, unless an extension had been granted due to the recent war. Anyway, neither Brotherhoods nor AGE, which had long established steam wagon building firms within the group, were prepared to contest the case. In June 1926 'It was decided to write off an amount of £10,149 off Stock in Trade & Work in Progress Account in respect of Obsolescent Stock, (including) Steam Wagons £745.0.0'.

Bearing in mind the development of internal combustion engines and use of petrol lorries during the recent war, it is perhaps surprising that Brotherhoods decided to enter the steam wagon market. However, they were neither the last nor smallest firm to try at this late stage, and they did not make the attempt half-heartedly. George Hutchinson Mann was a brother of J.H.Mann of Mann's Patent Steam Cart & Wagon Co. Ltd. In 1901 G.H.Mann, who had a workshop in Holbeck, Leeds, had patented a small boiler, and as his brother would not use it he and his partner set up the Yorkshire Wagon Company. Thus G.H.Mann was an experienced and knowledgeable person to head Brotherhood's new Steam Wagon Department.

A full description of the undertype Brotherhood wagon was published in *The Commercial Motor* of 5th July, 1921. It said:

> The outstanding features of this remarkably well-designed steam wagon are: Large loading space in proportion to the overall length, viz., 13 ft. against 18 ft. 6 ins; short wheelbase and small turning circle, an unladen weight of less than five tons and a rear axle weight within the eight-ton limit with the vehicle carrying a five ton load and full equipment; the complete protection of the engine motion, transmission and differential gear by dust-proof casings, and this, combined with simple automatic lubrication and wonderful accessibility of all the working parts, even when the vehicle is loaded; direct transmission by machine-cut gearing, combined with the use of a dead rear axle; a multi-tubular boiler with a heating surface much in excess of that of any other type of boiler on a steam wagon, thus dispensing with the need for forcing the boiler whilst hill-climbing; high economy in working owing to the very efficient boiler; steam driers, feed-water heater, and remarkably effective lubrication of the engine and transmission gear; easy and quick steering of the Ackerman type [i.e. with stub axles like on a car, and not the whole axle like on a traction engine]; free engine, and two-speed gear.

The Brotherhood wagon had a well-braced channel steel frame which carried Mann's totally enclosed return-tube type of boiler, mounted across the front of the vehicle. It had a central firebox, from which 42 tubes went each way to a combustion chamber either side, where a second set of six much larger tubes led to a small smokebox within the boiler above the firebox, and supported the chimney. The boiler had 2 $\frac{1}{2}$ sq. ft grate area and a total heating surface of 75 sq. ft and generated steam at 200psi. This boiler supplied, via a steam drier in the combustion chambers, to a 2-cylinder compound engine with HP cylinder 4$\frac{1}{2}$ in. x 8in. stroke on the off side of the chassis and the 7in. x 8in. LP cylinder was on the near side. When starting or needing a short burst of extra power HP steam could be admitted direct to the LP cylinder. This was so effective that the prototype wagon had not needed to use low gear at all in its first month of operation in London. The exhaust was taken via the pivots for the combustion chamber doors to nozzles pointing along the return tubes, so that they provided blast and reheated the exhaust making it largely invisible. The crankshaft drove a longitudinal shaft through one of two spiral gears which could move on a splined section of the crankshaft. The longitudinal shaft powered the differential, from which short shafts driven through bevel gears powered each wheel. The differential was protected from road shocks, and all the gears were enclosed. This was in contrast to most wagons of the period, where the final drive was by exposed chains. A powerful screw brake was provided. The water tank at the rear carried sufficient to run the vehicle fully loaded for 25-30 miles, and the wagon was equipped with 30ft of suction hose fitted with a brass strainer so it could take on water from streams etc when on the road. Fuel consumption was between 4 & 5lb per mile when loaded, using low quality coke. Lubrication holes were closed by a neat and simple method. In each case a stout brass split-pin was pushed into the hole and while the pin's spring was sufficient to hold it in position it did not prevent the pin being withdrawn easily when required.

Everywhere in its design this wagon displays a sound knowledge of engineering principles, at which one cannot be surprised when it is realised the makers have had many years' experience in the building of high-speed steam engines, petrol tractors [sic], and other forms of mechanism In no place throughout its design could be find any traces whatever of slipshod work

The prototype had been supplied to Schweppes, manufacturers of table waters, in early 1921. This was probably no coincidence, as the Brotherhood family owned at least 90 per cent of the Schweppes shares! A second wagon, and perhaps the third, had a tipping body, with the water tank repositioned behind the cab. These last two were used by the works for general haulage, taking compressor parts to Billingham and a complete ice making plant for J.Lyons & Co. Ltd to the Wembley Exhibition. Later they were used internally and one survived until the 1950s. Despite their good design, only these three wagons were built altogether.

Somewhat more successful was the tractor, intended to use expertise and equipment from tank engine manufacture. Even before joining AGE, Brotherhoods had engaged Joshua Howard, from the well-known Bedford agricultural machinery manufacturers James & Frederick Howard Ltd, to design it, and he was well aware of farmers' requirements. He attended and reported 'on the progress of Tractor work' to the monthly Board meetings from November 1919 until February 1920, but progress was slow. At the last meeting 'it was decided to increase the order for Paraffin engines for drawing Ploughing Tractors from 3 to 4.'

On 8th June, 1920, 'Mr Howard attended the meeting & the Tractor specification for distribution at the Royal Show was approved. It was decided that enquiries for material for 500 tractors be sent out.' The July Board meeting agreed that these tractors were to be ordered for stock, with delivery to commence in February and to be completed by July 1921. The Brotherhood 'Peterbro' tractor was awarded a Bronze medal of the Royal Agricultural Society of England at the 1920 Lincoln Tractor Trials.

The tractor and the Company were described in the magazine *Old Tractor* between January and May 2005. The design was based on the American Emerson-Brantingham Model AA tractor. The chassis comprised two rolled-steel channels bolted to a front bracket carrying the front axle and radiator, and the transmission casing of the gearbox acted as the rear frame member. A 30hp Brotherhood-Ricardo 4-cylinder paraffin engine with overhead valves provided power. The engine was started on petrol and then when hot the fuel was changed to the more economical paraffin. The prototype had the firm's 3-cylinder engine logo on the radiator, but later models had the word PETERBRO here and the AGE logo cast into the wheel centres.

The piston had a light tubular stem about 50 per cent longer than the piston stroke. Its lower section had an iron sleeve bolted to it which carried the gudgeon pin for the connecting rod. This sleeve was a close fit in an aluminium guide attached to the bottom of the cylinder, and the bearing surface was well lubricated by oil thrown up by the rotating crank. The piston itself needed little lubrication as its only contact with the cylinder walls was by its rings. Carefully sized and positioned holes in the iron sleeve drew a mist of air and oil from the crankcase into the cylinder on the up-stroke sufficient to lubricate the piston. Any unburnt fuel left on the cylinder walls (a problem with paraffin) trickled into an annular sump at the base of the sleeve, whence it drained into the carburettor and returned to the cylinder, any excess being drained off as necessary. This design meant that no fuel could touch the bearing surface between sleeve and tubular piston extension, so neither was the fuel diluted by lubricating oil from the cylinder walls, nor was the crankcase oil diluted by unburnt fuel left on the cylinder walls.

The cylinder water jacket and radiator had generous capacities so that the engine kept cool even at the height of the Australian summer, and the whole mechanism was thoroughly dustproofed. There is evidence to suggest the rear wheels were subcontracted to Howards of Bedford, also within AGE. According to testimonials in a brochure, the tractor could plough about two acres per hour, with a fuel consumption of approximately one gallon of paraffin to the acre. The Ricardo tractor engine was similar to the tank engine but smaller.

Options available included power take-off shafts and a gas producer unit, so that wood fuel could be used in places where paraffin was either unavailable or prohibitively expensive. The gas producer was the

Peterbro tractor fitted with producer gas plant instead of using paraffin fuel. Fuel (anthracite, coke, etc) stored in the vertical cylinder had air drawn through it, causing it to burn forming carbon monoxide, which was then passed as fuel into the engine where it was burnt to give carbon dioxide.

Clarke-Jones type supplied by the Parker Gas Producer Plant Company of London, and not as might have been expected derived from Ambrose Shardlow products. (During the Second World War in order to save petrol, some 550 London 48-seat petrol-engined buses towed a small trailer carrying a producer gas generator which looked like a corrugated metal dustbin. Official figures stated that each bus burnt a ton of anthracite each week, needed refuelling every 80 miles, and saved about 6,400 gallons of petrol annually, although they suffered some loss of power.) A half-track version of the tractor was made in 1925, having the chassis extended backwards and the rear wheels on each side replaced by a tracked bogie. However, only one seems to have been made.

Works folklore maintained, but so far no documentary evidence has been found, that an experimental full-tracked version was constructed and given trials in Fox Covert. Apparently it was not a success, as the front end tended to rear up and had to be held down by 1.5 tons of scrap! The extra weight broke the lugs on the cast-iron gearbox so a cast-steel replacement had to be fitted.

Unfortunately the Peterbro tractor was expensive, costing initially over £500, which compared badly with the contemporary Fordson at £280 or Austin at £300. In April 1921 the Board decided to assume possible sales of 40 tractors in a budget forecast, but in the event only

Peterbro roadless tractor ploughing.

about a dozen were sold that year. AGE had suggested reducing the price of tractors, but the Board had looked very carefully into the cost and 'it was not possible at present'. In November 1921,

> A very full discussion took place on the Tractor business – the question is whether we should continue the manufacture of those in hand & for which material had been ordered, or cease at once was considered, it was decided to complete 100 Tractors. The question of reduction in the selling price was also discussed, it was decided that in future the prices should be: Gross £440/-/- & Nett £395/-/-.

However, by June 1922 the price had dropped to £350, less 10 per cent trade discount. In December 1921 the question of liability on outstanding orders for material was discussed, and it was stated that a number of the contractors had agreed to reduce their claims, the question of the amount to be written off was left in abeyance until the question had been discussed with the auditors.

At this time the works were very short of orders. Tractors were assembled from existing parts as required. Once the tractor shop staff was even reduced to a single person. The two tractor demonstrator drivers left, and used their driving skills to set up bus companies: Jack Morley operating as J.S.Morley & Sons in Whittlesey (to the east of Peterborough) and Harry Patch formed Black & White Coaches.

Despite few orders within the UK, the Peterbro tractor sold quite well overseas, particularly in Australia and New Zealand. It won a Silver medal (highest award) at Christchurch, New Zealand, in 1922, and further medals at Dunedin, New Zealand, in 1926. A demonstration in Egypt was arranged in September 1923, and agents were appointed in South Africa in 1924. In November 1923,

> Messrs Noye's [an Australian firm, based at least in Melbourne and Sydney] letter re sale of Tractors & proposals as to supply was considered – it was decided to agree to Messrs Noye's suggestion that we supply them with 50 Tractors during the year commencing the 1st July last. It was also decided to ask Messrs Noye's whether they would be prepared to take up our other Agencies ...' or recommend any other firm who might. 'With reference to Messrs F.A.Hughes & Co's proposed Tractor Agency for the Baltic States, it was decided to write Messrs Hughes asking them what form the guarantee of the Lettish [Lithuanian] Government takes, & whether they guarantee payment on a gold basis.

Noyes asked for £1,000 pa in July 1924 to actively develop a market for Brotherhood machinery in Australia, but although the Board declined at the present time it was willing to offer 'particularly attractive prices for our machinery until it was sufficiently well known in Australia.'

There were requests in 1924 for a smaller tractor, but without definite orders they were ignored. In July 1925 a letter was received from Messrs Davey Paxman & Co. Ltd enquiring whether Brotherhoods intended to exhibit at the show of The Royal Agricultural Society of Egypt to be held at Cairo in February 1926, and whether they would be prepared to cooperate with themselves and Messrs Garretts (all members of AGE). It was decided not to go to the expense of a special exhibit but to write to Messrs Fendian asking whether it was their intention to exhibit at the show, as they might include the tractor. By June 1926 tractor sales had declined to the extent that the Board decided to write off £2,000 against tractors. A letter from the Australian agents in April 1926 'with regard to the state of trade in New South Wales & Queensland & pointing out that at the present price of our Tractor they were unable to do business in the countries named.' The possibility of another firm to take over Noye's Tractor Agency was to be investigated. Even so, in early 1927 Howard was sent on a sales tour to Australasia and the Far East. In May 1927 the Board considered

Mr Howard's report on his visit to Australia & New Zealand & the prospect of business. The question of the cost of new model Tractor was discussed and whether it would be advisable to go to the expense of redesigning the Tractor without guarantee of substantial orders being placed with us.

It was not enough. Discussion at the April 1929 Board meeting resulted in the decision to send a foreman to Australia to investigate certain complaints which had been made, probably cracked cylinder heads. In May 1929 'In view of the general slackness in the Tractor department, the Board decided that the services of Mr Howard should be dispensed with, & the Secretary was instructed to give Mr Howard notice to terminate his engagement with the Company on the 7th June next.' Despite this, in July

Mr Bryant reported that Head Office were anxious that we should resume the manufacture of Tractors. The matter was discussed by the Board particularly with respect to the question of finance. It was decided that further particulars as regards proposed designs etc should be obtained from AGE Ltd.

The tractor was entered at the 1930 World Agricultural Tractor Trials held at Oxford, but unfortunately it had to be withdrawn due to piston and connecting rod damage, probably caused by a loose nut in the crankcase. This was the last attempt to market it. Although so few tractors were made and sold, possibly only 100 altogether, several survive in preservation both in UK and Australasia.

Brotherhood-Ricardo 40hp petrol-paraffin engines, tractor engines with cylinders bored out to give extra power, were supplied to the Avonside Engine Co. One powered a 2ft gauge locomotive for the British Phosphate Company in 1928. Three others powered shunting locomotives built in 1929-31: standard gauge for paper mills at Keynsham near Bristol (where it lasted until the late 1960s), 5ft 3in. gauge for Union Cold Storage, Australia and 5ft 6in. gauge for the North Western Railway of India.

Tractor components formed the basis of the works shunting locomotive, noted by the author of an article about Peter Brotherhood Ltd in 'The Workshops of Great Britain', a series of articles published in *The British Engineers Export Journal* of September 1926, but otherwise virtually undocumented. Remembering his career at Brotherhoods, G.Forrave noted that '10/25 to 3/26 [he was making drawings for] the rail run-about for the yards (with a tractor engine)' – although I doubt this was his only work for six months!

Brotherhood-Ricardo tractor engines were also made for the larger Barford & Perkins road rollers. Type OE roller engines, designed by Coventry Simplex, were being made by Brotherhoods for that firm in

4-cylinder petrol engines for small rollers under construction, early 1920s.

1920 when that company failed. It seems likely that the Brotherhood BB roller engines were a joint design between Brotherhood and Barford, based on the Coventry Simplex design with which many parts were interchangeable. One of these small rollers, supplied in 1931, was still used by the groundsmen at Malsis Hall School, Yorkshire, in 1977. The 4-cylinder Brotherhood BB engine was the original, and had given very little trouble over the years.

Returning to December 1919, having run ahead to complete the steam wagon and tractor story, the firm took out a provisional patent for torpedoes with a wedge-shaped head (axis vertical) to improve underwater stability when in motion after firing. During 1920 Stanley was appointed High Sheriff of Northamptonshire. In June 1920 an agreement was made with Riccardo regarding retaining fees, royalties and experimental work, and it was decided to drop the manufacture of oil engines. In July the firm declined a request from the Victor Engine Co., Temple Chambers to manufacture a car or chassis as 'under present conditions not in a position to do so'. Mr Dunkerley was appointed a Director.

Barford roller powered by a 4-cylinder Brotherhood BB engine supplied to Malsis Hall School, near Keighley, Yorkshire, in 1931 which was still being used by the groundsman in 1977. Note this roller was fitted with a power take-off point.

The management in general, and Freestone in particular, actively searched for orders and would manufacture anything for which there was a possible market. Even so, at the worst period in the early 1920s the Company had orders for but three pumps and the workforce was two men, one in the tractor shop and one in the erecting shop.

Coal was the vital fuel then. A coal strike threatened in the summer of 1920, and Brotherhoods replied to an enquiry from the Nation Union of Manufacturers (an employers' organization) on 30th August:

> We have sufficient coal for about four weeks working. It would probably be necessary to cease work in less time so that some fuel would be available for resumption of work during the period of restoration of supplies. Stoppage of coal supplies would involve the discharge of the whole of our employees and the financial loss would be large. To continue working until all coal supplies are consumed would be unwise as the supply of other raw materials would probably be held up for some time after coal output had been resumed, and we consider that in such cases as ours it would be to the best interests of all concerned to give brief notice that our works would close within a few days of the declaration of a general strike of the coal miners.

As one of the first events after joining AGE in September 1920, Brotherhoods wrote a letter to the Associated Firms in AGE stating that there was surplus capacity in the foundry and offering to supply castings in aluminium, phosphor bronze or brass 'if necessary within two days from receipt of patterns'. Trade became ever more difficult and for the first time in the Company's history men were put on short time or laid off. Those who were sacked took any job going. As stated above, two men, Jack Morley and Harry Patch, developed local bus services to Bourne and Stamford respectively. The lack of orders was such that the works closed on Saturdays except for the foundry and pattern shop.

An existing order from A.V.Roe & Co. for 100 35hp Green aero engines caused concern. In April 1921 it was agreed to make 20 only and cancel remaining 80, for delivery within 12 months. Despite a lot of development work on various aero engines during the First World War, this engine appears to have been the only type built in any numbers, and was mainly used in the Avro Baby, a single-seat light biplane first flown in 1919.

In April 1921 it was reported that a reduction of 25 per cent had been made in Works Staff, and 'It was decided to close the Works on alternate weeks until further orders.' Mr Bryant had been appointed their proxy and representative by AGE. Also in April,

> The Works Manager ... stated his proposals as regards further reductions in the Works. It was decided to reduce the working hours forthwith to 30 i.e. 9am to

4pm Monday to Friday inclusive. The Foundry & Pattern Shop to close for 3 weeks, provided no orders are received to necessitate reopening, with the exception of 8 men in the Foundry, & a Charge Hand, & 2 or 3 boys in the Pattern Shop.

It was also decided to terminate Agency agreements as they fell in.

The order from Synthetic Ammonia & Nitrates Ltd for compressors and gas circulating pumps for Billingham was discussed at the May 1921 meeting, and it was decided to accept the order and proceed with the work. It was pointed out that if any further plant was ordered it would be necessary to obtain special machinery or alternatively to obtain assistance 'from any of our outside friends who were willing to help us.' Repeated breakdowns of the Blackstone oil engine in the power house were reported at the June meeting. At the same meeting the Board declined Messrs Dorman's proposals for the manufacture of petrol/paraffin engines, and 'It was reported that notices re the reduction in rates of wages had been received from the Engineering & the National Employers Association, & had been posted in the Works.'

Part of the high pressure compressor house at ICI Billingham, showing Brotherhood compressors. Note their size, with about 18 steps up to the intermediate platform and as many again to the top.   *Courtesy ICI*

Major changes were discussed at the Board meeting on 22nd July, 1921.

The question of further economies in view of the shortage of work was discussed at length & it was resolved to immediately close the Green Engine shop and transfer the work remaining in that shop to the main works. It was also resolved to do the same with the sight shop. The Drawing Office staff was reviewed. Although over the past four weeks a saving of £20pw been made, even so, it was decided to 'close the second part of the Drawing Office, & curtail all work that was not absolutely necessary for production, or for estimating & endeavour to reduce the present cost of staff by 50% or a saving of £3600/-/- per annum.

Seven clerks had been made redundant in the general office and the laboratory closed, saving £1,300pa. Also,

In view of the drop in output, & the amount of work in sight, it was decided that it would be necessary to reduce the permanent wages bill by an amount equivalent to 50%, and instructions were given to the Works Manager to carry this into effect. The number of Works Foremen to be correspondingly reduced.

Also in July a letter noted that the Brotherhood torpedo engine has been used for many years in the British Navy. An agreement had been made under which a small proportion of the engines might be made in the

Torpedo Shop at Peterborough, with four-cylinder engines under construction,1920s.

R.N.Torpedo Factory, in order to ensure continuity of manufacture under any circumstances, and all the remainder would be made by Brotherhoods. In consequence, all the engines used during the past 20 years were of Brotherhood design and practically all were their manufacture. Patented ideas to improve torpedo range, reduce weight, and maximize the proportion of warhead within it had used heaters within the engine cylinders.

Things were no better by the end of September 1921, although a manufacturing agreement had been signed with Finney Pumps. However, by April 1922 matters regarding this firm were to be placed in hands of solicitors unless payment was made. In October 1923, Capt Carnt reported to the Board regarding Finney Pumps that 'all the pumps in stock should have been taken off our hands by the end of October 1923 – a letter was ordered to be written to Messrs Finney asking what steps they were taking to dispose of the Pumps.' 1,364 were in stock.

Brotherhoods had invested in the Liquid Air Business in 1918, but by December 1921 it was struggling, and a letter had been received suggesting each Director 'put up an additional £100 to tide over the

Engine and generator units for Bull lighting sets. In addition, there were 'accumulators' (glass cells) to store electricity and a switchboard.

present stringency'. As some of this new money was for the preparation of oxygen bottles, it was agreed to anneal the bottles free of charge in lieu of sending a cheque.

By the end of 1922 the firm was making lighting sets, particularly for houses in the country. They were called 'Bull' lighting sets, so probably used generators made by Bull Motors Ltd, another AGE company. They were aimed mainly at those living in areas without mains electricity, although in fact in the 1920s electricity could often be generated privately more cheaply than purchased from a mains supply. A company catalogue pointed out that a Bull Lighting Set running on paraffin for lighting a house would make a saving of almost 70 per cent when compared with the cost of gas lighting. A typical installation consisted of engine, dynamo, a switchboard with instruments and fuses mounted on a polished slate panel, and a battery comprising 13 to 54 glass enclosed cells (depending on the voltage required) all mounted on a wooden stand. As many customers did not have mains water the lighting set could be made to drive a pump to lift water into the house storage tank, instead of pumping by hand. These lighting sets proved popular with country houses, vicarages, churches, cottage hospitals, schools, golf clubs and hotels. The village hall at Thornhaugh had one, described in the 1931 sale catalogue: '**Electric Light** is supplied by a "Bull" Lighting Set (25-volt, 13 cells), which is run by a $1^1/_4$ hp Peter Brotherhood Petrol Engine housed in an asbestos-sheeted shed.' Mr Kemp-Welch attended the December 1922 Board meeting and

> the position of the [lighting] business was fully discussed. It was decided to continue the business as it was considered that there was every prospect of good business being done. It was also decided to circularise all wiring Contractors & endeavour to get them to take over the sale of the sets, offering a commission on sales. It was decided to accept Messrs Blackstone's offer to place a set in their showrooms.

The meeting then discussed the question of reductions in the staff salaries, and it was decided to bring these into operation by two cuts, on the 7th January & 4th February respectively. However, overseas agencies were being continued. The Board considered the possible transfer of the Bull Motors Ltd business, at the request of AGE, on 14th February, 1924, but was not in favour, and decided to defer further consideration 'for the moment'.

The Engineer (24th February, 1922) reported that Peter Brotherhood Ltd had made the fan for the exhaust condenser at the rear of the experimental Armstrong-Whitworth steam turbine locomotive delivered to the

Ramsey 2-6-0+0-6-2 steam-electric turbine locomotive, built by Armstrong-Whitworth and tried on Lancashire & Yorkshire Railway. *Engineering* 24th March, 1922. The condenser fan was at the rear of the tender.

Lancashire & Yorkshire Railway in 1922. The condenser created an exhaust vacuum for efficient turbine operation. The turbine drove a 3-phase 890kW AC generator supplying power to four 3-phase 275hp AC motors, two driving each jackshaft. The locomotive was unsuccessful.

By July 1923 the new AGE Head Office was progressing well, and the 'Advisory Managing Board' wrote asking how much office space Brotherhoods required in Aldwych House. It was agreed to apply for three rooms on 6th floor, total size about 40 x 15ft. The following June was the first reference in the Minutes to AGE as the 'Parent Company'

Brotherhood's real salvation at this difficult time came from an agreement with the Liquid Carbonic Co. Ltd, later the Meyer Liquid Co. of Philadelphia. For years after, bottle cleaning and filling machinery formed a large proportion of the output. The bottle cleaning machines could automatically clean the insides and outsides of up to 10,000 bottles per hour. The process included a period for soaking the bottles in a caustic solution. The filling machines were specially designed to deal with gaseous liquids and with 50 independent filling heads had the same output as the washing machines. This plant was supplied to many large breweries.

The exhaust gases of an internal combustion engine contain a lot of potentially useful heat, and such 'waste heat recovery' with conventional steam turbines became an important part of Brotherhood's work in the 1960s. However, 40 years earlier, Mr W.J.Still had designed an engine which utilized the heat in the exhaust, and also heat from the internal combustion cylinder, otherwise lost through the cooling system, to generate steam which was then used within a steam cylinder forming an integral part of the engine. The internal combustion part of a Still engine could use either the 2- or 4-stroke cycle. A paper describing the engine was read to the Royal Society of Arts by Mr Acland in May 1919. In April 1921, Mr Bryant reported to the Board on the interview he had with Mr Hogg of the Still Engine Co. with reference to the proposed licence for the manufacture of stationery Still Engines. Having inspected the drawings 'it was found that there was a fair probability of our being able to manufacture the engines under commercial conditions an agreement might be entered into.'

At the end of 1922 January a special meeting was arranged with Messrs Hogg and Acland of the Still Engine Co. '& further explained & discussed the proposed terms of a Pioneer License [sic] for the manufacture of Stationary Engines under the Still system & a standard license for Engines for auxiliary machinery driving & other purposes except for traction or propulsion.' It was decided that a tender should be sent in for the Worthing Electricity Works and that the Licences should be signed 'when mutually agreed on in modified form.' At the Board meeting on 14th February, 1922, it minuted:

> Still Engine Co. Mr Bryant read the proposed general agreement & Pioneer License ... details not considered altogether satisfactory ... Bryant should have a further interview with Mr Hogg with a view to getting several of the clauses altered in view of the loss of the Worthing Contract.

Brotherhoods eventually obtained a 'Pioneer Licence' for the Still engine in mid-1922, but, like the tractor, the project rumbled on throughout the 1920s and again proved a disappointment.

By April 1922, as enquiries were fairly numerous, the Board considered it advisable to have an engine to show prospective customers, and it was decided to 'commence the manufacture of a "4 cylinder" $12^{1}/_{2}$" x 15" engine for running purposes.' A fee of £500pa was payable to the Still Engine Co. Ltd for the Pioneer Licence, and while Brotherhoods paid it, it was done reluctantly 'but the question was to be brought up again before any further payments were made.' Two years later, in April 1924,

Mr Bryant reported on his interview with the Still Engine Co with reference to the proposed installation of two 'Still' Engines. The Board decided that before accepting the order, Messrs Still should be asked to let us have without further payment, a Pioneer License for the 2-cycle engine for land use & for the same range of power & speeds as for the 4-cycle engine.

Great things were obviously expected on the Still engine, as the Minute of 26th September, 1922 makes clear:

With reference to Messrs S.Williams & Co's [probably at Dagenham, Essex] Contract for the supply of one 250/300 B.H.P. Brotherhood-Still heavy oil Engine, the Board agreed to accept the amended agreement, the amended clause to read as follows:

In the event of S.Williams & Sons being able to obtain a supply of current on more favourable terms than those at which they can afford to generate during the first five years from the installation of the Brotherhood-Still engine & failing other means of disposing of the plant enumerated in the tender of 10/8/1922, & should compensation not be received upon ceasing to generate and supply current, then Messrs Peter Brotherhood shall buy back the plant they supplied, at a price not greater than 50% of the tender price, or such lesser sum as shall be arrived at by gradually depreciating the plant by 15% per annum from the time of complete erection, the 15% depreciated during any year being calculated on the depreciated value at the beginning of that year.

By 26th September, 1923 Brotherhoods had built their experimental Still engine, as the Minutes record 'With reference to the unsatisfactory running of the Still Engine, the Board considered that Mr Still should be requested to let us have his proposals with a view to the engine giving better results.'

Commander Sillence went to the Still Engine Company's headquarters at Chiswick and his reported was considered by the Board on 16th June, 1924:

in connection with the enquiry for 2 2- stroke cycle opposed piston 'Brotherhood-Still' engines for Dunswell Pumping Station, Hull ... it was decided to accept the order for supply & erection of the plant for the sum of £9,850/-/-.

Payment for the Pioneer Licence continued to be a concern, probably in view of the problems experienced in making the experimental engine work reliably. In March 1925 it discussed

the payment by us of £1000/-/- per annum by way of contribution towards expenses. The Board considered that under the existing circumstances these payments were not justified, & it was suggested that a letter be written to the Still Engine Co with a view to getting them to agree to a reduction in our contribution.

By November 1926 this payment rankled. A Director

reported on his interview with the Chairman of the Still Engine Co Ltd with reference to the payment of our annual contribution in connection with the Pioneer Licence. A letter was ordered to be written to Messrs Still stating the feelings of the Board in the matter & informing them that owing to the unfortunate experience & great expense which had been incurred owing to the rejection of the first unit & the necessity of making new designs & patterns the Board considered that permission should be given us to waive payment of the annual contribution until such time as the engines for the Hull Water Works are a proved success, when the question would be reconsidered.

A Still engine, presumably the 1922 experimental one, with a book value of £5,180 had already been written off that June. In January 1927,

The question of further payment of the half yearly contribution to the Still Engine Co in accordance with the terms of the Pioneer License was considered. In view of the unsatisfactory results obtained from the first engine manufactured which had been left on our hands, & the subsequent trouble & expense incurred in connection with the engines for Hull, the Board felt compelled if possible to drop the Licence – it was decided to obtain legal advice on the subject before the next Board Meeting.

Bryant had an interview in March 1927 with the Still Engine Co. about their proposed reorganization. Brotherhood's cheque for their annual contribution was then due and was to be sent. In April 1927,

Mr Bryant reported on his interview with the Directors of the Still Engine Co Ltd with reference to the payment of our Annual Contribution under the Pioneer Licence. The Still Engine Co had agreed to grant us a moratorium in respect of the two instalments payable on the 1st July 1926 & the 1st January 1927 respectively, on the understanding that the half yearly instalment payable on the 1st July 1927, together with all future instalments will be paid as & when they fall due. The Secretary was instructed to write & confirm the arrangement arrived at.

In October the Secretary was authorized to pay £500 due to Still Engine Co. under the terms of the licence. The proposed reorganization of Still Engine Co. and consequent changes to licences were still being considered the following March, and the proposed changed to the

licences were being shown to solicitors handling the Hull contracts in
April 1928. In December,

> The Board decide to engage Messrs Torkey & Sillince to prepare expert
> evidence in case of a claim being made by Messrs Potter & Co in connection
> with the plant supplied to the Hull Corporation.

It was agreed to relinquish the Still licence in May 1929, and in July the
Board was advised to take Council's opinion if agreement could not be
reached with the Still Engine Co. On 29th October, 1929,

> Mr Dunkerley reported on the present position as regards the Still Engine Co
> & the terms suggested as a basis for a settlement at an interview held on the
> 21st October.

The Board suggested certain modifications which Mr Dunkerley was to
suggest to Still. There was no further correspondence with Potter & Co.
about Hull, so no further action was planned at present.

By the summer of 1926 two 400hp Brotherhood-Still engines were
under construction for the new Dunswell Pumping Station, then being
built for Hull Corporation. Officially opened on 16th October, 1931, the
station had two sets of pumps each capable of delivering five million
gallons of water per day against a head of 250ft when running at 19rpm.
Unfortunately the Still engines were not a success, breaking down
frequently and were therefore heavy on spares. They also suffered from
lubrication problems, possibly due to high running temperatures. The
dismantled engines were inspected by the Hull Water Committee on
27th April, 1932 and it was decided to replace them as soon as possible.
Following negotiations with Brotherhoods, in July it was decided to
install 6-cylinder 275hp, Brotherhood-Ricardo diesel engines developing
300hp at 800rpm. These were officially started on 13th January, 1933. The
higher speed of the new engines required additional reduction gearing
to be supplied, two sets double helical reduction gears from 300rpm to
75rpm, driving on to the existing gears which reduced from 75rpm to
19rpm. These new diesel engines gave very satisfactory service until
1958.

The Brotherhood-Still Heavy Oil Engine, to quote the title on the
general arrangement drawing, was an ingenious 2-cylinder vertical
engine. Each cylinder contained two opposed pistons which drove the
same crankshaft. The lower piston had a crosshead and connecting rod
in the ordinary way. The upper piston's massive crosshead was
extended sideways, and a pair of long connecting rods bracketed the

Hull Corporation, Dunswell Pumping Station, *c*.1933.On the left is a 400hp Brotherhood-Still engine and on the right the six cylinder 300hp Brotherhood-Ricardo diesel engine which had replaced the second Still engine. In the background is the reduction gear for the pumps. This remaining Still engine was later replaced by a second Ricardo diesel.

cylinder, to drive a pair of cranks either side of the first one and at 180° to it, causing the pistons to move in opposite directions as the shaft turned. Oil fuel was injected into the space between the two pistons, which functioned as a diesel engine. The hot exhaust gases passed to a heat exchanger behind the engine where they generated steam at 150psi. This steam was passed to the outer ends of the cylinder which functioned as a steam engine. In order to maximize heat recovery the cylinder water jacket was connected to the heat exchanger, and the exhaust gases also passed through a feed water heater. Each engine had numerous auxiliaries, including air, feed and circulating pumps, condenser, oil separators, scavenging blower, and a separate oil-fired boiler for starting purposes. Rated fuel consumption was 0.36lb fuel per bhp per hour, giving 30 per cent thermal efficiency.

Still engines of up to 1,200hp were offered but it seems that the only ones built by Brotherhood were the experimental one in 1922 and the two for Hull, the two enquiries in 1922 from Worthing Corporation and S.Williams not proceeding any further. Kitson & Co. Ltd, the Leeds locomotive manufacturer, built an experimental 2-6-2 incorporating Still's ideas in 1927. Brian Webb in *British Internal Combustion Locomotives*

1894-1940 (David & Charles 1973) said it used steam to start and for extra power, and changed to diesel at about 6mph. 'After initial troubles ... the unit performed reasonably well in service, bearing in mind its unique design, and was developed into a reliable machine in the course of some six years of running and trials', but the prototype was never sold and no others were built.

However, Scott-Still marine engines were proposed in two types, one with diesel on top of the pistons and steam underneath (as used in Kitson-Still locomotive), the other having diesel power on five cylinders and two conventional steam cylinders on same crankshaft (using a waste heat boiler). The first design suffered from the basic flaw of cross-contamination. Oil from the diesel part of the engine contaminated the boiler feedwater (which seriously cut down heat transmission in the boiler) and water also contaminated the lubricating oil in the diesel engine crankcase. The second type was fitted in at least two Blue Funnel ships, but required senior engineering officers to have *both* steam and motor qualification. The ships so fitted lasted about 20 years, so they

Large condenser, possibly one for Peterborough Power Station. Cooling water flowed through the many tubes and steam filled the remainder of the space within the casing. The condensed steam collected in the hotwell at the bottom for return to the boiler.

must have worked. Overall efficiency was claimed at 38 per cent, with 14 per cent of the power coming from the steam side.

Going back to 1922, and to more ordinary concerns, in February the Board considered the Head Office proposal that payment of future expenses should be made by the Associated Firms in proportion to share capital was discussed and agreed.

Torpedoes continued to be a product. In March 'A letter from the Admiralty with reference to the re-assignment to us of various secret patents was read ... as far as the Admiralty was concerned these need no longer be kept secret.' Then 'A letter was read from Societe Lyonnaise ... with reference to the suggested license for the manufacture of Torpedo Engines for the French Government, it was felt by the Board that it was advisable to keep up the Torpedo Engine Work ...' and further discussion was proposed. In addition, 'the order for Turbine & Condenser in connection with the Peterborough Corporation Electricity Works' had been obtained.

In April 1922 AGE enquired how the firm would handle whole or partial closure if lockout notices became operative. It would not close entirely, but continue with such men as were available plus foremen to deal with urgent work. It was agreed the works would close for the Easter holidays, closing at midday Thursday 13th April, reopening 9am Wednesday 19th April. It was decided not to take a place at the Peterborough Show this year. In addition, 'It was decided to extend Mr Denny's tenancy of the New England Cinema for a further two years, half the cost of Insurance of the whole Club Building to be paid by Mr Denny.' At the end of April 'The lockout notices expiring on Tuesday the 2nd May were ordered to be posted.'

In May the Directors agreed to relinquish their fees up to 31st March, 1922, and in fact did this on a number of occasions through the 1920s, but despite the hard times, it was still possible to recommend a 6 per cent dividend.

At the end of May, Viney's appointment as assistant torpedo designer was confirmed at a salary of £400pa, and Sillence as head of the Internal Combustion Engine Dept confirmed at £750pa. 'The question of the manufacture of small Refrigerating Sets for private houses was brought up by Mr Dunkerley and discussed, it was decided to go on with a suggested design & prepare estimate of cost.' These were intended to be built-in, to cool larders etc., and were not free standing kitchen units.

The agreement with Ricardo & Co. terminated at the end of June 1922, and it was proposed in the future to pay for services rendered 'in accordance with their usual scale of fees'. The Foremen's Pension

Scheme was discussed, and it was agreed that all foremen under 55 should join the Foremen's Mutual Benefit Society to secure a pension of £1 per week, but 'Those Foremen over 55 years of age to be allowed to remain in their Union.' Mr Denny was granted five year lease of the New England Cinema from 1st February.

It seems that in just under two years Brotherhoods had become disenchanted with AGE, and in June had written to Mr Maconochie about the possibility of severing the connection. After considering his reply, the Board

> decided to reply that in deference to their wishes & the legal difficulties, we have decided to remain in, although still of the opinion that it would have been better for this Firm & no detriment to the A.G.E. had we adhered to the proposals contained in our letter of October 25th 1921.

Unfortunately this letter appears no longer to exist.

In September there was a proposed contract for 60 torpedoes for the Argentine Government, so Bryant was to meet the Argentine Authorities in London. In December it was agreed to seek tenders for an oil-fired superheater for the works boiler. The works closed for Christmas 1922 on Friday night 22th December, reopening on Thursday morning 28th December.

The Minutes of 8th January, 1923 proposed a financial reconstruction of AGE, but nothing appears to have happened. An advertising board facing the railway, showing the company name and products was agreed. Lastly, 'The Board decided to pay Mr Viney the sum of £100 'in recognition of his services in connection with the proposed new Torpedo Engine'. In July his appointment as Manager of Torpedo Department was confirmed, with a salary of £1,000pa from 1st January. By 1918 it had been realised that the existing power plants for torpedoes had almost reached their limit of development, due to the high rate of air consumption. Experiments were made to use 'enriched air' with hydrogen peroxide, but this was dangerous to use. A history of torpedoes, *The Devil's Device* by Edwyn Gray (Seeley, Service & Co. Ltd, 1975) states:

> The Brotherhood Company's new Burner Cycle engine killed off the enriched oxygen venture – in the same way that Peter Brotherhood's first radial engine had spelled the death of Robert Whitehead's original power unit. The Burner Cycle engine was a success from the beginning, using, at first, air and then, much later, hydrogen peroxide. By 1945 the four cylinder unit was producing some 465bhp with speeds up to 50 knots and, basically, remains the standard

torpedo propulsion engine today – a far cry, indeed, from the performance obtained from Brotherhood's first three cylinder radial of 1876.

A list of Whitehead torpedoes showing how the specification and performance changed over the years from its invention in 1866 shows the Brotherhood 3-cylinder engine was the almost exclusive power plant from 1876 to 1905, with the speed increasing by half to 30 knots, the range increasing from 600 yards to 2,190 yards and the explosive warhead from 32lb to 220lb, most of the torpedoes being 14in. in diameter with a few 18in. 3-cylinder engines with a heater which were introduced in 1907 and 4-cylinder engines with heater in 1909, which by 1917 had a charge of 515lb and a range of 5,000 yards (2.8 miles) at 40 knots or 13,500 yards (7.6 miles) at 25 knots. The Brotherhood Burner Cycle engine was introduced in 1928 giving 21in. torpedoes a speed of around 40 knots over a range of 10,000 yards (5.7 miles) with a 750lb warhead. This is what was developed in the small torpedo room at the works.

Economy was still important. At the end of January 1923 the Board resolved to reduce the amount of advertising in trade papers. The advertising budget was to be allocated: Refrigerating Machinery 20%, Air Compressors 20%, Turbines etc 20%, Diesel Engines 20%, Oil Engines 10%, Other Manufactures 10%.

Applications for patents for Refrigerating Plant and improvements in the manufacture of ice were sealed in March 1923 and Mr Kemp-Welch commenced his new duties on 1st May, 1923.

Although it had been decided not to exhibit at the British Empire Exhibition 'unless more favourable circumstances presented themselves', in May 1923 the New Zealand Fruit Growers requested the loan of small refrigeration plant at their exhibit at British Empire Exhibition, but a decision was deferred. Then in July,

> The suggestion of the New Zealand Meat Producers Board that we should loan them a Refrigerating plant for use in the New Zealand Pavilion at the British Empire Exhibition was considered, it was decided to offer to loan and erect a complete plant designed and built in accordance with our standard practice. As the cooling equipment for the Meat & Dairy Show Cases would have to be specially designed & manufactured, it was to be understood that they were willing to reimburse us for expenditure on this special material.

At the end of the First World War, Brunner-Mond, head of a large chemical company, formed Synthetic Ammonia & Nitrates Ltd to take over and develop the government synthetic ammonia plant at Billingham. In the years that followed the Synthetic Ammonia &

Nitrates Ltd engineers A.H.Cowap and H.E.Humphrey often visited Peterborough to discuss the design of larger and better compressors with Mr Bryant. Eventually Synthetic Ammonia & Nitrates Ltd became part of Imperial Chemical Industries. Thanks to the generous help of staff at ICI Billingham it has been possible to record 50 years of Brotherhood plant with a large customer.

Brunner-Mond's No. 1 Ammonia Plant was at Runcorn, Cheshire, but following his acquisition of the Billingham works all production was concentrated there. The four compressors originally ordered by the Government formed the nucleus of No. 2 Ammonia Plant, which first made ammonia on Christmas Eve 1923. The advent of yet larger compressors rendered the original Billingham plant obsolete, so in the 1930s they were modified for the compression of carbon dioxide gas in the production of solid carbon dioxide, sold as 'Drikold'. The modified compressors were 3-crank 2-stage machines, with a single first stage and two second stage cylinders. The cylinder ratios were unbalanced to admit recycled medium pressure carbon dioxide, formed in the 'Drikold' process, direct into the second stage. At some stage the original steam engines were replaced by electric motors. The modified compressors were still in continuous use 24 hours a day over 50 years after they were delivered. Three similar machines, built for 'Drikold' work, were installed in 1936.

At the end of November 1923 the Board agreed the following values of machines in stock:

1,364 Finney Pumps	£2,722
3 Wagons & Parts	£ 900
48 Lighting Sets	£3,175
Parts of 400 Tractors	£4,640
55 Complete Tractors	£12,656
Parts of Green Engines	£ 90

Just before Christmas 1923 the contract for an air compressor for Reading Corporation Sewage Works was confirmed. The Christmas closure was from 5.30pm Friday 21st December, to 9am Friday 28th December. Also in December,

> ... in connection with the Torpedo Engine Agreement with the Admiralty. The Agreement between the Company & C.W.Bryant in which it is agreed that in consideration of Mr Bryant assigning to the Company all his interest in certain inventions & patents which are being acquired from the Company by H.M.Admiralty for the sole use of the Nation, the Company agrees to pay Mr

Bryant ... The terms stated, and the royalty due to Mr A.W.Viney, were also agreed.

At the Board meeting on 28th December, 1923, 'Oil Engine sales during last six months were reviewed, it was decided to finish off all uncompleted engines, & to order castings & rough forgings for a further 14 engines for stock.' Furthermore, 'A sum of £10 was ordered to be sent to Mr Pettican as an appreciation of work done at Billingham & the absence of trouble in running the machines.'

Stanley planned a visit South Africa & Australia, and had gone by mid-February, returning by mid-May. In his absence Bryant held the key to the Company's seal, which was used for several documents at the January and February Board meetings, typical items being: Application for Secret Patent 'Improvements in & relating to Internal Combustion Engines' and Application for Secret Patent 'Improvements in the utilisation of liquids & gases for Internal Combustion Engines'. Not all internal combustion engine patents were specified Secret, and the Minutes merely recorded 'Assignment to the Admiralty of Letters Patent for an Invention for "Improvements in & relating to Internal Combustion Engines used for the propulsion of Torpedoes".' Bryant reported that a letter had been sent to the Director of Torpedoes & Mining stating that Brotherhoods

would be prepared to give an undertaking that we would accept no foreign orders for Torpedoes or their components, & that we would not admit representatives of any Foreign Government to the Works in which Torpedoes were being made by us.

He had pointed out that they did not expect a large volume of orders at the present time, but 'we believe that it would be useful to have our Works available for production & capable of rapid expansion when needed.' Prophetic words!

In March 1924 the advertising budget was reduced to £1,000pa and 'A list of advertisements to be dropped or curtailed ... to be given to Mr Kemp Welch.' It was decided to install a time register clock for the use of the staff, and a central telephone switchboard was considered. 'It was felt that there would be a considerable saving of time if various offices were connected up to the trunk system. The Board decided that the Telephone Company be instructed to carry out the work.' Sillinoe suggested a modified programme of oil engine manufacture for stock, cutting out the smaller units, which the Board agreed. An extra 10 ton crane was bought for the foundry for £450 from George Cohen & Armstrong Disposal Corporation.

The Metropolitan Borough of Islington had ordered a turbine generating set in May 1924, Brotherhoods being paid for the whole unit, and the English Electric Co. Ltd had accepted Brotherhood order for one 6,250kW 2-Phase Turbo Alternator for the project. In November 1925

> The Board expressed their satisfaction at the manner in which the Islington Contract had been carried out, & letters of appreciation were ordered to be written to Mr Dewar in connection with the design & to Mr Davis & Mr Freestone for the time they had given in connection with the erection and trials of the plant.

The Board agreed to prepare a draft licence for 'Single Sleeve Valve Engine Patents, in connection with the Ricardo-Burt engine for Rail Cars, Aeroplanes & Airships'.

By now Gwilyn Rowland was Chairman of AGE, and he seems to have begun trying to extract money from member firms. The Board minuted on 15th July, 1924: 'The contribution of £8,500 towards Head Office expenses for last year was confirmed, although a year later the agreed contribution was only £2,000.

In 1924 the August holidays were a whole week, closing at noon on Saturday 2nd August and reopening at 9am on Monday 11th August. The Board met although the works were closed, and agreed that the London agent, Mr Reid, could visit South Africa in association with several large schemes for installing refrigeration plant. There were possibilities which 'would eventually prove very advantageous to us'. Six month's absence was agreed.

Later in 1924 the tender for machinery for Walton (Surrey) Pumping Station was confirmed (Metropolitan Water Board). In November it was agreed to purchase a gear cutting machine for turbine gears 'in view of the large amount of work in hand'.

The British Broadcasting Company began regular radio broadcasts in November 1922, and in December 1924

> A letter was read from the Radio Club in connection with the Works, asking for permission to erect an Aerial in connection with a proposed wireless installation in the Workmen's messroom – the proposal was approved in principle, & Mr Bryant was asked to interview the committee.

The Christmas holiday started at 5.30pm 23rd December, the works reopening at 9am on 30th December, although the offices reopened at 9am the previous day.

A single-cylinder high speed compressor of 200 cu. ft capacity with a sleeve valve was authorized to be made in January 1925. In April the firm agreed to pay £400 towards the fund of the Walton War Memorial Hospital over four years, starting on 25th June, 1925. Mr Reid's report following his South African visit was considered, as was his request to return there. 'The Economy Policy was further discussed'. The Whitsun holiday was from 12 noon on Saturday 30th May to 9am Wednesday 3rd June. In July the Board proposed to increase the working capital from £30,000 to £100,000. It agreed to consider question of 'procuring new plant to cope with the orders placed with us by the Synthetic Ammonia & Nitrates Ltd' and deferred a decision to the next meeting. The August holidays were a week, as in the previous year.

Airships became steadily lighter as their fuel was used, and thus they tended to rise and gain altitude. In order to maintain a steady height it was therefore necessary periodically to vent some hydrogen to reduce the lift. Brotherhoods and Ricardo worked very closely on engine development, and for airships they produced a hydrogen/kerosene engine to use vented hydrogen which was otherwise wasted. They were intended for the R100, commercially built by Vickers in 1924-29. The engines weighed a total of 9 tons. The contemporary airship R101, a state enterprise, was built at Cardington near Bedford 1925-30. It was driven by large diesel engines which were started by small 35hp Brotherhood engines. These starting engines were themselves kick started, so a strong handrail had to be fitted for the mechanic to grasp to prevent himself from being propelled backwards from the gondola. Rue Hardy went to a great deal of trouble to put a good finish on the external aluminium work of the engines, only to be told to spray them all over with black cellulose! Although the R100 made a number of satisfactory flights, including a return Atlantic crossing in July-August 1930, the crash of the R101with heavy loss of life in October 1930 effectively terminated British airship development.

In the early 1920s the Company had been conscious of the fuel savings to be made if a steam turbine exhausted into a high vacuum, and used this as part of its advertising for water cooling towers, as has already been mentioned. A Turbine brochure dated 1929 gave the saving as 20 per cent over exhaust to the atmosphere. However, it went on to make the point that high pressure steam could be generated for very little more fuel than low pressure steam. Figures given showed that 1,000lb of steam at 50psi needed the consumption of 140lb coal,

Sleeve valve hydrogen-kerosene engine, using kerosene (paraffin) and/or surplus hydrogen as fuel under test, attached to a dynamometer. Built for the R100 airship but in the event not used (late 1920s).

while 180psi needed only 144lb coal for the same weight of steam, 75 per cent more energy from only 2.8 per cent more fuel. This being the case, the brochure argued the case for power generation as a by-product of low pressure steam required for various industrial processes. Turbines could be designed to exhaust some or all of their steam to low pressure mains, or to a condenser. If the turbine had several stages it could be designed to accept steam from a variety of sources at various pressures. With turbine speeds in the range 3,000 to 10,000rpm the rotor stored a considerable amount of kinetic energy and so gave a very smooth drive. Being a sealed unit foreign matter was unlikely to be a problem. In fact, during the 1926 Coal Strike a turbine had been totally submerged for six months but was able to be used again as soon as pumping had uncovered its control valve. Turbines were used for generators, gas exhausters, boiler feed pumps, etc.

When Engineer Commander Hardcastle retired from the Navy in 1925, the Board offered him 'the direction of the Torpedo Department at a salary of £1,000 per annum.' Construction of a works road between the foundry and main works was proposed in July 1925, but instead a rail track was laid.

Davey Paxman enquired whether Brotherhoods would be prepared to supply a steam-driven generating set for show at the forthcoming Laundry Exhibition (late 1925, early 1926). The Board decided to quote for a '54 B.H.P. Double acting high speed engine coupled direct to a 35KW Bull Motor [sic].'

Remembering that Peter's works on Belevedere Road had been fitted with steam heating pipes, it is strange to realise that this feature had not been incorporated in the Peterborough factory. In December 1925 the Board minuted that stoves in the drawing office were to be replaced by steam pipes due to risk of fire. In the works themselves heating was by drums of burning coke in the shops until the Second World War As a means of economizing on steam, and hence coal, it was agreed to install a 100kW hot bulb oil engine & dynamo, using the set standing in stock.

Mr Sillinoe was ill in January 1926, and as he was reluctant to retire on pension the Board eventually had to agree to dispense with his services with effect from 1st September, 1926.

Brotherhoods created debentures for £85,000 at 0.5 per cent of Bank of England at the end of March 1926, repayable £50,000 on 31st March, 1927, £25,000 on 30th September, 1927 and £10,000 on 31st March, 1928, these 'debentures to be in favour of Agricultural & General Engineers Ltd'.

In May 1926 Mr Stokes, a foreman, was granted a pension of 30/- per week on his retirement after 41 years of service with the firm. The threatened General Strike also occupied the Board:

> The general position as regards the Strike was discussed. It was announced that the Pattern Makers & Trimmers had given official notice that they would cease work that night & there was a probability of the other departments following suit. It was decided to keep the Works open for those who wished to remain at work, & if necessary give assistance to apprentices to return to their homes. The question of those employees whose services could be dispensed with, was discussed. It was decided to take out an Insurance Policy against Civil Riots & Commotion for a sum to be decided upon after getting into communication with the Underwriters.

Considering staff sickness,

> It was decided that in future, members of the Staff who might be absent from work through illness & being contributory members to the National Health

Insurance scheme or the Foremen's Mutual Benefit Society, should be paid as follows:
For the first 4 Weeks   Full pay, less half the amount received from Insurance
For the second 4 Weeks   Half pay less full Insurance

However, this Minute was rescinded in May 1927 and firm reverted to the plan originally adopted.

Even torpedoes were not exempt from economies, as the Board decided to place Captain Hardcastle and Mr Viney on half-pay as from the 1st June. Also in June 1926:

It was decided to write off an amount of £10149/-/- off Stock in Trade & Work in Progress Account in respect of Obsolescent Stock, & made up as follows:
Steam Wagons   745.0.0
Lighting Sets   149.0.0
Green Engines   2075.0.0
Still Engine   5180.0.0   [presumably the experimental one]
Tractors   2000.0.0
               £10149.0.0

A contract to supply electrically driven HP air compressors and accessories to the Imperial Japanese Navy was confirmed. Negotiations were in progress with the Italian Professor Emilio Vianello regarding drawings and calculations for a 150 cubic feet rotary compressor. Basically, this type of compressor had a number of discs on the same axle, each disc being isolated from its neighbour by a diaphragm with suitable leak-proof packing on the axle. The discs were designed so that each would compress the same amount of gas, the gas under compression moving progressively from stage to stage along the machine as its pressure increased.

The Works Manager, Mr Freestone, attended the October Board meeting to discuss suggestions regarding economy. The number of men discharged owing to lack of fuel and material and other reasons since the 1st September amounted to 100, the reduction in the main factory being 24.6 per cent and in the foundry 19 per cent. Mr Davis, chief draughtsman, reported that economies in the drawing office had been effected since July amounting to £43 per week.

The possibility of manufacturing petrol engines for lorries constructed by Messrs Richard Garrett & Sons Ltd, another AGE member, was discussed. Garrett's, a long established builder of steam road vehicles, was trying to break into the market for vehicles with internal combustion engines, but for various reasons their 1927 petrol lorry was unsuccessful, and only three were made. Brotherhoods had probably been considered as they were within the AGE group, in the same way as Blackstone was chosen to build the engine for their later diesel lorry.

Capt Carnt retired with effect from Saturday 26th March, 1927, which the Board accepted with 'very great regret.'

Railcar engines had been supplied to General Electric Co. for 'the Railway Administration in South Africa'. It seems there may have been problems with them as in May 1927 Bryant reported an interview regarding these engines.

Soon after the First World War, Ricardo had begun investigations into high speed compression-ignition (diesel) engines. An experimental 50hp single-cylinder sleeve valve diesel engine (S50) was designed for research in 1924. It was intended, eventually, to form the basis of a complete family of 2, 3, 6 & 8-cylinder industrial engines of varying capacities and interchangeable components. By 1927 Brotherhoods had constructed five prototypes which were undergoing service trials, including Brotherhoods' Works, Ricardo's base Bridge Works, and

Brotherhood-Ricardo diesel engines were made in a range of sizes for many years. This 8-cylinder diesel generating set was supplied to the New Zealand Shipping Co. Ltd for MV *Empire Windrush* in January 1949. Output was 300kW at 220 volts dc when running at 800rpm.

Worthing Corporation Power Station. By 1928 all the teething problems had been resolved and production of the Brotherhood-Ricardo engine began. The engines were far in advance of anything else that had then been achieved, and they enjoyed considerable commercial success, being produced in large numbers.

Introduced in 1928, the Brotherhood-Ricardo high speed diesel engine was the first heavy oil engine using a single sleeve valve to be manufactured on a commercial scale. The circular sleeve, which fitted between the piston and cylinder wall, worked in an elliptical path at half crankshaft speed, the elliptical movement ensuring it had good lubrication. The inlet and exhaust ports were triangular holes on opposite sides of the cylinder wall and gave a tangential swirl to the air. Normally out of alignment and so closed, the holes could be aligned by the movement of the sleeve, so opening the port. Since the motion of the sleeve was by direct gearing from the crankshaft, wear had no effect on timing. In addition, the numerous valves, rockers, springs and cams of the conventional 4-stroke engine, together with associated inertia and bounce problems, were eliminated. Fuel was injected through a single-hole atomiser in each cylinder by a pump under control of the governor. Engines were offered having from one to eight cylinders. Each cylinder was cast separately and rated at 20/25hp at 1,000/1,300rpm, 50hp at 900rpm or 63hp at 800rpm, thus outputs of 20 to 500hp were available. A 4-cylinder air engine of special design was used for starting.

These high speed diesel engines were more compact and lighter than previous slow speed engines, so could be used in existing buildings without the need to dig expensive deep foundations. The smaller lighter parts were easier to handle during maintenance, and it was possible to transport a completely assembled engine to a customer. Brotherhood-Ricardo diesel engines were supplied mainly for service as a stationary generating engine or an auxiliary marine engine. They powered launches and excavators, and could be directly coupled to drive fans, generators or pumps. The engines were made in a range of sizes giving 40-500hp, at speeds of 800-1250rpm. Many 8-cylinder engines were supplied to drive 300kW generators on RN ships.

The general policy as regards the manufacture of 'Ricardo' engines was discussed in July 1929, being followed by the decision to advertise in October for a salesman to handle Ricardo diesel engine business. By 6th November, 1929 Mr John Barker had been engaged as

salesman for Brotherhood-Ricardo Diesel Engines in Great Britain, at a minimum salary & commission of £500/-/- per annum for the first 2 years in addition to reasonable travelling expenses', to commence on or about 9th December next.

John Boothroyd, a 17-year old junior draughtsman employed by the Bolton Superheater Company, had been interested in a new air compressor being installed on the premises of the Liquid Air Company, and had called in on his way home. The installation engineer had started the plant and had reached a pressure of 175 atmospheres (2,625psi) when a copper pipe burst 'with a deafening crash' and Boothroyd fell with fractures in his skull. He was taken to Stockport Infirmary where he died the following morning, 26th March, 1927. At the inquest it emerged that it was a new design of compressor, the first of three, and that a pipe intended for the first or second stage, wall thickness $^1/_8$ in. (3.175mm) had been used for the third stage, the correct pipe having design wall thickness $^7/_{16}$ in. (11.11mm). Brotherhoods' Works Manager, Freestone, said that the pipe had withstood a nine hour running test, and an hydraulic test, but he agreed that pipes of such similar appearance should be identified, and said it was due to 'a lapse on the part of an employee ... (who) ... had failed to work to the drawings'. The boy's parents had made a claim, and Mr Boothroyd had accepted the offer of £200 in full settlement of all claims arising from the death of his son. Messrs Liquid Air Ltd agreed to share the liability.

In July 1927 the supply of an air compressor for Sunderland Technical College was confirmed. Tenders for two 150kW steam-driven electricity generator sets for Metropolitan Water Board were confirmed in October, as was an agreement with Kobe Steelworks for the manufacture of air compressors and accessories in Japan. The interim award amounting to £25,000 under the Awards to Inventors Act was received, and the following sums had been paid out in accordance with agreements, the balance being carried to Revenue Account: Mr C.W.Bryant £7,916, Mr A.W.Viney £1,250. This was later followed by a further award of £100,000 when the *Daily Mail* reported (10th October, 1931) 'Closely guarded national secrets are associated with the award, which had been made for "improvements in internal combustion engines".' No details were given to the reporter as 'we are sworn to secrecy'.

The meeting on 25th October, 1927 also discussed the enquiry from Synthetic Ammonia & Nitrates for new plant at Billingham - 'practically a repeat of their order now under construction'. The continuing rising demand for ammonia and its derivatives in the 1920s caused progressive expansion at Billingham to meet it. No. 3 Plant used two

pairs of Brotherhood compressors (1 & 2) built in 1926. This was
followed by No. 4 Plant with two more pairs (3 & 4) in 1928, and No. 5
Plant with a single pair (5) in 1934. Each Plant received H-gas or N-gas
(gas mixtures rich in hydrogen or nitrogen respectively) at 10
atmospheres pressure (150psi). The intermediate compressor raised the
pressure to 52 atmospheres (780psi), and the gas then passed to an
adjoining building where scrubbers removed carbon dioxide. The gas
was then returned to the compressor house where the high pressure
compressor raised the pressure to 250 atmospheres (3,750psi). Another
scrubber removed carbon dioxide and the pure hydrogen and nitrogen
mixture then passed to the catalyst for conversion to ammonia.

At the time of construction, this group of compressors formed the
largest high pressure plant in Europe, requiring 60,000hp to power it.
Compressors 1 to 4 were originally driven through David Brown double
reduction double helical gear boxes by Brotherhood 3,000hp passout
turbines, exhausting to the factory low pressure steam main, while No. 5
compressors were driven by 40 cycle Mather & Platt electric motors.
However, changing steam and electricity requirements within the whole
works over the years caused the replacement of most of the turbines by
motors to restore the total energy balance. (The 40 cycle motors were a
relic of the lack of standardization before the Nation Grid was formed,
and in 1977 the works still generated some power at 40 cycles although
most was converted to 50 cycles before distribution.) The turbines had
five stages with the final disc 31in. in diameter. They took steam at
250psi and exhausted at 15psi, and ran at 4,000rpm.

The specification for No. 3 Plant, dated 12th May, 1926, required all
the bearings to be of ample size 'to allow for continuous working 24
hours per day and seven days per week. The machine in the ordinary
course of events will not be stopped unless it is found necessary, due to
mechanical defect or for overhaul.' In practice the compressors were
found to be 'remarkably reliable machines' and were in continuous use
until 1971. Then they were only displaced by changes in chemical
engineering technology, and until 1977 they were occasionally run as
stand-by to other machines. During their forty-odd years' life they
produced 8.8 million tons of ammonia and half a million tons of
methanol, besides producing 1,600 tons of hydrogen during the Second
World War: for RAF barrage balloons. In December 1928 the Board
minuted 'With reference to the Methanol Plant supplied to the Imperial
Chemical Co at Billingham this had now been completely installed &
was running satisfactorily. The Board regretted that a loss had been
made on this particular plant, but as repeat orders were likely to be

placed these should become a paying proposition.'

The original plant extended for half a mile along Ammonia Avenue, commencing with batteries of coke ovens and a water gas plant to provide the raw hydrogen. (Coal gas from a coke oven was impure hydrogen. Water gas, made by passing steam through red hot coke, made a mixture of hydrogen and carbon monoxide.) A total labour force of about 800 was needed for a daily output of 1,200 tons of ammonia. In the 1950s the gasification of heavy oil, and later still of naphtha, replaced coal as the primary raw material. North Sea gas was later used as the feedstock for the Company's modern plants. The latest of these in 1977 was across the road from the old compressor house. Designed to produce 1,100 tonne/day of ammonia it was a single stream plant with one large centrifugal synthesis gas compressor.

Compressors 1 to 4 (1926 & 1928) were 3-crank 2-stage machines. The intermediate pressure compressors received 4,000 cubic metres of gas per hour at 10 atmospheres, and the high pressure compressor received the equivalent volume at 52 atmospheres, less 30 per cent carbon dioxide which had been scrubbed out. The single-acting cylinders for the two stages were in tandem, with a common piston rod, compressing gas in the bottom cylinder (first stage) on the down stroke and in the upper cylinder (second stage) on the up stroke. Gas leaking past the glands was collected and recycled. No. 5 compressors were slightly smaller than the earlier machines but had the same output due to the use of double-acting cylinders for each of their three stages. The intercoolers were networks of vertical pipes fastened to the outside walls of the compressor house, down the outside of which ran cooling water.

The compressor house was a vast building, like the nave of a cathedral, with the compressors arranged in two rows along its length. Each intermediate pressure (IP) compressor faced its corresponding high pressure (HP) machine. The great height of the building enabled natural ventilation to disperse any gases that escaped. At one end of the building was the elevated control room, its huge glass window giving a clear view of the 10 Brotherhood compressors (and four others) housed within. The operator in charge adjusted the compressor speeds by remote control to regulate the pressure and composition of the synthesis gas going forward through gas purification stages to the ammonia synthesis converter. His task was a demanding one, since the orders to cause any changes required in the gas composition might have to go right back to the gas generators at the coke ovens, with all the delays that entailed!

Unlike a cathedral, the compressor house was filled with a pulsating roar which made normal conversation impossible. Consequently the men working there developed a system of gestures which permitted conversation despite the noise and distance. It was even used by the controller in his office, having caught a man's eye, although he did have a telephone as well. Brotherhoods were very proud of these compressors, and they featured in publicity until the 1960s.

The proposed sale of house property in Belham & Thistlemore Roads was discussed in November 1927. The suggested price of £380 by the Auctioneers

> was higher than the enquirers are prepared to give... The best offer received for the vacant house was £300/-/-, & it was decided to write to the Chairman of the Parent Company (i.e. AGE) suggesting that we proceed with the sale of the house at this figure & asking his concurrence. As regards the remaining 47 houses, the Board considered that the most satisfactory method of dealing with the property was to offer it by Public Auction & suggested a reserve of £270/-/- to £280/-/- [£8600 – £8900] on each house.

The April meeting saw 23 conveyances of house property sealed, with six more in October, five in November and one in December.

Winter gales caused about £200 of damage to the roof of various shops. Also in January 1928 'It was decided to resign our membership of the Society of Motor Manufacturers & Traders as the Board did not consider that any useful purpose would be served by continuing as members.'

The April 1928 meeting heard that the debentures held by the parent company had reduced by £34,760 during the year. Also 'The Board learnt with gratification that the Works Ambulance team had won the Challenge Cup in the competition held at Bedford with teams composed of representatives from the other associated companies.' In May

> The question of repairing & reglazing the Green Engine Shop & other parts of the Factory was considered. It was decided only to carry out repairs which were absolutely necessary – the work to be done by our own men when they could conveniently be spared.

In June,

> An application from Mr B.Pettican, Foreman in charge of Synthetic Ammonia & Nitrates Co's Contract at Billingham, for an increase in salary was considered – it was decided not to grant an increase, but in view of the efficient manner in which his duties had been carried out, the Board, to show their appreciation, decided to grant Mr Pettican a bonus of £50/-/-.

The question of insuring members of the staff against accidents which might occur in the course of their employment, where salaries exceeded £350 per annum and consequently did not come under the existing Employer's Liability policy was discussed in October 1928. It was decided to obtain cover at the quoted rate of $\frac{1}{6}$ per cent.

The question of the desirability of taking in hand contracts for Foreign Governments for the manufacture of Torpedo Work was discussed in November and before arriving at a decision it 'was considered advisable to put the matter before the Director of Torpedoes & Mining at the Admiralty.' There was also a request from AGE to pay £15,000 towards expenses, plus £3,000 income tax, which was merely 'Noted'. This was followed in December by a letter from the 'Parent Company asking us resign our individual membership of the British Engineer's Association as from the 31st December. Agreed to comply.' Two staff items were also recorded: 'It was decided to allow H.Read, an old employee, a pension of £1/-/- per week as he was in very straightened circumstances.' Also letter was sent to Mrs Satchell expressing the Board's regret at the death of her husband, an employee for over 40 years.

Advertising was discussed and it was agreed to put the production of a new Turbine catalogue in hand, that the new Water Cooling Tower catalogue be ordered, and to draft an entirely new Compressor catalogue, but no new publicity in connection with oil engines was to be put in hand. In addition, it was decided to reduce advertisement in the *Motor Ship* to half-page, and to suspend the advertisement in *Colliery Engineering*, thus saving £192 pa.

In October Mr Bryant reported an enquiry for 150 torpedo engines was likely from the Admiralty. He also

reported that the 2 following Resolutions were passed at the A.G.E. Board Meeting held on the 28th September, that Messrs Brotherhood be instructed to proceed with the manufacture of 6 Kerosene Engines suitable for the Tractor ... and that Messrs Peter Brotherhood Ltd be authorised to proceed with the manufacture of the Ricardo Diesel engine ...

There was also a request from Sociedad Capanola of Cartagena, Spain, for permission to construct seven Y6 type Brotherhood air compressors for destroyer Flotilla Leaders under the licence granted them in 1917. This was granted, subject to payment by them of a royalty of 10 per cent of the selling price.

Although most of the firm's products went all over the country and the world, local needs were met too. Local orders located in surviving records were quite varied, in both product and size. They show how the firm was prepared to chase any order, particularly in difficult times.

G.Milner, Esq, of Lords Fen, Yaxley, about five miles south of Peterborough, close to the GNR main line, ordered a 30bhp paraffin engine for driving a centrifugal pump by belt in August 1922. The order has the note 'Engine Brotherhood-Ricardo Tractor Engine to be taken from stock'. Peterborough Rural District Council in January 1924 ordered a vertical spindle slow speed centrifugal pump for Walton Sewage Disposal Station, to pump 250 gallons per minute of untreated sewage against a 40ft head, at 750rpm. In June 1925 the Marquis of Exeter, of Burghley House, Stamford ordered a 1kW portable Bull lighting set. Enquiries in 1977 found no trace of it at Burghley, indeed until 1956 there was very little electricity in the house, as it had been lit by gas for many years from its own small plant in the park. Maybe the Marquis used it elsewhere on his estates. The Whittlesea Brick Co. ordered in November 1925 one 2in. MD pump, 70gpm against 15ft head at 1,410rpm, having a 3bhp motor, and coming complete with 12ft of 2in. suction pipe and 2 foot long water strainer. The Peterborough Gas & Coal Co. ordered two 2-cylinder compound engines of 50kW at 550rpm in 1928.

The Minutes for 10th August, 1926 state that the contract for the

The works' Peterbro tractor delivering a condenser to Peterborough Power Station along Lincoln Road, New England in 1924.

supply and erection of a 6,000kW turbo alternator set for the Corporation of Peterborough was confirmed. The Central Electricity Generating Board described the unit as a 6.5MW Brotherhood turbine driving an English Electric alternator. It was commissioned in 1926 and scrapped in 1968. This was thought to be only the second machine of its type, the other having been designed by Ernest Dewar and supplied to Islington power station, where it had been scrapped about 1950. Soon after this turbine had been commissioned Dewar received a letter from congratulating him on 'the highly satisfactory results obtained [being] due in a large measure to the care and ability displayed by you in the design of the machine.' Peterborough Corporation had previously ordered a 26in. vertical spindle centrifugal pump, capacity 15,000gpm against 35ft head at 730rpm in May 1926. The new Peterborough Power Station was formally opened on 6th September, 1923, the original one, in Albert Meadow beside River Nene having been opened in 1900. The original plant had a capacity of 120kW, increased to 1,340kW by 1919 by which time there were 583 consumers. In 1920 new work was commenced to enlarge the capacity to 7,000kW to supply 1,211 consumers. Peter Brotherhood Ltd supplied one of the three turbines, part of the condensing plant and the circulating water pumps. Peterborough Power Station closed in October 1976.

Dewar's appointment letters survive and show the speed with which a senior appointment could then be made. The post was advertised in *Engineering* of 17th February, 1922. Dewar wrote from Sale, Cheshire, applying for the post on the 18th, which the firm acknowledged on the 22nd, asking for further particulars, salary required and 'if you are able to visit us for an interview we can see you at any time'. On 6th March Brotherhoods' wrote 'We confirm our telegram of this morning reading as follows: "Appointment [as Assistant to our Chief Engineer] decided in your favour please commence duties as soon as possible."…. Please reply by return stating when you can take up your appointment.' His salary would be £300pa, increased to £350 'in three months from date of commencement of your duties if your work is satisfactory'.

As the 1920s drew to a close the affairs of AGE deteriorated, and Stanley Brotherhood become increasingly concerned over the future of his company. Brotherhoods were obviously wary of AGE's practices, as in January 1930,

> The Secretary was instructed to write to Messrs Agricultural & General Engineers Ltd asking that in view of the fact that the Debentures held by the Parent Company had been liquidated & that this Company is now in credit whether steps will now be taken for the return of the Debenture.

On 11th December, 1930 the Minutes recorded:

> The Chairman & Mr Bryant reported the negotiations & arrangements which had been made for the acquisition by Mr Brotherhood & his friends of the whole of the Ordinary Shares of the Company by purchase from Agricultural & General Engineers Ltd. ... it was obviously to the advantage of the business of the Company & to the whole of the Shareholders that A.G.E. should no longer control the business of the Company ....

and details of the necessary financial arrangements followed. On 15th December the Board formally accepted the new financial arrangements for Peter Brotherhood Ltd. Two days later Debenture Stock totalling £100,000 was issued: £66,667 in names of Hon. Clive Pearson & Sir Clarendon Golden Hyde of 47 Parliament St, SW1, £27,777 Charles William Bryant of Westwood House, Peterborough, and £5,556 Henry Montgomery Dunkerley of The Hill House, Wansford, Peterborough. A meeting on 30th December resolved to increase the number of Directors to eight, the additional five being: Mr A.H.Carnt, Mr F.H.Davis, Mr W.T.Freestone, Mr J.Kemp Welch, and Mr A.M.Neal, the new members of the Board 'retaining their present duties'.

Using the profits from the beer machinery, at a cost of £100,000, completing (without payment of the contract price £6,180) three 150kW turbo-generating sets for Garretts (another firm in the group), together with some other financial adjustments, in December 1930 Peter Brotherhood Ltd had managed to buy itself out of AGE before the crash came. Much later, Barford (*see page 128*) said he himself had become increasingly concerned at AGE's performance and practices. In early 1930 he discovered gross irregularities in the finances of Aldwych House, which appeared to have used most of the rent monies received to make large loans to AGE. Then he says he also discovered a fraud involving the sale of obsolescent agricultural machinery to South America using the government Export Credit Guarantee Department, with a much larger one planned. He challenged Rowland – and was dismissed. Fighting back, the ensuing publicity caused questions to be asked and investigations to be made. Finally Rowland suddenly disappeared leaving no address and a receiver was appointed around February 1932, to be followed by a liquidator in April. The group's liabilities were shown to be £829,895 of which £139,029 was unsecured; assets were £644,940 less £972 for preferential claims and £618,939 for debentures, leaving £25,027 to meet unsecured claims. The total deficiency was £2,625,000. Some of the constituent companies managed to survive, but by then Peter Brotherhood Ltd was no longer involved or affected.

CHAPTER EIGHT

1930s, STANLEY AFTER
AGRICULTURAL & GENERAL ENGINEERS LTD

From December 1930, free from external control by AGE, Peter
Brotherhood Ltd continued operation much as before.

The Institution of Mechanical Engineers included Peter Brotherhood
Ltd in its annual visits arranged for July 1931. The party seems to have
been based in Cambridge, with excursions over at least two days giving
opportunities to go to firms in Ely, Letchworth, Northampton, and
Peterborough, and nearby centres. In the Peterborough area visits were
made to the London Brick Co., Forders, Ketton Portland Cement Co.,
Barford & Perkins and Peter Brotherhood Ltd. The report of the visit in
the Institution's Proceedings included a brief description of the works
and its products.

The workshops covered an area of about eight acres. The iron foundry
was a separate building, with a floor area of 34,000 sq ft (about ³/₄ acre).
It had a railway siding so fuel and pig iron could be brought in direct.
Later it included a 30 ton weighbridge, which could also be used by
lorries. The cupolas could produce castings up to about 18 tons weight.
Nickel-iron alloy was used for castings of an intricate nature or
subjected to heavy wear or high pressure. Behind the administrative
offices were the main workshops, comprising pattern shop and stores,
non-ferrous metals foundry, welding and cutting shops, main machine
shops, erecting and testing shops, smithy, coppersmith's shop, and
water testing shop. Power was supplied from three power houses, two
having been added to meet the increasing output of the works. One
contained three Babcock boilers with continuously moving chain grates
supplying steam to three Brotherhood high-speed generating sets with a
total of 550kW capacity. The power house on the other side of the main
building contained four horizontal heavy-oil engines, two by Blackstone
and two by Brotherhood, with a total output of 500kW. The third power
house, separate from the other buildings, contained a Brotherhood twin-
cylinder heavy-oil engine of 150kW, a 50kW Brotherhood-Ricardo
engine and dynamo, and a vertical suction-gas engine and 100kW
dynamo. The electricity supply throughout the works and offices was
220 volts DC.

The main products listed were: high-pressure compressors for air and
gas for the chemical industry, and auxiliary air service for motor ships
(compressed air at about 1000psi was used for air blast fuel injection in
early engines, for manoeuvring to turn the main engine at low speed, to

start diesel engines, as well as sundry other purposes); internal-combustion engines including the Brotherhood-Ricardo high-speed diesel engine; steam turbines; steam engines; refrigerating machinery; 'and many other machines of a specialised character'. Motor ship development really began after the end of the First World War. At that time Peter Brotherhood Ltd was the only British firm really qualified to construct suitable compressors, with the result that the majority of early motor ships had Brotherhood auxiliary compressors installed. The company continued to be a major supplier, both in Britain and abroad, even when other firms entered that market.

A event which must have caused some grief to Stanley took place in the Angel Hotel, Peterborough, on Saturday 17th October, 1931 at 2pm. It was the sale of much of the Thornhaugh Estate, 'in 45 convenient lots', although the Hall itself was not included. If pencil notes on a surviving catalogue are correct, Stanley realised about £23,000. Perhaps this was necessary in order to help repay loans arising from the escape from AGE. Facilities enjoyed by the properties, most of Thornhaugh village, a few in Wansford, and some in the country between, varied. Only two properties, both in Wansford, had 'Company's water'. The others mainly had a well on the property or used a pump. Most of Thornhaugh village had a supply pumped from a well on the village green. A couple of properties were supplied from the Hall itself, 'by ram', for which an annual charge was made, usually 6s. 8d. Only five properties had a WC and cesspool. The village hall had its 'Bull' lighting set, previously mentioned, but only one other property had electric light 'supplied by the private plant in the barn'. General Information included

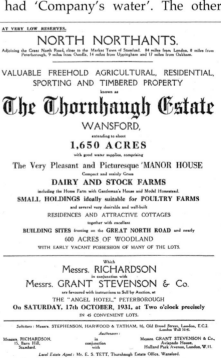

AT VERY LOW RESERVES.

NORTH NORTHANTS.

Adjoining the Great North Road, close to the Market Town of Stamford. 84 miles from London, 8 miles from Peterborough, 9 miles from Oundle, 14 miles from Uppingham and 17 miles from Oakham.

VALUABLE FREEHOLD AGRICULTURAL, RESIDENTIAL, SPORTING AND TIMBERED PROPERTY

known as

The Thornhaugh Estate

WANSFORD,

extending to about

1,650 ACRES

with good water supplies, comprising

The Very Pleasant and Picturesque 'MANOR HOUSE

Compact and mainly Grass

DAIRY AND STOCK FARMS

including the Home Farm with Gentleman's House and Model Homestead.

SMALL HOLDINGS ideally suitable for POULTRY FARMS

and several very desirable and well-built

RESIDENCES AND ATTRACTIVE COTTAGES

together with excellent

BUILDING SITES fronting on the GREAT NORTH ROAD and nearly

600 ACRES OF WOODLAND

WITH EARLY VACANT POSSESSION OF MANY OF THE LOTS.

Which

Messrs. RICHARDSON

in conjunction with

Messrs. GRANT STEVENSON & Co.

are favoured with instructions to Sell by Auction, at

THE "ANGEL HOTEL," PETERBOROUGH

On SATURDAY, 17th OCTOBER, 1931, at Two o'clock precisely

IN 45 CONVENIENT LOTS.

Solicitors: Messrs. STEPHENSON, HARWOOD & TATHAM, 16, Old Broad Street, London, E.C.2.
(London Wall 3146).

Auctioneers:

Messrs. RICHARDSON,   in   Messrs. GRANT STEVENSON & Co.,
15, Barn Hill,   conjunction   Avispado House,
Stamford.   with   Holland Park Avenue, London, W.11.

Local Estate Agent: Mr. E. S. TETT, Thornhaugh Estate Office, Wansford.

Cover of catalogue for the sale of the Thornhaugh Estate on 17th October, 1931.

Vertical compressor and a steam turbine in the shops. Note the turntable instead of points on the workshop railway.

sporting attractions in the neighbourhood: Burghley Park Polo Club, hunting – the Estate being in Fitzwilliam country and the Cottesmore and Woodland Pytchley both meeting within easy distance, the Bucks Otter hounds hunted local streams in the spring and early autumn, excellent pheasant and partridge shooting, and there were several golf courses in the area.

The manufacture of Dorr-Oliver filters began in 1931. The filters comprised several large discs covered with straining cloth. The lower parts of the discs were immersed in the liquid, for example cement slurry. The interior of the disc was subject to vacuum, so the water was sucked through and the solid material was left on the cloth, where it was dried by compressed air and scraped off.

Other products made at this time were homogenisers and carbon dioxide recovery compressors. The homogenisers contained a triple pump which forced the liquid through a small spring-loaded valve. The tiny orifice broke up the particles of liquid to such an extent that immiscible substances no longer separated out. All the parts of the machine which came into contact with the liquid were designed for ease of cleaning, and were made of materials which would not taint the liquid in any way. Homogenisers were made for a wide variety of substances: cosmetics, disinfectants, furniture polish, ice cream, salad cream, sauces, etc. If required, they would be 'tested at the works with the material it is intended to treat, provided that a sufficient quantity of the same is supplied by the purchaser free of charge'. One day, when a homogeniser was being tested, one 'Brookie' was told by his mates that it was making hair cream. He used a handful, only to discover, too late, that it was salad dressing!

Carbon dioxide recovery was a potential source of revenue from fermentation processes as the gas had a ready market in mineral water manufacture, sugar refining, refrigerators and the chemical industry. Brotherhoods supplied the complete equipment: hoods to cover the fermentation units, a vertical 3-stage compressor, the liquifier, and the bottling/storage units. The compressor compressed the first and third stages on the upstroke, and the second on the down, thus balancing the loads. The gas was washed and dried after the first stage. The valves were arranged so that access was possible without breaking any of the gas or water connections.

An addition to the range of pumps was the Brotherhood-Gill Axial Flow Pump in 1931. Unlike centrifugal pumps the direction of flow of the liquid was not altered by the pump. It could be used in any position, horizontal, vertical or inclined, against moderate heads up to 30ft. The scientifically designed impeller which pumped the liquid offered little resistance when idling in the stream, so the pump could be incorporated in siphons or intake scoops. The pumps were used for circulating cooling water on ships, irrigation, chemical liquors, cement slurry, sewage, wood pulp and mineral sludge. A 42in. irrigation pump delivering 46,200 gallons per minute against a 13ft head absorbed 226hp at 380rpm, while a destroyer's circulating pump delivered 15,400 gallons per minute against a 14.5ft head when driven at 725rpm by a Brotherhood turbine. The pumps were very efficient of a wide range of capacity and head.

In the early 1930s the Company pioneered the use of fabricated steel baseplates for diesel engines and compressors. These were lighter yet stronger than castings. The first one constructed was for a diesel engine fitted to HMS *Grampus*, a mine laying submarine, sunk off Italy in June 1940.

By the late 1930s the firm had a steam crane by J.Booth, of Rodley, Leeds, operating in its sidings. It seems to have been purchased second-hand at an unknown date. It could have been in use from around 1907, unloading incoming raw materials. Equally, it could have been obtained in the early 1930s specifically for use with the annealing furnace

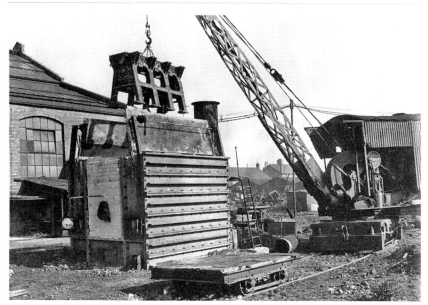

Booth steam crane 'Lifting Engine Columns out of Annealing Furnace'. Although the crane has a coupling hook and buffer beam, they are so low that it is unlikely the crane shunted main line wagons, but only the low trolley shown. In the distance, visible between the furnace and the top rungs of the ladder, is one of the steam road wagons.

In an attempt to reduce shunting costs the LMS ordered a number of different diesel locomotives to assess their potential before placing bulk orders. The Hunslet Engine Co., Leeds, built several locomotives with different engines, 7053 having a 150hp Brotherhood-Ricardo diesel. Although this locomotive was broken up around 1954, an externally very similar locomotive is preserved on the Middleton Railway in Leeds. *Collection S.A.Leleux*

required for the fabricated diesel engines it had started to build.

Research by the London Midland & Scottish Railway (LMS) showed that shunting occupied 50 per cent of freight locomotive hours, so the company decided to investigate the possibilities of diesel locomotives, and in 1932 placed orders with five different manufacturers for nine different locomotives. Number 7053, one of three different 0-6-0D built by the Hunslet Engine Co., Leeds, was powered by a 150hp Brotherhood-Ricardo RZS 6-cylinder diesel engine. The final drive was by a jackshaft and side rods. No. 7053 was loaned to the War Department in 1939, and eventually resold to Hunslet for rebuilding and resale, which did not take place, and the locomotive was dismantled around 1954. An externally very similar locomotive, but with a different make of engine, originally LMS 7051, is preserved on the Middleton Railway in Leeds.

Brotherhoods obtained the licence to manufacture Junkers 2-stroke diesel engines in the early 1930s. The small high speed British Junkers diesel engines had from one to three cylinders, each generating 10/12hp, and were aimed at the marine and DC generation markets. Each cylinder, of 65mm bore, had two opposed pistons with 210 mm combined stroke, giving uniflow scavenging.

This engine was used to power a range of small 2ft gauge locomotives, intended for contractors, sand, gravel and clay pits, etc. Although the sales leaflet for the 'Rickanpick' [all-British diesel locomotive gives the name only of Richter & Pickis, Brick and Tileworks] Engineers and Contractors, of London EC3, the locomotives were made at Peterborough, and Brotherhoods still have drawings (dated July and September 1932) of all the component parts except the radiator and engine. (To put this development into perspective, two major British manufacturers of small diesel locomotives were Motor Rail Ltd, who had made petrol locomotives since 1915, made their first diesel in 1929, and Ruston, Hornsby Ltd whose first locomotive was a small diesel in 1931.)

The name against the initial order for these locomotives was Richter & Picklis, possibly a joint venture with Brotherhood, as it provided an outlet for the British Junkers engine they manufactured, as well other useful work like gearboxes which were well within their capability. The fact that the company was prepared to produce a full set of drawings from scratch for this small order strongly suggests that there was some sort of collaboration.

Six 20hp locomotives were ordered for stock, plus 100 yards of 2ft gauge track, on 6th September, 1932, and haulage trials for a 20hp $3\frac{1}{2}$ ton locomotive were recorded on 21st November, 1932. The locomotive had deep plate frames carrying four 14in. diameter wheels set at 2ft 7 $\frac{1}{2}$ in. wheelbase, and supported the longitudinally mounted 2-cylinder engine. The drive went to a gearbox giving three speeds in each direction, and thence by chains to each axle. A sturdy cab was provided as standard (unlike the two firms previously mentioned!). Several photographs were taken in the works, and it is thought one was tested in a gravel pit at nearby Eye. Later, in January 1935, one of the stock locomotives was altered to 700mm gauge 'For Pinang [sic]'. The locomotive having square cab spectacles was possibly the prototype, as a photograph published in the *Industrial Railway Record* (No. 103) taken in a Ringwood, Hampshire, scrapyard in 1965 shows a R&P locomotive with different axleboxes and circular cab windows. Despite being in at the beginning of commercial exploitation of a new idea, unfortunately production did not proceed beyond the initial order. Construction by a general purpose manufacturer instead of a locomotive specialist probably told against them, and may well have been reflected in the price each firm charged.

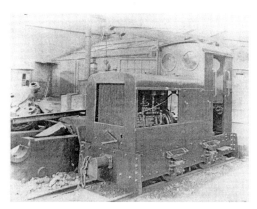

Richter & Pickis 'Rickanpick all-British' 20hp 2ft gauge diesel locomotive in the works yard, 1932-3.

Drawing of Richter & Pickis locomotive.

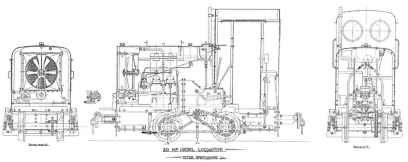

The first diesel-electric tug, the *Acklam Cross*, was built for Robinson & Crosthwaite of Middlesbrough in 1933 by Hall Russell & Co., yard number 728. This firm was the last Aberdeen shipbuilder to survive, closing in 1992. The tug was powered by a pair of 300hp 6-cylinder Brotherhood-Ricardo diesel engines. With a battery-powered electric starter for the main diesel engine, and an easily reversible electric motor driving the propeller, the captain could control the engines direct from the bridge thus saving on crew. In fact the vessel only needed a complement of four, making for economy in operation. Unfortunately, at £30,000, the first cost was double that of a conventional tug.

Brotherhoods built standard Admiralty pattern diesel engines for British S and the later A class submarines.

In 1931 the Grand Union Canal Company obtained Parliamentary permission to widen locks north of Berkhampstead. The ultimate aim was to enable traffic to be carried in 12ft 6in.-wide barges all the way from London to Birmingham instead of 7ft-wide narrow boats. One prototype timber barge, the PROGRESS, was built by Bushell Bros of Tring. It carried 66 tons and was powered by a British Junkers engine supplied by Brotherhoods. At the same time a Grand Union subsidiary, Associated Canal Carriers Ltd, experimented with small compartment

Set of 4 articulated compartment canal boats built in 1932 for Associated Canal Carriers Ltd. Each boat carried 10 tons, and the set would fit a standard narrow lock. Note the sloping front of the leading boat. The raised framework was to support a tarpaulin sheet for weather protection. The set was to be hauled by a tug. The boats appear to have been coupled by loops of light chain passed over horizontal pulleys on each side of each end of the intermediate boats and rear end of the leading one. Print dated 24th February, 1933.

boats towed by tugs. In 1932 four such welded boats, each 18ft by 7ft by 4ft 6in., intended to carry 10 tons and fit together into a standard narrow lock, were ordered from Peter Brotherhood Ltd (*Canals of the East Midlands*, Charles Hadfield – David & Charles, 1970, page 242), and were completed early 1933.

The use of hollow pistons of large depth, to ease heat transfer, was developed at this time in a range of double-acting single-stage compressors, with output at 100psi. With long, narrow, water-cooled cylinders and water-cooled cylinder heads they absorbed only 10 per cent more power than equivalent 2-stage compressors.

Another company formed following the collapse of AGE was Perkins Engines, based in Peterborough in the former works of the bread and biscuit manufacturer Baker Perkins. In 1932 Perkins Engines had a staff of a couple of draughtsmen and Brotherhoods did all Perkins' machining and constructed their first engines. Rue Hardy remembers that an order for 50 engines was 'wonderful'. The first Perkins diesel engine ever fitted in a commercial vehicle was done in the old sight shop in the mid-1930s. What intrigued everyone in the works at the time were the rubber-mounted blocks on which the engine rested. Accustomed to rigid installations, it appeared a kind of heresy to have an engine which could be rocked at the touch of a hand!

The Company had, and still has, a reputation for making almost anything, but perhaps the most unusual order was from Oscar Brumner in about 1936. Brumner appears to have been a 'character' in his own right, greeting Neal (then Stanley's assistant) with a Nazi salute and 'Heil Hitler! Good morning Mr Neal!' who would mutter 'silly old b---'. Others described Brumner as 'a blooming old scrounger'. However, he had done a lot of work developing welding torches which worked under water, and he went on to design a boiler with the fire within the water space. He formed a syndicate in Birmingham to exploit this boiler, and an associated turbine-driven compressor supposedly 125 per cent efficient! Surprisingly, people invested in the scheme and Brotherhoods were asked to build the equipment. Although the boiler itself was made to work it suffered from severe corrosion. The other trials were most unsuccessful. An old horizontal engine, 'imported from a Belgian user' made no improvement and the project collapsed. Another of Brumner's ideas was to extract oxygen from seawater, so a set of large tanks was built in a corner of the works to hold the water, but nothing came of this idea either.

During the 1930s the management had the courage to diversify and actively sought orders anywhere, often abroad, for products old and new. Freestone's invariable reply to the question 'Can you make it?' was 'Of course'. The works were thus kept in reasonably full employment even in those difficult times. The beer, filtration, and sewage pumping machinery were especially important. One idea exploited by the Company was to manufacture goods for American companies. Being of British manufacture they were within the tariffs which then protected the British Empire, so that the parent company could reach markets which otherwise would have been closed.

Holidays at Easter and Christmas were unpaid, so workmen paid 2/6 to 5/- per week, stopped from their pay, into a holiday fund, and withdrew this at holiday times, receiving between £6-5-0 & £12-10-0 There was no sickness pay, so the men ran 'sick and dividing clubs' on the shop floor, 1/- per week contribution, and if off sick with a doctor's certificate it paid £2pw to 'supplement the poor government sick pay'. If you were receiving sick pay you were not allowed out after 6pm!

Peter had always been interested in the welfare of his employees and this interest was maintained. A Sports Club opened in 1908 with 20 members who played football and cricket at ground off Marholm Road. In 1911 it moved to a playing field behind Paul Pride Inn, and 1918 to a site at New England. From 1919 to 1939 the headquarters of the Club was in Occupation Road, but in 1939 a sports pavilion, given by the firm, opened at New England. There was a Kemp-Welch Cup at the Sports Club. Membership in the late 1970s was 700 covering 14 different sports. Brotherhoods' Club & Institute in Occupation Road, opened on Boxing Day 1919, similarly had 550 members.

In the inter-war period senior staff, especially Works Manager Freestone and his assistant Thompson, tended to treat their employees with little consideration. Their attitude was often bullying and a man might be fired at any time at an hour's notice (although, to be fair, they were often reinstated a few days later). This, however, appears to have been typical of the period. The situation is illustrated by Freestone's reported conversation one day with yard foreman Arthur 'Sargeant Major' Smith: 'Have you any labourers to spare?' 'I'll find one for you, sir.' 'Get rid of him!' Despite this attitude he was trusted by the men. When Thomas Sewell was an apprentice he was working one day beside a man machining an aluminium aero engine case. As Freestone passed the man asked for extra pay, due to the difficulty of working aluminium. The reply was, 'Get on with your job, I'll see you're alright!' and the man knew that it would be. He was an excellent manager, never failing to produce orders on time.

Stanley and Neale were always interested in their employees' families, and would frequently enquire after them. Neale had a strong sense of family traditions of working for a company. He approached one young man: 'Barnett, are you married?' 'No, sir.' 'What a pity! I wanted to have three generations of Barnetts here.' Boys were almost guaranteed an apprenticeship if their fathers worked for the Company.

Conditions might have been hard and the public faces of the bosses tough, but they were always approachable, and it was known that they did care. If a man was in trouble, especially if he needed expensive medical treatment in those pre-National Health Service days, a quiet word to the Manager or a Director would bring assistance. Strikes were unknown except when they were forced out in the 1926 General Strike.

In the late 1930s the Company instituted a Pension Fund in conjunction with an insurance company, with contributions made up since the employee was 21. It is now a contributory fund for management staff and non-contributory for works staff. On 29th June, 1937 Stanley had signed a contract to act as Chairman and technical adviser for 10 years, at a salary as technical adviser of £4,600pa, in addition to his fees as Director and Chairman.

Stanley was Peter Brotherhood's second son. He had hoped to go into the Navy, but following the death of his elder brother he had received an engineering training. Despite this, and having been works manager for his father, he was not really an engineer, but instead took a keen interest

in administration and finance. He had the ability to attract and retain men brilliant in their respective fields. His bearing and manner were aristocratic, and he would wave his stick to make a point if he met Freestone in the works. He used to open all the mail, no matter to whom it was addressed, and kept a series of notebooks listing all orders won. Besides being Chairman of his own company he was a director of Humber Cars and Price's Candles.

Stanley Brotherhood entered public life soon after coming to Thornhaugh. He became a member

Stanley Brotherhood as
Master of Fox Hounds

of the Soke (of Peterborough) County Council, for Wittering division, in June 1913 and was elected to the Education Committee the same day. He retained this Council seat without opposition until withdrawing in 1934. He was made JP for the Soke of Peterborough in 1917, and was High Sheriff for Northamptonshire in 1920. This might have been the reason he was granted a coat of arms, with the motto, loosely translated as 'Authority and vigour'.

> Mr Brotherhood entered into all sports with the enthusiasm and thoroughness expected of a country gentleman. A keen rider to hounds, he was a regular follower of the Fitzwilliam and for a period, after the war, was Joint Master with the late Mr Geo. Fitzwilliam, with whom he was on terms of intimate friendship. On relinquishing the office he was presented by the followers with a silver tray. A notably good shot, Mr Brotherhood frequently spent a holiday with his gun on the moors, and he was also a devotee of angling. A generous helper in other people's games, he held office in various clubs including the sports club at the Walton works. Mr Brotherhood was a Conservative...his interest in agriculture was betokened by his membership of the National Farmers' Union.

Stanley had a great interest in the Peterborough Show, and 'he stood as its friend in a very critical period in its history'. There had been a successful show in 1914, and none during the war, so a period of reconstruction began in November 1918. Stanley was the first post-war president, and, most unusually, he was also president for the following year. While several people had been president twice, no-one else apparently had been president two years running.

> A good whip himself, he was a member of the Coaching Club, and devoted to the picturesque four-in-hand, a class which he established and endowed at Peterborough, but unfortunately it was not well supported and did not survive the war period. [His daughter Sheila added that his many prizes included the champion four–in-hand at Olympia in 1914]) Mr Brotherhood exhibited teams at Richmond and other shows, and his name had appeared in the prize list at Peterborough many times for hackneys and hackers. He was also a greatly honoured judge, officiating at many shows, including the classic Richmond Horse Show.

He was a vice president up to the time of his death, and was a member of the Institution of Mechanical Engineers. His clubs were the Carlton and Orleans.

The Navy remained his great love, and the naval work was always of great interest. According to Sheila, the loss of naval work and turning to commercial products was a great grief to him. He took a great interest in his workers and donated the Brotherhood Sports Ground. He was a perfectionist and all-round sportsman. He was the only Englishman to swim Lake Neuchatal, reputedly the coldest lake in Switzerland. He was a kind generous man. Always unassuming, he helped many people and did many kind acts which have never been heard about. His wife Vera was a well-known hostess, and many Society gatherings were held at Thornhaugh Hall. An obituary was also published in *The Engineer* of 20th May, 1938.

Stanley and Vera had three daughters. I was in touch with the eldest, Helen, in 1961 when I was researching for the first edition, but being primarily interested in Peter regrettably I failed to ask any questions about her. She had married Claude Nicholson before 1938, and later married Mr Jackson. I was in contact in 1977 with the second daughter, Sheila, who provided information for the previous paragraph. In April 1937 she became the second wife of Admiral Cyril Douglas-Pennant, a member of the family which owned the Penrhyn slate quarries near Bangor. They had no children. Later she married Marshall Warmington. The youngest, Elizabeth, married John Thomson in 1935. He was a Director of Barclays Bank 1947-78, being Chairman 1962-73, during which time he oversaw the introduction of Britain's first credit card (Barclaycard). He was knighted in 1972, becoming Sir John Thomson, and died in 1998, some 20 years after Elizabeth who had died in 1977. There were no children.

There was a catastrophic fire at Thornhaugh Hall on 24th November, 1937. The *Peterborough Standard* had two whole columns for its report, which began 'Nearly the whole of Thornhaugh Hall ... was gutted by fire ... apart from the servants' quarters, practically the entire interior was in ruins. Only the walls remained standing. Preliminary estimates of the damage put £20,000 as a conservative figure.' The fire seems to have started in the 'stokehole of the hot water heating system, which is beneath the ground level in the east wing of the Hall' at about 9pm, then spread up the staircase into a pantry where it took hold, despite the efforts of Mrs Brotherhood and staff with chemical fire extinguishers and attempts to beat out the flames. The Peterborough Volunteer Fire Brigade and the Stamford Fire Brigade were both summoned at about 9.20pm. Stanley was ill in bed with bronchitis (which he had for the past month), and had to be well wrapped against the cold when taken by his wife and nurse in a bath chair to a groom's cottage where he spent the night and where he remained at the time of publication of the paper. The fire brigades tried to restrict the blaze to the east wing but were hampered by a lack of water – two ornamental ponds in the grounds were soon pumped dry so the pumps had to be moved to a stream about half a mile away – and by the difficulty of getting the hose into the roof which was made of thick boards covered by stout local Colyweston tiles. Later the firemen were joined by a squad from nearby No. 11 Flying School, Wittering. With flames the length of the roof, despite the efforts of about 70 firemen, the decision was taken to save as much of the furniture as possible. It was stacked on surrounding lawns and in outhouses. By midnight the flames had spread from the roof downwards through practically the whole of the Hall, although it did prove possible to save an Austrian oak staircase valued at £4,000, and the servants' quarters. The blaze died down in the early hours of the morning, leaving 'grounds piled with furniture, carpets and pictures, and trampled lawns.' Sheila and Elizabeth both came the day after. Six months later, when Stanley died, the house was still a ruin, but eventually it was rebuilt, with one floor less. For a time it was owned by Baker-Perkins for hospitality, but by 2006 it was again a home.

An important step in 1937 was the conversion of the firm to a public limited company. Perhaps Stanley was influenced by having no son, although he had three daughters. It did, however, make it easier to raise capital for expansion. Employees were, and are, encouraged to hold shares in the firm. Stan Laxton, then chief cashier, bought his in order to have a vote at meetings that he had to attend anyway. The original capital of about £500,000 was subscribed within a minute, with 5/- shares fetching 15/- each, but employees could purchase them at par.

Thornhaugh Hall, as rebuilt without the top floor.

Unfortunately Stanley's health began to fail soon after the formation of the new company, and he died on Sunday 8th May, 1938, aged 62, so he was never able to take the chair at an annual meeting of the public company. His successor was Marcus Neal who had been groomed by Stanley, despite their similarity in age. Although he had no link with the family he maintained the atmosphere in the difficult years that followed. The Chairman's Office remained unaltered. From 1937 rearmament caused work to build up, and defence contracts were to be important for the next 10 years.

The Directors in 1938 were given as: Stanley Brotherhood MIMechE (Chairman), Alexander Marcus Neal AMICE (general manager), Wheaton Thos. Freestone (works manager), Francis Henry Davis (chief designer), Alan Hubert Carnt (departmental manager), Howard Kemp Welch MBE (London Office manager), Engr Rear-Admiral Frederick George Hardy MVO. 'It is notable that no one may be a director of the firm who is not a British subject.'

Stanley Brotherhood died from tuberculosis and heart disease in the Hyde Park Hotel, Knightsbridge on Sunday 8th May, 1938. According to an obituary, he had suffered 'almost ten years of continuous ill health', possibly a result of the trials with AGE. His funeral was held at Thornhaugh on the following Wednesday afternoon (11th May) with a simultaneous memorial service at Paston Church, the parish in which the works was situated. The *Peterborough Standard* gave extensive coverage, over half a page, to the funeral, while there was a third of a column in *The Times*.

People lined the church path at Thornhaugh to pay homage. 'The Church was almost full some time before the funeral which took place at 2.30pm.' There were 109 floral tributes. The coffin arrived by road from London at 1.20pm and was taken into church:

> The mourners arrived a few minutes before 2.30 and by this time the Church was crowded. A robed choir was in attendance, and the choral service was conducted by the Rev W.Marshall Selwyn, Vicar of Holy Trinity Church, Brompton, assisted by the Rev J.H.R.Duke [Rector of Thornhaugh]. The coffin, borne by four employees at the Works and four members of the Hall staff, was lowered into a brick grave lined with moss, wild orchids, bluebells, clematis and woodland flowers.

The plain oak coffin had oxidized silver fittings and was inscribed 'Stanley Brotherhood, died 8th May, 1938'.

In addition to family members there were many official representatives including Capt E.Mark-Wardlaw (also representing the

Engineer-in-Chief of the Admiralty), the Mayors of Peterborough and Stamford, while 36 'employees of the firm travelled in a special bus to the funeral'. The works closed on the afternoon of his funeral.

> At the same hour as the funeral at Thornhaugh, a memorial service was held at Paston Church, conducted by the Rector (Canon A.Lethbridge). The Church was full, the majority of the congregation being members of the works staff, clerks and workmen, in some instances with their wives. In a few cases men prevented from being present were represented by their wives. The service followed the same order with regard to music and prayers as that at Thornhaugh.

Two Church members who were also 'of Brotherhood's staff' were sidesmen. Directors Carnt & Davis were present, also the 'resident Naval Ordnance Inspector'. Also among those present were A.T.Savage, J. & Mrs Savage, and T.F.Sewell.

The same issue of the paper reported: 'The following amounts received during the month of April are gratefully acknowledged by Mr Joseph Stephenson FSAA, honorary secretary of the Peterborough and District Workpeople's Hospital Fund: ... Peter Brotherhood Ltd., employees 34-0-0'.

Stanley's grave is behind Thornhaugh Church. The inscription on the headstone reads: 'In love remember Stanley Brotherhood Jan 10th 1876 May 8th 1938 also Vera his wife who died March 20th 1950.' His estate was valued at £382,934-4-0, some £15m today. His chauffeur later became a Brotherhoods progress chaser.

Stanley Brotherhood, and the coat of arms, loosely translated as 'Authority and vigour', on his memorial in Thornhaugh Church.   *S.A.Leleux*

CHAPTER NINE

MARCUS NEAL (1938-1961)
THE SECOND WORLD WAR TO 1961

Brotherhoods was a family firm, having been founded by Peter Brotherhood and then passing to his son Stanley. Although Stanley had no son to carry on the business, he had groomed as his successor Marcus Neal, who had joined in 1911 and took control in 1938. As one of Stanley's executors and a member of the Brotherhood Trust, he was always very conscious of his duty towards Stanley's daughters, whom he regarded as his special responsibility, and he maintained the firm's atmosphere in the difficult years which followed.

Before the Second World War the men worked $5\frac{1}{2}$ days per week, with one week off at Easter and two days at Whitsun. Peter W.Goodale entered the factory for first time in January 1937, 'not prepared for the noise of the machinery cutting metal and the squealing belts and pulleys'. He was placed in the turret shop on a Drummond lathe, near the foreman's wooden office:

> The steps outside the office were where you stood before entering to receive a 'dressing' down for some misdemeanour, being late, breaking a drill or worst of all scrapping a component, all this for nine shillings a week! Every Friday

Bottle cleaning plant loaded for delivery. Note the use of two separate trailers, and the crane mounted on the Scammell tractor unit.

was payday and you would collect your tin with your clock number stamped on the lid. Sometimes we apprentices would be errand boys sent to the stores for a 'long stand' or a 'smooth file', but this gave us the chance to see other areas of the factory, iron and brass foundries, Green Engine shop, Grindery, heavy turnery, steel stores and all sorts of other 'cubby holes'. There was the hallowed front office and drawing office with an array of busts on pedestals, the Commissionaire in his uniform and his waxed moustache. The so-called ambulance room with its cold slab like mortuary, the little sentry box outside the toilets where you were given a piece of paper and timed in and out. The canteen for the 'workers' was equipped with a gas oven to heat your 'Shepherds Pie' or just to sit and eat your sandwiches. The 'torpedo' office tucked away in the remote corner of the factory approached by a flight of wooden stairs where the occupants kept a bucket for a toilet, which was emptied out of the window when full! There were many characters ... the Works Manager walking round the factory in a check plus fours suit prior to leaving for the local golf course.

Donald A. Laxton also joined as an apprentice in 1937 in the pattern shop under Horace Bye, working on a pattern for 'the big Billingham Compressor that had to be made plus the big base plate' (six skilled pattern makers had worked on the base plate). He was offered the chance to see it being cast in the foundry, and jumped at the offer:

When we arrived at the foundry they were just tapping the furnaces for the molten metal pouring it into two big ladles. This was the biggest casting they had ever done there. I forget the actual tonnage. The pattern was so large the pit the pattern was to go into was made bigger and deepened. They started pouring the metal into the mould from both ends. When the mould was full the molten metal would come out of the top of the mould ... then they should stop pouring, but they emptied both of the ladles and still the mould was not full in fact there was no metal at all in the mould. The next day Horace said to me, Don we are lucky to be alive today. I asked him what he was talking about. He said they found that as the mould pit had to be deepened they were just on top of a drain. The molten metal had broken through into this drain and flowed under the foundry under the Lincoln Road towards the railway bridge. It was a dry drain, if it had had water in it the foundry would have gone sky high and us with it.

Presumably the metal is still there, somewhere under the A47 flyover. He was then aged 17. When war broke out in 1939 all the apprentices were transferred into the works and put onto machines in the machine shops. He remained in the works after the war turning the parts on a centre lathe that had made the jets for the first nylon machine for ICI. He left in 1948.

Peter Roy began his apprenticeship with Brotherhoods in March 1938, and kept a record of life in the works. Age 15$\frac{1}{2}$, he was given a letter of introduction to Mr Davis, a Director. He was taken to watch a turner, there being no vacancies in the electrical department where Peter had wanted to go:

> Having never been in a factory before I was rather bewildered by the noise as I entered, above each row of lathes revolved a long shaft with pulley wheels, each lathe driven by a heavy flat leather belt from the pulley above, initially the noise of the pulleys and the slap of the belts was somewhat frightening but after a few days it became a normal sound.

After three weeks he still had not been allowed to touch the lathe, so he complained to the shop foreman. Next day he was taken to the tool and gauge making department under 'Honest John' Mansfield, an Alderman and ex-Mayor. Here he did Brinell hardness testing (of materials), tensile testing of steels, roughed out plate gauges and recalibrated pressure and vacuum gauges. After three months he was offered post in the electrical department where a vacancy had arisen, but John Mansfield was 'so pleased with my work he would like me to stay and train as a toolmaker and ... I decided to stay.' He was put to work on a bench beside three toolmakers whose job it was to teach him his trade. Tools and gauges were cut out by hacksaw and file, and made correct to one thousandth part of an inch by hand. A set time was allocated for each type of gauge. If one was made quicker than the set time then the surplus time was shown as bonus, if it took longer then any bonus earned was reduced by that amount. As an apprentice he used to eat his lunch on Fox Covert, then a patch of scrub with a small pond. Later, John Mansfield trained Peter Roy to be his backup, and when he retired in 1955

> he recommended me to fulfill his job. The way I was promoted, typical in those days, Mr Freestone the Managing Director called me into his office and said 'Mr Mansfield recommends you to take his job on his retirement can you do it?' I replied 'Yes'. He then said 'The job's yours don't let John down' and so it came about. The lads backed me 100% as we had worked together as a team for several years and continued to do so.

He was responsible for the purchase of all small tools throughout the factory, as well as the tool stores and issue of tools and gauges. He was Stores & Stock Control Manager 1974-80 and completely reorganized them, reducing 16 separate stores to one! Requests from naive staff, such as a ball of Whitworth thread, a long wait, or a skyhook, were still common when he retired.

Peter Roy's notebook of his experiences continued:

> The toilet facilities were most austere, outside the door of the two lavatory blocks stood a sentry box manned by the toilet cleaner. If you needed to use a cubicle during working hours you had to ask the cleaner for some toilet paper, no tissue in those days, he would tear off a few sheets of the hard, shiny, Izal type then record your name and clock number in his record book, you were allowed ten minutes and when your time was up he would kick the cubicle door and tell you to come out. If you had a stomach upset you had to get a note from your foreman to be allowed to use the lavatory more often. Harry Holmes was the lavatory cleaner as well as the first aid man, so, if you had an accident, a cut, or an abrasion you had to fetch him from his cleaning to dress your wound after a quick swill of his hands.
>
> Eating and drinking during working hours was forbidden and if one was caught by the Works Manager who prowled the shop floor during the day, even eating a sweet, he would call your foreman over and instruct him to give you a fifteen minute passout to empty your mouth. However, smoking was allowed from 9am to 11am and from 2pm to 4pm.
>
> As apprentices our first job on a winter's morning was to take the [45 gallon drums with holes punched in the sides] out into the yard, stoke them up with paper, wood and coke and when they were glowing nicely and no longer smoking we would pass a steel bar through the holes and carry them back into the workshop (where they stood on bricks beside the gangway) where coke would be fed to them in small quantities to avoid smoke and fumes, even when you got home at night you could still taste the acrid fumes.

Eventually, during the Second World War, steam heating was introduced in the factory. Working hours were marked by a hooter at 7.30am when the night shift finished, at 7.55am as a warning, and at 8.00am to start work. When the hooter finally went the gatekeeper would slam the 6ft high wooden gates shut, even if someone had their bicycle wheel half inside. After five minutes the gates were opened, the person's name and clock number were taken by the works policeman, and they were let in, losing 15 minutes pay. The hooter sounded at 12.00 lunch, 12.55 warning, 1.00 start. 5.30 finish, or 7.00 if overtime was being worked, and at 7.30 when the night shift started.

Peter Roy was issued with a papier mâché helmet as protection against falling glass in air raids. His recollection continues:

> During World War II the night shift had a half hour break from 2.30 to 3am this is when one's metabolism is at its lowest so many workers would snatch a short nap whilst others would go to the canteen for a plate of chips. 'Nodder' Winch, the Night Manager, would sit in his office at the end of the Turret Shop, at 3am a bell would ring for work to resume then Nodder would rise from his

chair to take a walk around the factory. He was nicknamed 'Nodder' as when he walked he nodded his head. Now 'Linnet', a well-known character in Peterborough, was a shop labourer during the war, the only job he was ever made to do in his life. He would hide behind No 1 Lathe in the Heavy Turnery and watch for 'Nodder' to rise from his chair then would make a noise like a sheep, Baa, Baa, this call was then relayed round the factory so that everyone was aware of 'Nodder's' coming and would be busy on their machines... [On the outbreak of war] our Company became under Admiralty control manufacturing large diesel engines for the 'S' class submarines, turbines, torpedo tubes, warheads, paravanes [mine sweeping device], Bofors guns, aircraft landing gear and many other military items. I did not serve in the forces as I was only 16 years old at the commencement of the war and was more useful in the manufacture of munitions than in the forces, my reserved position was reviewed by the Ministry every six months.

Then in 1941 Managing Director Bill Freestone and a few of his pals bought some piglets and had some outbuildings behind the foundry converted to pigsties. The law at that time was, if you kept pigs they had to be declared, as meat was rationed. The pigs had to be officially slaughtered and all the meat accounted for, but because of the secrecy and cover up on these pigs that were fed on all the canteen waste we believed they were not declared. One dark night during shift the 'boys' went to work on the pigs painting them with red,

Submarine engine leaving the Walton Factory. The caption on the front reads 3,500bhp, but on the back of the print in pencil it reads 2,150bhp at 460rpm. Note the low loader owned by Edward Box & Co. Ltd has pneumatic tyres only on the front wheels of the tractor, all the other tyres being solid. Note, too, the many overhead telephone wires and their massive poles, a contemporary feature of main roads. Bearing in mind Peterborough tramways had closed in 1930, but the rails are starting to show through the tarmac laid over them, the date is late 1930s.

white and blue stripes around their bodies and legs. The next morning there was hell to pay with much investigation and interrogation but no culprit was found and Wally Biggs the Yard Foreman and a couple of his men spent most of the day trying to clean them. Two days later a cartoon appeared on the front of the Works Manager's office depicting the pot-bellied profile of Bill Freestone gazing down at a painted pig, the caption read, 'What does a Brotherhoods fat pig weigh? Answer – Freestone'! [three stone – of 14 pounds, 42lb total, or 19kg].

In the latter part of 1942 there was an intake of C3 men [fitness category] from unreserved occupations whom Roy had to help train in engineering skills. Shifts were 12 hours long, with one weekend off in three. Food was rationed, but mid-day meals in the works canteen were 'off the ration'. Many of the new workers were women – from December 1941 unmarried women aged 18-30 could be conscripted into war work or agriculture. Over 2,000 women were employed at Brotherhoods during the war as machinists, fitters etc, and proved very capable. Some of the women were local and some had been evacuated from London. Mrs Afford was in charge of women's welfare. Many lived in what became the hostel for out of town apprentices, built 1941/42 at 191 Lincoln Road, Walton. Other workers were collected by special buses or even lorries from out in the fens. Eventually during the war some 5,000 staff were employed. Peter Roy's wife was a Norfolk girl who had worked in a hairdressing shop and had then been trained as a machinist in Norwich. At the end of her six weeks' training she was given the

option of working in a factory in Welwyn Garden City or Peterborough. She chose the latter, as her grandmother and aunt owned the Albion Hotel in North Street, and she was sent to Brotherhoods where she worked on lathe outside Peter's stores office window. This led to 49 years of marriage. Sister Cullen in the sick bay then lived in the former police sergeant's house.

A new wartime problem was the blackout. Thomas Sewell was appointed Air Raid Precautions

Bofors gun made in the Second World War.

(ARP) Officer. His first jobs included emptying the lofts of rubbish, in case of fire, and then to organize the blackout and camouflage of 15 acres of roof. He remembered the figure well! Due to the blackout permanently obscuring the windows in the roof, the lights were on continuously, and fumes from the home-made coke stoves could not escape, so conditions in the shops could become very unpleasant.

Peter Roy wrote:

> During the night shift if the air raid siren blew for a 'yellow' warning all the top lights in the workshop went out leaving only the individual light over your bench or machine. Then if the 'red' alert sounded, which meant that enemy planes were in the area, the power would be cut so all lights would be extinguished and we would have to make our way to the air raid shelters guided by storm lanterns placed at intervals along the gangways throughout the workshops. We had a labourer from the brickyards who had lost all the fingers from both hands clearing bricks from off the press too soon, his job was to see the storm lanterns were topped up with paraffin regularly and kept alight during the hours of darkness, needless to say he was known as 'Aladdin'.

Cutting the power also stopped all the machine tools, which often caused their tool bits to shatter as the tools and/or work pieces stopped moving. Drivers of the overhead cranes could only access their control cabins from special platforms built beside the overhead rails. With no electricity the cranes could not move to the platforms and the drivers would have been marooned. To overcome this problem, the crane drivers were each given a rope ladder which could be dropped to the floor, and so enabled them to climb down to safety. Air raid shelters were provided all over the site, but standing water was a problem in them. Petrol was strictly rationed during the war so almost everyone had to walk or cycle to work.

A local order completed in the early years of the Second World War was for the 'City of Peterborough Waterworks Undertaking' at Etton, to the north of the city. The works here had been opened in 1907, and demand had outgrown its capacity (and of Wilsthorpe, dating from 1880), so improvements had been planned from 1936 onwards. Modern electrically-driven pumps were installed at Etton, with steam-driven generating plant as stand-by in case the mains supply failed. This was built by Brotherhoods, a $14^1/_4$ & 24 x 8in. 2-crank engine and alternator working at 150psi with output 200kW in December 1939 at a cost of £4,250. It was very similar to plant supplied to HMS *Hood*. The new works at both sites were opened on 28th August, 1941.

Gladys Cowling (née Rushby) remembered the war.

In 1940 [then aged about 19] I was working in domestic service for a local butcher's family. As the war progressed my father told me, in no uncertain terms, that unless I changed my job to one involving the war effort, I would almost certainly be called up for one of the Services. As I had no wish to be sent away from home I applied for, and got a job, at Peter Brotherhoods ... On reporting for work I had to complete various tests, one of which was reading a micrometer which I was able to do. As this apparently was not something that everyone was able to do I was set to work on a Herbert No 4 lathe making the screws for breech blocks to be used on submarines.... I was single and living at home so I used to cycle to and from work even going home for my midday meal, a distance of about 12 miles per day in total. I used to do 12 hour night shifts and when my friend Evelyn Higgs and I used to cycle past the Town Park on Sunday evenings we were very envious of the people walking and enjoying the summer evenings whilst we had to go to work. During my time at Brotherhoods I married ... and only left there when I was expecting my first baby in 1944.

For many years a reminder of those times was the continued use, even in 1977, of women drivers for the overhead cranes spanning the workshops. After some trouble replacing skirts by trousers, as access to the cranes was by open stairs, they took over in the early days of the war and remained there. (There had been women turners in the heavy turnery in the First World War but they had been replaced after the war.) In 1977 some of the crane drivers had served up to 20 years, lifting weights of up to 25 tons and carrying them about the shop. One of their most skilled jobs was lifting work from between the centres of a lathe, without damaging either the work or the machine, as the rope slings 'gave' a little when a load was applied.

Thomas Sewell was also responsible for the spotter posts with Lewis (light anti-aircraft) guns which were on top of the roof. One gun was at the office end of the heavy turnery and the other above the Green engine/fabrication shop, at the end of the pattern shop. The each gun was manned by a couple of regular soldiers, billeted in a camp just across the railway. One grey damp day a German plane suddenly appeared out of the low cloud and flew past along the railway, but the gun remained silent – it still had its cover on to keep off the drizzle! On another occasion a plane dropped five bombs in a nearby field, and a plane once machine-gunned nearby buildings, but the works was never damaged by enemy action.

Naval work was prominent, with torpedo centre and after bodies, submarine compressors, compressors and lighting sets for ships,

Twin torpedo tube. Note the main line wagon brought right into the workshop

pumps, diesel engines, Bofors guns and their sights (made in the new gun shop), and paravanes (a device which cut the mooring wires of mines so they came to the surface and could be destroyed). Some civilian work continued, mainly brewery machinery as it was for the food industry. There were also orders for spares, including some for machines built in the old London works. Torpedo engine cylinder blocks were machined for other firms who could not master the casting technique.

Sometimes there were exceptional demands. One Sunday the factory manufacturing hydraulic landing gear 'Oleo Legs' for Warwick and Wellington bombers was destroyed by enemy action. Brotherhoods had them in production again on the following Friday, after adapting machines to do the job. The machine shop manager, William Thompson, was an expert at modifying machine tools! One day there was the urgent order for a spare plunger for the HP compressor on a warship due to sail from the Clyde the next morning. The spare was made, but by then the last train north from Peterborough had gone. Nothing daunted, Alfred Savage, a railway enthusiast, suggested using the 'Night Scot' which was due to pass through Peterborough around midnight. Arrangements were made immediately with the railway and the Admiralty, and the train was stopped specially so the plunger could be loaded. The ship sailed on time.

Brotherhoods also used the premises of several local firms during the war. Stores were kept at a Fletton brickworks and wooden patterns, being a fire risk, were kept on the showground at Eastfield. Torpedo after-bodies were manufactured at the British Horticultural Society bulb factory. Brotherhoods became the area's secure bonded stores for non-ferrous metal, then in short supply, from which other firms could draw when suitably authorized.

An anti-aircraft rocket battery (Z Battery, 101 Northants Batt. Home Guard LAA Rocket Battery) was installed in nearby Fulbridge Road, on the playing field behind the school, in 1942. It was manned by civilians (i.e. Home Guard) from 7.00pm to 7.30am. Brotherhoods supplied two troops of 64 men, one troop from each shift. When working nights they would report for duty on their night off (Saturday), when working days would report for Sunday night. Living and sleeping huts had been erected at the gun site in Tennyson Road. The site was controlled by regulars from the Royal Artillery, whose sergeants tried to get some military training into them. They had little success as the men were working 12 hours a night during the week and this was officially their night off. Each evening on duty they practised gun drill until 9pm, then they had supper after which they were allowed into the NAFFI (Forces canteen) until lights out at 11pm. The corrugated-iron sleeping huts contained 32 double bunks (one above the other) and were heated by two cast-iron coke stoves. 'We slept in our clothes in case of a call-out during the night.'

Despite pressure from defence contracts some special development work continued on a reduced scale. The policy of 'tailor made engineering', building anything for anyone, born out of the need to survive in the inter-war years, had been recognised for its value and was about to bear real fruit. In 1944 Courtaulds approached several firms, including Brotherhoods, for the construction of prototype machines for the embryonic synthetic fibre industry. Freestone was able to examine an existing American machine, sized it up for a few minutes, and gave a price. Brotherhoods got the contract, which soon led to the contract for the equipment for the British Nylon Spinners' Pontypool factory in 1946. Much of the post-war prosperity of the Company was due to synthetic fibre plant orders.

The transition to peace was easier but slower in 1945. Unlike 1918, many defence contracts continued, and on the civilian side the synthetic fibre plant was being developed, turbines were produced for Boving for worldwide use on hydro-electric schemes, and on top of this there was a flood of orders from breweries, sewage works, etc. to replace equipment they had not been able to afford in the Thirties nor to have built during the war. For 10 years the new gun shop was devoted to the manufacture of Liquid Carbonic Company machines. Bank note printing presses were made for Thomas De La Rue & Co. in 1948, and subsequently made for export to Japan, Russia, and the United States.

As a result of their war work both Messrs Freestone and Charlton received the British Empire Medal. A major problem of the early post-war years was shortages, especially of raw materials. Most materials needed a licence before they could be ordered, and actual delivery was unpredictable. Under these conditions orders were executed as materials arrived, and the final product delivered when everything had finally come together. Dates were meaningless.

The *Peterborough Standard* of 28th September, 1945 carried a report about the Company. The Chairman, Marcus Neal, noted that output was down by almost a third from the previous year, due to the cancellation of many Service contacts. He considered the time had come when details of the firm's war work could be revealed:

> Our manufactures for the Admiralty during the six years from September 1939 have consisted of torpedo engines and components, torpedo tubes, turbo-generators, high pressure air compressors, high speed diesel engines, main propelling diesel engines for submarines, gun mountings, and a number of other items too numerous to mention. In addition to these we have manufactured hydrogen compressors and aircraft landing gear for the Ministry of Aircraft Production, and a considerable volume of chemical plant machinery for the Ministry of Supply, the total value of our output during the six years referred to, amounting to some ten and a half million pounds. The transition period would be a testing time, but we have on our books a large number of orders including air compressors for diesel-driven vessels, steam and water turbines for export, brewery machinery, refrigeration machinery, and general structural work. He acknowledged on behalf of shareholders and the Board the loyal services rendered by the staff and workpeople during the immediate pre-war and the wartime period, amounting in all to nearly ten years.

More Brotherhood compressors at Billingham were in the Urea plant, near Ammonia Avenue (an internal road). In the 1940s six vertical carbon dioxide compressors were supplied, two low pressure ones of 400hp and four high pressure ones of 200-250hp.

As unusual order in 1949 was to supply 24 transportable 500kW self-contained turbo alternators mounted on steel sleds. Single-stage turbines had long been produced in their hundreds for refineries and

A vertical compressor loaded for transport, c.1950, still on solid tyres.

gas works, and by the mid-1950s they were also being supplied to sugar mills around the world. The typical sugar mill required four single-stage turbines to drive the cane mills, one to drive a cane shredder and a small multistage turbo generator to provide electrical power for the mill. An order for Cuba in 1968 required 51 machines, and thereafter that type of turbines was known as a 'Cuban'.

The Company continued in the marine field. A new range of marine alternators of up to 1,000kW was developed in 1947, to meet the demand as shipping lines replaced wartime losses. The first set was supplied to the *Madelana* but it did not see much use as the ship ran aground on her maiden voyage! However, much equipment, including the generator set, was salvaged and put to use in Brazil. Spares were still being supplied for it in 1975. This type of turbo alternator was ordered for many liners built in the late 1940s to mid- 1950s. It developed a package of steam-driven auxiliary machinery so that the ship owner had to deal with only a single service engineer and hold one firm's spares. For example, the 101,000 ton *Texaco Westminster* was supplied with Brotherhood turbines to drive cargo, ballast, main circulating and tank cleaning pumps, and with two 1,000kW back pressure turbo alternator sets. Vertical shaft turbines, first produced in the 1920s to drive circulating water pumps in battleships were now required for use in tankers for handling oil and ballast. One large order in 1952 was for 72 vertical turbines driving Hayward Tyler pumps for Anglo Saxon &

Eagle Oil tankers. The Company was well placed to meet the needs of the tanker boom of the late 1950s onwards.

Textile machinery manufacture began in earnest in 1947. Brotherhoods had a joint project with Courtaulds and ICI through British Nylon Spinners, making machinery based on Dupont (USA) technology. ICI then developed a new fibre, terylene, the first terylene plant being constructed for ICI at Wilton (Middlesbrough) during 1951. This was followed by a steady flow of orders throughout the 1950s and a flood in the 1960s, reaching a peak in 1965. Brotherhoods supplied synthetic fibre machinery for ICI contracts in Poland, Russia, Turkey and elsewhere. A lot of experimental work was required to develop new machinery. Textile spinnarets, which actually formed the individual fibrous threads, were 3in. (76.2mm) diameter stainless steel discs $^3/_8$ in. (9.52mm) thick, each disc having 100 holes. Each hole was $^3/_{64}$ in. (1.19mm) diameter with the final '10 thou' (thousandths of an inch, 0.254mm) drilled by hand to ten , eight or even four thou (0.254, 0.2032, 0.1016mm) diameter. Synthetic fibre business peaked around 1965 and then dried up very quickly. Brotherhoods also equipped an artificial leather factory at Kings Lynn in the early 1970s. The synthetic fibre market is one reason why Brotherhoods survived when so many firms failed or were taken over.

Most compressors built prior to 1958 had been vertical units, but in that year a new range of horizontal, balanced opposed, reciprocating

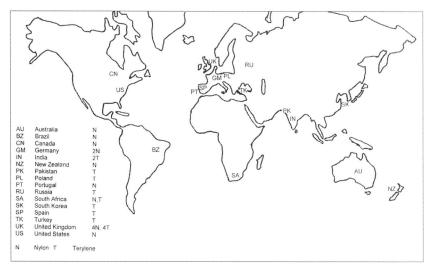

World map showing location of artificial fibre machinery sales.

Horizontal compressor in ICI, Billingham, Urea plant. Note access points for the valves.

Courtesy ICI

compressors was introduced. These were cheaper to make, easier to house and maintain, and were much more compact. The range had compressors up to 14,000hp with outputs up to 10,000psi. By 1977 a pair of these modern Brotherhood horizontal compressors had been installed at ICI Billingham. They each absorbed 3,500hp, taking 10,000 cubic metres of carbon dioxide per hour at 5psi and compressing it to 220 atmospheres (3,300psi). These 5-stage 3-crank machines had three first stage cylinders on one side of the crankshaft, and the cylinders for the other stages were on the other side, with the fourth and fifth stages having a common piston. Each cylinder had its own water jacket so the whole compressor had a 'knobbly' appearance. A sight glass containing a light ball was provided in the water circuit for each cooling jacket so it was easy to check the flow of water. The design permitted the water jacket of each cylinder to be isolated, so it was only necessary to drain the jacket of the affected cylinder to change one of the flat disc valves, which took only two hours. Horizontal compressors, besides needing less headroom and being more accessible, could be fastened down much more rigidly than vertical ones. I stood a coin on edge on the cylinder block of this particular machine at Billingham while it was running.

Another development in compressors was the use of aluminium pistons with cast-iron centres, or having hollow pistons, both being means to minimize the effects of inertia in large low pressure stages. High pressure cylinders were cast steel with drilled water passages. Piston rod packing was either metallic or carbon, and self-adjusting for wear.

About this time there were changes in the Company leadership. First Bill Freestone retired, in 1958, having completed 50 years' service in October 1957. A very able engineer and strong union man (one reason for his early promotion had been to keep him away from the union!), he had already been bitterly disappointed that he had to be content with being Vice Chairman following Stanley's death. Perhaps he had hoped he could succeed Marcus Neal, who, in fact, outlasted him, retiring in September 1961. The private road between works and offices was their 'no man's land'! Bill Freestone's attitude had been 'Give us a drawing and we will make it'. This was the sort of skill that made some traditionalists consider that 'Once the MD was a financier and not an engineer then the firm went down-hill!' If he caught anyone eating – even sweets – or drinking in works time, there was a 15 minute penalty!

In the late 1950s hip replacement surgery was becoming more common, and the local hospital had the need for instruments to scrape clean hip joints. Could Brotherhoods make them? 'Of course we can!' Unfortunately, despite searches, no trace has been found of one of these instruments.

The Company always had a reputation for a willingness to build prototypes or small batches, whereas many firms only mass produce standard designs. Following Bill Freestone's reply 'Of course we can make this' the works would then discover how. Indeed, on occasions the object would be made and the proper drawings prepared afterwards. While he and his assistant William Thompson might appear to be brash 'know alls' or 'slave drivers' they were also very talented engineers. This positive attitude towards customers' requests remains and is one of the Company's biggest assets.

General engineering experience gained over many years in many fields enabled the firm to suggest improvements and modifications to both prototype and later designs. Indeed, some machines, for example those for synthetic leather manufacture, were designed by Brotherhoods from a broad outline given by the customer. In other cases machines were built to a rigid design supplied by the customer. Either way accumulated expertise was put to good use for mutual benefit.

For most of its existence the Company was independent of any other company, which meant that trade secrets were secure, as there was no parent company which could bring any pressure to bear to divulge them. Brotherhoods also accepted advertising restrictions from customers; for example, synthetic fibre machinery production was secret for years.

The combination of expertise, willingness, and independence, backed by skilled men throughout the works, contributed largely to the Company's survival. For years it was fortunate, too, in having three main markets: marine, fibres, and general industry, and while one might often be depressed it was rare that two were.

Apprentices, whether it was Rue Hardy or Thomas Sewell in 1915 or Norman Sismey in 1955, used to receive their training on the shop floor. A boy entered his apprenticeship at 15 and qualified when he was 20. In the meantime he passed through every department in turn, machine shop, patternmaking, foundry, fitting, draughtsman. The apprentice would watch an experienced man for about a week and then commence the job himself. Gradually day release courses at local technical colleges were provided for apprentices, but it was not until the 1960s that the Company took apprentices off the shop floor into a purpose built Training School. Besides freeing the apprentices from the rigours of commercial production they could also demonstrate their skills in public.

Brotherhood apprentices undertook a number of projects to benefit local causes. These have ranged from overhauling and fitting new

Items made by apprentices for St John the Baptist Church, Werrington.

bearings to a church weathercock to giving thorough overhauls to steam locomotives for the nearby preserved Nene Valley Railway (0-6-0ST *Jacks Green* in the early 1970s was followed by 4-6-0 No. 73050, completed after two years' work in 1980). A set of stainless steel altar ornaments was made for Peterborough Hospital Chapel and other items for Werrington church.

A Brotherhood apprenticeship was and is a very useful asset. Apprentices used to come from far afield, and in 1941 an apprentice hostel was opened in Lincoln Road in nearby Walton. In the 1950s many had come from South Wales, but later the majority of apprentices were local boys so it closed in 1963. Some companies, for example ICI and Shell, sent graduate engineers to Peterborough for a period of practical training. From 1945 until the late 1950s all young men had to do two years' National Service; although apprentices and students might obtain deferment but not exemption. An alternative taken by a number of apprentices was service in the Merchant Navy, which enabled useful engineering experience to be obtained under conditions thought to be preferable to those in the armed forces. Training was sometimes given to customers' staff, either at Peterborough or on site during the erection of the machinery.

Several graduate apprentices have sent their memories of time at Brotherhoods. John Willetts was one of eight ICI graduate trainees sent in 1948-49 to obtain practical works' experience. Having served from 1944 as an Engineer Officer in the Navy he only had six months at Peterborough while the others had eight to twelve months. He stayed in the apprentice hostel while some of the others found digs with local landladies. Brotherhoods was chosen as it supplied so much plant, particularly gas and air compressors, to ICI at Billingham. He worked in various departments including

the Foundry, Electricians, Assembly Shop and the Test Beds. This latter was always the most popular and interesting because it was fascinating to see the products – turbines, air compressors etc – turn over for the first time having helped to build them and prepare them for test... Every few months the Engineering Director of ICI Sir Ewart Smith came to visit us to check on our progress. I was most impressed that such a senior person took such an interest in us young trainees. An example of management at its best! I am proud of having worked for a short time with an elderly fitter (perhaps about 70 years at the time) who was trusted with the highly skilled and important job of blading all the steam turbines. He was a proud engineering fitter who took great pride in his work. He wore a white shirt, a wing collar and bow tie, and came to work in a bowler hat! Those were the days when such men were looked up to as the cream of their profession and dressed accordingly!

Later, about 1955, he was working for ICI Metals Division and needed some crucibles for a new plant being built to produce titanium. A small Birmingham engineering company had supplied some crucibles, but he thought Brotherhoods might be interested, and so he took the drawings to Peterborough where he met Mr Freestone.

> He studied the drawings for about five minutes and then said 'Yes, we can do those for £80 each! [This was the same price as they had paid the local company]... I was most impressed with his total command and an outstanding example of a practical engineer who had reached the top to run a successful engineering company. Finally, I have a permanent and treasured reminder of my happy days at P.B. Every time I open my tool box I am confronted with a hammer and pair of pliers stamped with P.B.Ltd on them! They were given to us by the various departments in which we worked. The Electricians were noted as being particularly generous!

John Norsworthy was one of six ICI graduate apprentices in 1951.

> We were spread about the factory. In each workshop one was allocated to work with a craftsman and was given manual or minor technical duties both to keep us occupied and to avoid interfering with the piecework system. These craftsmen were specially selected volunteers. They were friendly and informative and the two-way exchanges benefited both. I started in the Foundry and spent a month working with a pair of foundrymen who were producing sizeable castings for air compressors. We enjoyed each other's company and, I believe, they commended my work to the Shop Foreman. He, on my last day there, asked how I got on. My reply that it had been good fun drew a snort and a frown. 'This is work – not fun' he declared stonily, then shook my hand and bade me well. On to the Pattern Shop where I beavered away. I rough planed large wooden patterns ready for the craftsmen to finish them off. What puzzled me was the occasional cry of '$2\frac{1}{2}$'. This, I learned, was a shop warning that the Foreman was on his way back. The rarer cry of '1 $\frac{1}{4}$' signalled the approach of the Chargehand. ... In the big boring shop we could only stand and watch. Later, in the Plate Shop, I was taken aback by the accuracy of the plater when marking out thick plates to allow for torch cutting and a chamfer to allow the plate to be bent to shape. Even more so to allow for the extra margin for torch cutting stainless steel to avoid burning deterioration of the metal when cut to size. In the compressor assembly shop, I came across a particularly inaccessible stud on a large compressor. This could only be tightened with a specially designed spanner (designed and made by the craftsman). In my opinion, moving the stud by one inch would allow any spanner to deal with it. 'Ah, yes' said the craftsman, 'if only you knew how difficult it is to get the Navy to allow a change, you wouldn't even think about it!' I enjoyed my apprenticeship at PBL and learned a lot of practical engineering.

Main gate at close of work, 1950s, with many bicycles and a solitary scooter. The workshops are visible behind the end of the office block. The person in white coat controlling traffic on the main road is probably a works policeman, as he has neither the helmet nor boots that an ordinary policeman would wear.

Christopher Warman was an ICI graduate apprentice in 1958. His memories are very similar.

> The few months I spent working in the ferrous foundry were particularly enjoyable. The size of some of the compressor castings was especially impressive. I found the mould makers a very likeable and friendly band who accepted the young upstart that I was without question. [He lived in digs] with a couple who, in their daytime work, were chefs in the managers' restaurant at Baker Perkins; the menu was amazing!

Derek Claxton started as an apprentice in 1956. The interview panel included the Managing Director, Mr Thomson, Sister Watson and three other members of staff. Mr Thomson said that he had trained as an apprentice with Derek's grandfather, Samuel Claxton, who had later helped to develop 'three-piston engine which was part of the Dry Torpedo'. Apparently there had been a plaque with a chrome torpedo commemorating this Brotherhood achievement at HMS *Vernon*, the

Navy's Torpedo School. Once he became 18, Derek was given the opportunity to work at Portsmouth, fitting Brotherhood equipment in a new frigate, HMS *Leopard*, and finally going on the sea trials to ensure it all worked satisfactorily. This was followed by helping to install nylon spinning machinery. He left Brotherhoods at the end of his apprenticeship for a career in the Royal Fleet Auxiliary as an Engineering Officer. Many pranks took place while an apprentice, being 'famous' for balancing a file in the flow of compressed air from an air-line clamped in a vice, and helping to nail the greasy bowler hat which Taff Evans always wore at work to the bench with a specially made 18in. nail!

In an article headed 'Jubilee of Brotherhood's Move to Walton', the *Peterborough Standard* of 2nd August, 1957 reported that the works then occupied more than 20 acres, mainly under cover. It was self-contained except for the supply of heavy forgings and stampings, and raw materials. The office block had about 400ft frontage along Lincoln Road, almost all on one floor. The main workshops comprised five 40ft bays 450ft long, each with one or more overhead travelling cranes running whole length. New heat treatment plant had been installed. In April 1955 a new pattern-making facility was opened in Lincoln Road, Werrington, comprising pattern stores and pattern shop, all with new equipment.

A new field was entered in 1960 when a prototype gas turbine was built, and also a centrifugal compressor, although they were not pursued due to pressure from the volume of other orders on hand. Another new field, or a logical extension of an existing one, was also entered in the late 1950s. Brotherhoods were approached by BP Tankers Ltd to provide a waste heat recovery turbine, using heat in the exhaust gases from the ship's main diesel engine to raise steam. With steam conditions typically from 220psi down to 50psi these machines are characterized by a large number of stages for a relatively small heat/pressure drop, to achieve good efficiency. From small beginnings, by 1979 Peter Brotherhood Ltd dominated this market. By then the Company had supplied about 200 units for ships plus others to general industry. Waste heat recovery meant that diesel and gas turbine exhausts yielded about 14 per cent and 30 per cent respectively more power from the same fuel. Factory chimneys and chemical plants offered similar opportunities for energy saving, while a corporation refuse incinerator produced 4MW for every 10 tons of rubbish burned. An agreement was signed with the Thermo-Electron Corporation, of Boston, Massachusetts, in 1975 to supply the American market.

Typically, the heat exchanger (boiler) was placed in the ship's funnel. The engine exhaust gases passed through it before being discharged to the atmosphere. The steam raised was then used to supply turbines driving alternators, thus producing useful electric power. Naturally the supply of steam depended on the temperature of the exhaust gases, which in turn depended on the type of engine, but a typical installation generated steam at 70 to 180psi and 570°F. An article in *Shipbuilding & Shipping Record* (11th December, 1970) discussed the economics of steam auxiliaries on motor ships. At 1967 prices a 400kW turbo-alternator set, including heat exchanger, for a typical 50,000 ton bulk carrier cost £34,000. The annual saving in running costs over a conventional diesel generator was estimated to be £7,400, so the steam unit paid for itself in five years and thereafter contributed towards a reduction in operating costs. An additional benefit was the elimination of one noisy diesel engine from the ship's engine room.

The number of orders for fibre plant and compressors in the mid-1960s led to congestion in the works. As local expansion was not possible, and sub-contractors could not keep pace, suitable premises

Compressor erecting shop with, in the foreground, a 6-cylinder horizontal carbon dioxide compressor for Kanpur, India. The pistons can be seen through the valve openings. The crank case is the height of the shoulders of the man standing at the left hand rear corner.

were sought elsewhere. The Crossley Bros factory at Sandiacre near Nottingham had recently closed and was available. It was purchased in 1965. Of comparable size to the Peterborough works, it was brought into production in 1966, but it had a much smaller labour force. The manufacture of large compressors was transferred there, and it also helped with general machining. A later recession caused the flow of orders to decline to a level within the capacity of the Peterborough works, so Sandiacre was closed and sold in 1971, with the unfortunate loss of 300 jobs, the first 250 redundancies leaving on 7th May. It was the first time that the Company had to lay off men since 1945. The site had been operated since 1967 as a partnership between Brotherhood and the Derby engineering firm of Fletcher & Stewart, and Sutcliffe & Wild, the partnership terminating in June 1971. The company's offices in Mark Street (once used by Crossleys) survive, and by 2006 were being used by Three Valleys Housing Ltd, formerly the Housing Department of Erewash Borough Council.

Turbines for sugar mills were important in the late 1960s, the largest order being 51 units for Cuba. Hydraulically-operated winch gear was introduced in 1966, while factory pumps designed by Tetmark were made between 1967 and 1971 to extend coverage in the industrial process field. In the 1960s Brotherhoods made many compressors for gas turbines.

During the 1950s Brotherhoods Sports Club, in Lincoln Road, New England, organized meetings under AAA rules with athletes from all over the country, but with no financial support from Brotherhoods they later had to abandon them. There were three Brotherhood marathons around this time as well, but they stopped when the London Marathons began. In 1966 the then Chairman, Mr Wilks, gave a £400 grant to fund a Works Family Day, which was a great success, and was held for several years, with sideshows, 'Miss Brotherhood', go-cart racing, 'It's a Knockout' etc.

Marcus Neal (1886-1963) was born at Kettering in 1886, and came to Peterborough in 1911 after four years as engineering master at nearby Oundle School. The headmaster, F.W.Sanderson, ran the school on very original lines and he had engineering workshops where the boys worked to a very high standard (classics, science and farming were also taught at this time) (*A Secret Well Kept* by Constance Kell – Conway, 2017, page 136). Neal was appointed to the Board in 1930, and became General Manager in 1935 on the death of Mr C.W.Bryant. Marcus Neal had a totally different personality from Bill Freestone. Besides being an able businessman and good engineer he had the manner and bearing of a gentleman. He could not be thwarted, and was adept at diverting conversation from complaints or of talking people out of requests he could sense but did not want. The continued existence of the independent company was probably a tribute to Marcus Neal's policy. He was content with a reasonable salary and did not want to be too adventurous. Growth to him could mean a less personal atmosphere in the works, might cause problems in finding skilled labour, might make a takeover more likely. As the last consequence could well result in old employees being made redundant, and affect the fortunes of Stanley's daughters (who took no direct interest in the firm), he had good reasons for continuing in the old ways. Later, the financial policies of various governments made financiers wary. In any case, the firm's success was due in no small part to its independence and trustworthiness. He retired in September 1961 having been Chairman for 23 years. Marcus Neal had been a Justice of the Peace since 1942. He was involved with Peterborough Sea Cadets and was also a governor of King's School, an ancient local foundation. He owned a 1938 Rover car which he would not change, and whose poor acceleration was probably a contributory factor in causing his death in an accident while crossing the A1 near his home at Water Newton, a short distance south-east of Wansford, on Sunday 10th November, 1963, aged 77.

Peter Roy was known to be interested in locks and keys. One day Marcus Neal was having problems with his front door of his house as the key would not work properly, so Peter met him by his car at lunch time and was taken to his home:

> [Peter] completed the job and expected to go back to work but Neal said 'Come and have a drink before you go back', and opened a bottle of port. In conversation it came up that I enjoyed shooting so out came the guns from his cabinet and we had an enjoyable discussion over the next hour before he returned me to work at 4pm much to the distain of my boss who wanted to know why it had taken me so long. I told him the truth, if the big man says you stay, you stay! After that I serviced his guns when necessary.

The workforce also had strong, if not stronger, family links with the firm.

In 1957 the *Peterborough Standard* reported two employees completing 50 years with the firm. William Law had joined as an apprentice fitter on 29th April 1907, but soon became a turner, and was then still employed in the heavy turning shop. For many years he had taken an active interest in works welfare, and was a works representative on the Hospital Committee. The other was Mr Freestone, already mentioned. In

August the previous year a fitter, Mr W.C.Willis, had completed 54 years with Brotherhoods.

Albert Viney (1874 – 1960) was born and educated in Barnstaple. By the time he was 12 he had learned all the local school could teach time, so was set to instruct the younger pupils. He became an engineering apprentice at Miller Bros, Barnstaple, where his father was foreman, then went to Maudslay Sons & Field where he worked on the erection, installation and sea trials of engines for the Admiralty. Transferring to Woolwich Arsenal in 1902, he became responsible for developing an improved type of compressed air engine for torpedoes. Using air heated to 300°C the range was more than doubled, from 1.4 to 3.7 miles. Viney held the patent. In 1912 he transferred to the RN Torpedo Factory, Greenock, where he became manager. During the war he worked seven days a week. Possibly because he found it irksome to work under Navy men in the factory, he was sent in 1917 to Whitehead's factory in the little village of St Tropez, which was making torpedoes for the French and Italian navies. He was awarded the MBE for his work on torpedo engines. On returning to England in late 1920, he worked briefly for British Thomson-Houston at Rugby, then went to Brotherhoods to do research in connection with the development of torpedo engines. His appointment as manager of the torpedo department was confirmed in July 1923, backdated to 1st January. He was one of the patentees of the torpedo engine used by the Royal Navy in the Second World War. After the successful torpedo attack on the Italian Navy by the Fleet Air Arm at Taranto on 12th November, 1940 the Admiralty sent him a telegram of congratulations. Although by then he was of retirement age, he was too valuable to lose and joined the Board in 1940. He first became involved with Peterborough City Council in 1937, and from there on was much involved with local government and community life. He was a County Councillor, Mayor in 1945-6, and was made an Alderman 1953. A prime mover in establishing Peterborough Technical College, he was its first Chairman of Governors. Earlier, he had been much involved with establishing Peterborough Memorial Hospital.

CHAPTER TEN

INDEPENDENCE
LOST AND REGAINED (1961-PRESENT)

William 'WT' Thompson succeeded Neal in 1961. He had followed Bill Freestone for years, as Assistant Works Manager and then as Manager. He was a strong character and a word of warning always went ahead of him when he walked round the works. When he retired in 1965 his departure marked the end of the family firm. While many senior staff continued to be former apprentices others came from outside, particularly ICI. However, the traditions of care, interest and help were maintained, while better job definitions, union agreements and the like reduced the responsibilities which in former days used to be given to even quite junior employees.

Production in the 1960s and 1970s followed the usual pattern of turbines, compressors, and fibre plant, interspersed with other machinery of all kinds. A turbine for the main engine of the Royal navy Research Ship *Challenger* was built in 1971. Noise and vibration problems were overcome so that the ship was able to hover while drilling for samples in the sea bed $3^{1}/_{2}$ miles below. The civil engineering contracting firm McAlpine ordered a tunnelling machine in 1972, to be capable of working in hard or soft ground. Following trials in 1973 at Chinnor, Oxfordshire, it was intended for the Channel Tunnel contract. A sophisticated self-propelled sweeper for factory floors and shopping precincts was developed in conjunction with Melford Engineering Ltd in 1974, but economic conditions prevented many sales so it was discontinued.

Two major developments in conjunction with ICI were made public in 1973. One was plant to make a new fibre, Cambrelle. The other was the Merolite system of bottling aerated drinks, in which the conventional bottle and cap was replaced by a printed plastic sachet with a pull-off tag. Both types of machine subsequently entered production. The Merolite sachet looked like a sausage of beer. During testing there were a number of problems, sachets broke, and beer went everywhere!

The works, power houses were modernized in 1953. Two new turbines, one providing 600kW ac and the other 600kW dc were installed, replacing three old Brotherhood high speed compound steam engines, and four horizontal heavy oil engines, two by Blackstone and two by Brotherhood, although the Brotherhood-Ricardo diesel engines were retained.

0-6-0ST *Jacks Green* under restoration in the early 1970s.

Half of a pair of ship stabilizers. The fin can be controlled to constantly create a force opposing a roll. It can also be retracted into the hull when not required or the ship docks.

Although normally the works later obtained electricity from the National Grid, the three power houses were retained for emergency use (a third had been built during the Second World War, complete with blast walls and a thick layer of sand on its roof). During a national Miners' Strike in 1972 the Company was able to overcome the power cuts which affected the country by generating a large proportion of its own electricity, just as it used to before the National Grid was constructed. One, or maybe two, of the Brotherhood-Ricardo diesel engines in the power house were reputed to have been supplied originally for HMS *Belfast*. One certainly had a heavily repaired base frame, which looked as though it had been split from end to end and welded up. This damage could have been caused when the ship was severely damaged by a German mine in 1939, and the engine, being too good to scrap but not good enough for active service, had been repaired and put to work in the power house.

Other developments arose from existing products. For example, synthetic fibre spinning machinery was modified to produce synthetic food protein, and bottling plant expertise was used to develop high speed food canning machines. Stabilizers for ships were manufactured in 1977. Servo motors caused the blade to tilt to counteract the tendency for the ship to lean either way, and the whole assembly could pivot into a slot in the hull when not required. At this time about three-quarters of the orders were for turbines, and about three-quarters of the output was exported.

An extensive programme of modernization in the works was begun in 1974 and largely completed by 1976. The majority of machine tools installed in the two million pound project were electronically controlled, so that the Company could continue to provide tailor-made engineering to extremely high standards.

These developments were not, unfortunately, accompanied by a steady flow of orders. Although Brotherhoods was buoyant in 1973, a world-wide recession came and everything changed. Many firms delayed expansion or the replacement of equipment. Expected orders failed to materialize, and at the end of 1976 the Company had to declare 500 men redundant from its staff of about 1,500. These were the first redundancies since Sandiacre had closed 10 years before, and the first at Peterborough since 1945. Despite this setback the future of the Company seemed assured for as long as there was a demand for individualized high quality engineering, since it sold facilities and skills rather than products. Nationally, the 1970s gave industry a 'wake up' call as it became very obvious that traditional ways had to change if a business was to survive.

Even in the late 1970s the sense of continuity with the past was still very strong in the offices. In the Directors' dining room it was clearly understood that the Chairman, if present, would carve. More publically, Peter's plates still remained on the pillars of the main door and the Company's trade mark was still a symbolic radial engine, a mark which dated from at least 1907 as it was carved in a stone above the main office door, although it did not appear on products until about 1920.

Many of the staff retained the strong family connections. Ted Brooks' grandfather came from Belvedere Road. There had been a notice in the works inviting people to move to Peterborough, and he moved, becoming a 'slinger' on an overhead crane, and sometimes drove the tractor. Although Ted's father went on the railway, his uncle came to the factory, and his maiden aunt was a machinist in the works in both wars. Ted was thus the third generation to be involved. He became the Director responsible for textile machinery in 1957. While neither worked long for Brotherhoods, his own daughter and grandson have both had work experience here, making five generations altogether.

Thomas Sewell, appointed to the Estimating Department by Marcus Neal when he was discharged from the army at the end of the First World War, rose to become chief estimator by the time he retired after 52 years' service in June 1967. He was a devoted member of the St John's Ambulance Brigade in his spare time, and retired as Senior County Officer after a record 60 years' service.

The Coombs family connection with Brotherhoods spanned 100 years and four generations. Farnham Coombs was born near Frome, Somerset, in 1859 and moved to London about 1875. In 1879 he married the daughter of the owner of a pub at 3 Compton Street, near Peter's first factory, and they lived in New Charles Street round the corner. As Peter's father Rowland did a lot of work around Frome on the GWR it is possible Farnham moved to London deliberately to work at Peter's factory. In the 1881 Census he is given as an 'Engineer's Labourer'. Farnham's eldest son Frank was born in 1880, and is known to have worked for Brotherhoods at Belvedere Road and then at Peterborough. Frank's ambition was to work for Brotherhoods for 50 years, and was not far off when he retired in 1947 at the time of his wife's death. He died in 1961. His eldest son, also Frank, started at Brotherhoods as an apprentice fitter in 1919, aged 16. He was laid off in the Twenties but later rejoined and worked as a driller until retiring in 1968. He lived all his married life in Paston Lane, within walking distance of the factory. Frank Senior's second son, Cyril, was a cabinet maker, but following redundancy in the early 1930s joined Brotherhoods and trained as a

McAlpine's tunnel boring machine
crossing the A1 near Huntingdon.

Tunnelling machine on trial at
Chinnor, Oxfordshire, 1973.

welder, working in the Green Engine shop, eventually becoming its foreman. He lived in Montague Road, and died aged 63 in 1975. Both brothers were able to leave home at the sound of Brotherhoods' siren (known locally as the 'buzzer') that sounded five minutes before each work session to summon the local workforce. Until she married in 1937, Cyril's wife, Elsie, had worked as live-in housekeeper for Works Manager Freestone at his house at 10 All Saints Road and later at a larger house in Fulbridge Road. One of Frank Junior and Cyril's sisters, Annie, had married Arthur 'Reg' Hankins who worked in Brotherhoods' time office for over 30 years, and was instrumental in helping Cyril to gain a job with the Company. Annie herself worked in the factory during the Second World War. The youngest of Frank Junior's children, Margaret, worked as a shorthand-typist for Mr P.Wholley, the Technical Manager, from February 1965 to June 1967, and was thus the fourth generation of the family. Her husband Peter Bools had served his student apprenticeship with Brotherhoods from August 1962 to September 1966, then became a draughtsman, eventually leaving the firm as stock controller, second to Peter Roy, in 1974.

Sections of the works had their traditions. From 1945 to 1970 the drawing office was controlled by Alfred Savage. He was a very religious man, churchwarden at nearby Werrington for over 35 years, and used to inspect every drawing carefully before it went out. Late comers in the morning used to be 'banged in' when they arrived, by the staff hitting their desks with any convenient object. One day Savage was late ... and was banged in! He turned, gave everyone a good dressing down, threatened to remove their privileges, and reached his office in silence. As he was about to open the door one stunned draughtsman came to and muttered 'What b----- privileges?' Even in those days there were a few girls in the drawing office, and one boy was told 'I am putting you at the back, next to Rose. You are a serious minded lad and she won't distract you.' Shortly before any of his staff, male or female, were married he would call them to his office and give them a homily on marriage, and ensure that they knew the facts of life. Incidentally, it was through a mutual friend, the vicar of Werrington, that he learned of my interest in Brotherhoods and arranged for me to visit in the early 1960s. He retired on 31st December, 1970.

Bank of England figures show that the value of money halved in the five years 1974-9, which was very detrimental to Brotherhoods, and the firm succumbed, despite the optimism of the early 1970s. The Thermo-Electron group, which had first invested in Brotherhoods in 1974, steadily expanded its holding from 7 per cent to 100 per cent, and

Probably the last 3-cylinder engine made, 1992. Supplied to Ravenscraig Steelworks.

thereby acquired the Company in May 1983. The Company continued in business under its new owners, although many redundancies occurred. A link with the early days occurred in March 1987, when a 3-cylinder engine was supplied to operate coke oven doors at Ravenscraig Steelworks, Motherwell. This was the last reciprocating steam engine sold for industrial use in the United Kingdom.

Changing technology and over-capacity in the foundry industry meant that castings could be bought very cheaply, leading to the closure of the foundry in 1985, with the 150ft-tall, brick-lined, cast-iron chimney being felled soon after dawn on Friday 22nd May, 1987. This 12 acre site was then redeveloped for a retail park, approached from the Lincoln Road by Brotherhood Close.

Meanwhile all was not well at the Lincoln Road site. The war and later arrears of maintenance had taken their toll. For example much of the roof needed heavy repair and there were many Health & Safety issues that required attention. The works were too big anyway for the current level of work. Closure was considered, but the Company still gained orders and had a good reputation. Accordingly, an alternative location was sought, particularly after Safeway, a large supermarket chain, had made an offer for the existing site. As there appeared to be nowhere suitable in Peterborough the Company looked further afield, and made a provisional agreement to move 20 miles to Spalding, whose council would make land available. This was not welcome news in Peterborough! To counter this threat, the Peterborough Development Corporation provided the present site on Papyrus Road, Werrington, on an industrial estate just beside Werrington Parkway, a dual carriageway that has replaced parts of Lincoln Road, about a mile north of the original works. A much smaller but well equipped factory (12,000m²

Nacelle of 1MW wind turbine for Ballymena, Northern Ireland. For scale, note fitter working towards rear of unit.

manufacturing area – three acres) with many modern machine tools was built on the 12 acre site at Werrington, with an integral office block. In 1994 it cost £16 million, comprising land £2 million, buildings £10 million and plant £4 million. It was officially opened on 17th March, 1995 by the then Prime Minister, the Rt Hon. John Major MP.

Modern CNC (Computer Numerically Controlled) equipment meant it became far easier to machine turbine blades whose section varied along their length. By now Peter Brotherhood Ltd was the only steam turbine manufacturer in the United Kingdom. While turbines had been supplied to many industries from the 1920s, since the 1950s a major use has been in waste heat recovery systems, especially on diesel-engined ships. Sizes currently manufactured ranged from 1 to 40MW. Over 1,000MW of Brotherhood equipment is now currently installed in plants using renewable energy, particularly crushed cane in sugar mills where Brotherhoods have supplied turbo-alternator units up to 26MW. There are also many combined cycle turbines, utilizing steam raised from the exhaust gases of diesel engines or gas turbines.

Gas compressors for hydrogen and many other gases have been made since 1917 and continue to be manufactured. Most run at medium to low speed to increase reliability, and are made with a range of strokes. After-sales support can include on-line remote monitoring (at Peterborough) of any compressor to assess its performance and maintenance needs.

At that time Peter Brotherhood Ltd was a partner in, or supported, a number of specialized services including wind turbines. The largest so far was a 1MW unit installed near Ballymena, Northern Ireland, made for Renewable Energy Systems. Brotherhoods were responsible for the overall design and manufacture. The nacelle was fully assembled in the works before being sent to the site where it was mounted on the Welsh fabricated tower and fitted with Danish-built blades. Brotherhoods later set up a joint venture with the German wind turbine manufacturer, RePower, to sell and service their units in the UK. In the first year of operation it sold £50m worth of RePower wind turbines.

The Company has also investigated technology to obtain energy from waves, for example using air turbines driven by pressure changes as a column of water oscillates in a closed tube. Aircogen is a patented CHP (combined heat and power) system, being an energy efficient way of producing heating, cooling and electric power from recycled waste heat from gas engines. Many factories and warehouses are heated/cooled by Aircogen systems.

Although the Thermo-Electron group was involved with waste heat recovery, following an internal reorganization in 2003, it was felt that Brotherhoods was outside its main interests. Accordingly, Peter Brotherhood Ltd was sold to a management buyout team led by Stephen Fitzpatrick in March 2003 and became independent again. This led to five years of growth. When Fitzpatrick took over the order book was £25M which had tripled to £80M when he left, with the workforce rising from 240 to 360, although under later owners it has shrunk to about 150. However, Fitzpatrick had made his mark, and he recouped his investment by selling most parts of the company to the US firm Dresser Rand in 2008 for £31 million. The Aircogen part was later absorbed into Guascor, another Dresser Rand business. Dresser Rand itself was acquired by the German industrial giant Siemens in September 2014. A year later, in October 2015, the Hayward Tyler Group, an engineering company founded in 1815 and based in Luton, Bedfordshire, specializing in pumps, purchased Peter Brotherhood Ltd from the Dresser Rand arm of Siemens for £9.7 million, so once again the company has regained its independence.

However, despite all the changes and modern surroundings, the

3-cylinder stone on lawn outside Walton Works. The plaque reads:
'This monument to Peter Brotherhood Ltd was unveiled on 17 March 1995 By Dr George Nhatsopoulos Chairman of the Board and President Thermo Electron Corporation
The stone at the centre of this plinth is a schematic representation of a three cylinder engine patented in 1872 by Mr Peter Brotherhood, founder of the company that now bears his name and which has been a world leader in engineering since 1867. From 1907 until 1994 the stone carving was above the main entrance to the company's former headquarters in Lincoln Road, Peterborough – less than two miles away. It was brought to this site when the company moved to this new building in October 1994.'   *S.A.Leleux, 17th October, 2005*

Company keeps links with its past. The carved '3-cylinder' stone from above the main office door was preserved when the old site was cleared and is now mounted on the lawn outside the main entrance to the present works at Werrington. Just inside the door of main reception is Peter's bust. Upstairs in the offices are pictures of both Peter and Stanley, and of an early naval action where a torpedo was fired. There is a display of medals won at exhibitions long ago: two from Vienna in 1873, Paris 1878, Paris 1881 International Electricity Exhibition, two from Paris 1889, Royal Cornwall Poly 1906, and Royal Agricultural Society 1920 for the tractor. In a glass case are three models: a one-eighth full size standard gauge wagon as supplied by Rowland to the GWR in 1865, a vertical boiler supplying steam to a single-cylinder vertical engine driving a machine which could be a sugar cane crusher, with the works plate reading 'Peter Brotherhood number 1353', and a torpedo on its launching ramp (not a tube) made by C.W. Bryant.

A number of examples of Brotherhood products have been preserved. The Science Museum has a lot of Brotherhood products in its large exhibits store at Wroughton, near Swindon, which has periodic open days and can make specified items available for viewing by prior arrangement. The Kittoe & Brotherhood beam engine preserved at Coldharbour Mill near Cullompton in Devon has been described earlier.

Despite the changes, in location and technology, Peter Brotherhood Ltd continues to trade. Well qualified staff, excellent facilities and high quality products enable it to continue to meet the engineering needs of a wide range of customers, worldwide. Peter would be pleased, and Rowland proud of his son's success. What will the future bring?

APPENDIX ONE

ROWLAND BROTHERHOOD'S AUTOBIOGRAPHY

Rowland Brotherhood wrote this interesting document shortly before his death, and it merits reproduction in full. Notes in italics were written on the original which Marcus Neal, the then Chairman of Peter Brotherhood Ltd, borrowed for me from Rowland's grandson E.C.Lowther in 1961. The spelling, use of capitals, underlining and punctuation follow Rowland's handwritten copy, now held by the Wiltshire & Swindon Record Office (some typed copies differ from each other and the hand written one). As Rowland often used the same mark for both commas and full stops in some places I have inserted the character that seemed most appropriate. Some letters and a newspaper cutting, all originally with the document I saw in 1961 but now filed separately, are also included. My additions are all within square brackets.

Copy sent to James December 9th/81

Part 1

My Grandfather, Harry Brotherhood, lived at Witton, near Hounslow Middlesex. He was a fine well built active Man. Standing six feet two inches high, he worked hard up to nearly Eighty and died at Hounslow, at 91, or 92, years of age. His occupation was partly that of a woodman in winter, felling heavy elm timber &c in the Valley of the Thames, between London and Windsor. I have often seen him in life and in pictures since, going to his work on a cold frosty morning, clothed in a tanned leather coat, with his light axe, in the belt, pipe in his mouth, and old dog by his side.

In Spring he felled oak, for Ship building, and barked the same for the tanners. In Summer he cut a great quantity of heath round turf for sale, which was dried in the sun, and then stacked in ricks for winter. Turf at that time being the principal fuel used in the neighbourhood of commons, before the enclosing act was passed [date 1845 inserted on one copy]. After that, he did something in the way of road making, fixing posts and rail fences ditching and planting the quickset hedges to enclose fields & allotments &c likewise did Harvest work, and other sundry jobs.

My Grandfather, John Wilder, lived at Littleton near the common, and afterwards by the side of Witton Common, he was a sheep owner, or sheep farmer, he used to attend some of the West Country, large yearly fairs, purchase lambs or young sheep and graze them up through the various commons and green lanes, onto Hounslow heath, where he fed, sheared, and Kept them, until they were old enough to be fatted, when he sold them to the Farmers, or Gentlemen who had estates to finish them for the London or other Markets.

And after the commons where enclosed, he took a farm near Feltham, where I afterwards used to go, to help him reap and house the corn &c. He died there at a good old age. My Grandmother, then removed with her youngest daughter and Grand Son, Wilder, who used to manage her sheep after, to Ditton Marsh and in a few years died there also at a good old age.

My Father William Brotherhood, was born in Witton Dean in Janry 1788, and died at Hounslow, through a fall from his horse, Janaryth 26th 1839, only 51 years of age. He was rather short, but well and strong built, and a very active energetic man. Was the eldest Son of a numerous family, and put to work at a very tender age, he continued to work with his Father a few years, until he went to sea as a Servant to a Captain Bowls, after a few years Service, in which he was at the first taking of Copenhagen by the English [1801], he returned and after a short time he settled down again with his Father at their old calling. And he then added the Night soil work, which was one of their very best paying jobs. There were no sewers at that time.

At the end of the great Comet year 1811, he Married Charlotte Wilder, when he became a partner with his Father. Their business increased very slowly until after the battle of Waterloo. When peace was proclaimed, the people began to settle down to business, and instead of war, the Nobles and Gentry also began to improve their grounds and estates, so that the Brotherhoods became more noticed and busily employed, and as money increased there was a great deal of building commenced, which gave them more work, in Well Sinking, diging cesspools &c., as each house had one. There being no water works, nor sewers there at that time. There business gradually improved on to 1821, and after.

As to Myself, I was born in Witton Deane October 5th 1812. I remember Hounslow heath being all open, and partly covered with heath and furze. The Miss Campbells used to take me into the house or grounds give me lots of grapes and other fruit, set me on a stool and paint me off, and give me plenty to take home. I also used to get plenty of fruit milk &c from Sir Bengiman Hobhouse, Gostlings, and Calverts at Kneller Hall.

I also remember being taken to my Grandfathers Sheep shearing dinners, when Grandmother gave me lots of plumb pudding and mutton pie. I also heard and felt the shock, of some explosions at the powder mills, which killed Many Men and broke our windows. I used to be taken to see a Aunt in London and have seen many of the Streets lighted, with the old oil lamps, and paved with large round bolder stones, from the sea shore, and have been jolted over them in the old hackney coaches &c, and have seen the Ladies carried in their Sedan chairs, which were afterwards supplanted, by the Bath wheel chair. I also saw many of the old watchmen, and heard them cry the howers.

I saw some of the first steam boats that run to Richmond, there was salmon caught in the Thames at that time. I afterwards saw Hancocks Steam Carriage on the common roads, it ran over my Fathers fat pig for which he received three pounds.

I saw George the thirds funeral. [1820]

When old enough was sent to a Dames School in the Vilage. But as there was a numerious family comeing on, and work was thought the most important thing, to be attended to at that time, and my father having been put to it very young, and as I seemed to like being out in the open better confinement at school, I commenced at the end of December in the year 1821, being nearly $9^{1}/_{4}$ years of age first to carry tools to the Smith Shop to be sharpened and repaired, to pick up chips hewn from the large timber trees, and also to scrapenig and sanding the wheeling planks [for barrows, to prevent their wheels sinking into the ground, or to bridge gaps] & Stages in the Mud work, and in a veriety of light jobs.

I never shall forget my first start. My Grandfather, Father, and Uncle Jack Brotherhood, who had come out to work a short time before me. He was always fond of a joke or lark, and would do a bit of mischief sometimes. They were felling timber for Lord Waldegrave at Strawberry Hill, Twickenham, the ropes and small tools were locked up in a spare coach house at night, and Uncle Jack took me with him and some of the Men, one morning to bring out the tools, not letting me know what I should see, and when the door was opened there stood a large stuffed Lion, and a Jack hall [jackal] by his side, and I got my first fright and a good laugh from Jack.

There was a Gentleman, on the estate by the name of Gibbs. I think he was some relation to her Ladyship, he was a very clever turner in Ivory, Wood, and Iron, he showed us a piece of wood which [he] said was so well turned that it would run uphill, of itself, he put down a wood framed incline on a long table, put the piece of wood at the bottom and it did go up the incline, and we could not see nor find out how it was done, he also showed us the first electric machine I had then seen, he put me up on a stool and gave me a shock which I did not forget for some time after, he also darkened the large long room, and made the lightening run all round at the top of the walls, he had several other clever little machines, but I do not remember their use. But from what I have read of late, I think his electric machines must have had something to do with the piece of wood going up hill.

Any one who who [twice on original] has passed up or down the Thames, between the Brentford & Isleworth, ferries would have seen a very large or long meadow in front of the Duke of Northumberland Sion house there is a sunk fence or Ha-Ha, throughout between the meadow and pleasure ground. There was genearlly a number of Cows and often a Bull with them, and it was said that every Bull put into that medow went wild and always run at all who came near him, so one day Uncle Jack thought he would have a lark, he could run fast so he got out into the meadow, and as the Bull was feeding some distance off, & before he saw Jack the latter had got some distance from the wall, but as soon as bill [Bull] saw him he gave chase, and Jack ran for the wall and tried to jump it but slipped & fell back, and as the Bull was getting close he ran along the bottom of the Ha-Ha, and the Bull after him when my Father who had just come down a tree with his clambers on which had spikes inside at the middle of the foot, he stood on the top of the wall until Bill came along with his back a little below, he jumped on his back and drove his spikes into the Bulls sides which so starteled him that he left Uncle Jack and run up the slope and across the meadow as hard as he could gallop while father was spurring him with his spikes, untill Bill gave up and went down on his two fore Knees & father jumped off, and the Old Bull did not run at any one fore some time and Jack did not give him a chance anymore, to run after him.

Soon after we were cleaning out the lake in the pleasure grounds and one day when I was sanding the wheeling planks, I slipped and fell on my back into about seven feet of mud, but was soon pulled out with a plank hook. After a few more suchlike larks in various places, Father bought or had made several small or light tools for me, and he was not long learning me how to use them. One of my first jobs to try with some of them was to help make a Ha=Ha thus [sketch of section of a Ha-Ha here, with a vertical wall on one side and a slope into up the meadow on the other] all across the park in Kew gardens, to Keep the cattle out of the old Palace gardens, these fences are generally built with brick or stone wall on the upright side, but this was made with all earth work & covered with green turf, although the greater part was filled in when the

Syon House from the Kew (Surrey) bank, 1821, around the time Rowland started work. The dark line across the park could well be a ha-ha to prevent animals from approaching too close to the house.   *Courtesy Hounslow Local Studies Library*

A typical ha-ha (in Wollaton Park, Nottingham), showing the vertical wall (about 6ft high) against the formal gardens and the slope into the park. Nearby is pedestrian access into the park, with a gate from the garden.   *S.A.Leleux, November 2006*

great alterations, were made a few years ago a speciment peice is left between the New Conservantories, this with other works done at Kew, was early in the reign of George IV [1820-1830].

Both farther and myself soon found how necessary it was that I should learn to write and figure a little so I went to a Night school in winter for that purpose, at that time our working hours, were from daylight to dark during a great part of the year, and some times all night at certain work. I went then to Sunday School nearly all the year round, there were no Bank holidays then for us.

My father was very particular he would have the very best possible tools, and all work turned out accordingly, and if there was any difficult or dangerous work to be done either up a tree or down a well, or anything else, he was always the first to face it, lead the way and show the men and me how to do it.

We were doing some work in the gardens for the Marquis of Ailsa at Saint Margarets near Isleworth, when there was a high flood in the Thames which met a high Spring tide, and the water got up the drain into the lower offices at the house, where many of the Sco[t]ch servant girls slep, and when they got up the next morning, they jumped in the

Another place where Rowland worked, the Marquis of Ailsa's home St Margaret's House, seen from the River Thames in 1830. The possibility of flooding, as described by Rowland, is obvious.   *Courtesy Hounslow Local Studies Library*

water nearly up to their Knees, and as soon as we came to work we had to ge[t] out the fire engin and a lot of Stable buckets to get out the water, which we worked at it hard all day, and the Girls fastened up their cloathes like a kilt and some much above their knees, they worked well carrying their goods & chattles to higher and dryer quarters, and Uncle Jack had plenty of fun that day, the old Butler gave us so much of their Scoch ale and it went down like mils [milk?], and when night came some of us could not walk home.

Soon after this Uncle Jack and I parted, at that time and before, their being so many Gipseis fiddlers round us, he had become a good rough dancer, and could do a little in the way of the fishers and sailers hornpipes &c, and when we had work near some of the large houses the servants when they could get a chance whould get him in to give them a step, and as he was always fond of the cooks, he often came away loaded with pudding &c &c, he was fond of riding, and would ride the wild colts unbroken on the heath, when he could get a chance. One day as he wished to see a little more life than our work gave him, he inlisted into the 4th light horse, and went off to Bengal and soon became rough rider to the rigiment, and used to go out with the Officers hunting and sticking the wild pigs, he also went with the army through the Ciber [Khyber], & Boling, passes the first time they went to Cabul, he was a fine young man & stood six feet high when he went out but after some years he came home covered with scratches and scars, and quite an old looking old man.

I help to make one of the early sewers, from the ponds in the green park to the thames west of the old Parlimant houses I had a tent in Hyde park, all one summer we were sinking wells and fixing iron pumps for watering the roads, as there were no water pipes in the park for the purpose at that time. We also laid a pipe from the Serpentine for the Duke of Wellington to his house at H.P. corner.

We were sinking a well at the corner of Fitzroy square, when Lord and Lady Wallingham was burnt in their bed in Harley street And at another time when there was a fire at a pawn brokers in Tottingham Court road a Poleiceman stole 15 watches.

We were doing some work close to Brentford, ferrie and I had [to] pass through the end of the long meadow thinking that as the Bull was a good way off I could clear the meadow before he could reach me. I started and soon did he, but one of our men was looking out for me, when I reach him he caught me up and carried me through the creek up to his middle in water so the old Bull was done.

We were cleaning out a pond for Col Clitherow at Boxton between

Brentford and Hanwell, when the servants brought out what they called broken victuals, some legs and sholders of mutton with only one slice cut out. And the strong beer was brought out in the Stable buckets it was the good old times then.

I saw the funeral of the Duke of York. [1827]

Some three or four hundred years ago Sion house, was supplied with Spring water from the gravel bed on Sion Hill, it was conveyed by a lead pipe five inches diameter and half inch thick, it became choked up with the fine roots of the lime trees, and I helped to take it up, and lay down two rows of cast iron pipes. The old lead paid all expences of every thing and there was a large sum to spare. Hampton Court-Palace was supplied by such a pipe laid under the Thames to Combe Warren Wood. I worked at several improvements at Sion. The Marquis of Ailsas, Marble Hall and many other places. And I believe by the time I had served seven years, I had done a share of every kind of work named in this paper. Prior to 1828 except cutting the heath turf which I was not quite strong enough to do when the commons were closed.

And Some Time after I had commenced the second seven years, as our work increased we had to devide, and at sixteen I had to take to the Management of some of the jobs. Measure the Work receive the Cash and make all payments.

And soon after My Father has a very nice wooden house made on wheels. I then left home with it, and attended to the most distant works, removing it as each was completed, and as I generally had a younger brother or a good man with me was very comfortable and always on or close to the works.

I saw the funeral of George the IV. [1830]

I had the house with me one winter felling timber for the Earl of Jersey, on the Osterley Park estate.

Also on the Duke of Kents estate castle bar hill, and a very grate deal of work at Sion. It was with me when the great Alterations were made by Sir Wm Cooper between Isleworth and Railshead. Such, as the new road high brick walls, tunnel divertion of the river Concrete Wall or banks, and the laying out of the new Kitchen gardens and pleasuregrounds, pile driving and the campsheeting [?], by the Thames Side.

I used often see our <u>Queen</u> [Victoria] when a little girl playing in the grounds at Sion, when under the care of the good Duches of Northumberland. There has been two Dukes & two Duches since that one.

I believe that by the end of 1834, I had executed work in some shape or form, on most of the Parks, Towns, and principal estates, between London, and Uxbridge, Slough, Stanes & Windsor. Much of which can be seen at the presant day.

I was married [at West Moseley, Surrey] on Sunday, Augs^t 30th 1835, to Priscilla Penton, daughter of Mr Wm Penton, Excise Officer, and formerly of Alsford [Alresford, near Winchester] Hants, and severil Tablets of their ancesters can be seen in Winchester Cathedral. Men who have been Mayers, of that town, and some of a very Old date.

Priscilla has not only proved herself to be one of the best of Wifs Parteners and helpmates to me, but also the very best Mother to our fourteen children, and I shall have more to say of her further on.

Copy sent to James December 23rd/81

Part 2

Having some tide work going on when we were married, I was compelled to be there early next morning, so started soon after 5.am, and was on the work at Isleworth firry when the men came at six, so there was not much working time lost over our little job.

Soon afterwards I went with Father to Manchester when it took us a day and nearly two nights to reach there on the Old Stage Coach. We cut out zoological gardens there, from the plans of Richard Farrish, the Landscape Gardener. Who had worked under Mr Heaton at Kew, when we made the Ha-Ha there. He afterwards became head gardener to the Duke of Northumberland, he was also the Designer of the Clifton Bristol Zoological gardens, and other works.

Just before we reached Manchester there had been a heavy storm of rain, and the water ran down the street by the Old Church, and got behind a high retaining wall and drove it into the river, the force of air and water knocked down Colyers factory on the other side of the river, but as it was at a meal time, no one was ingered.

Soon after we returned home, the Great Western Railway, was about to be Commenced. We did some of the borings, trial shafts &c, and Father undertook the first excavations, which was for foundations of the Wharncliffe viaduct, over the valley of the old Brent at Hanwell, Messrs Grissell & Peto, doing all the brick work.

It was arranged that I should take to the management of this excavation, so I did, and gave up the Old Connection for the new Railway work. I took a younger Brother with his portable wooden house with him, and on February 1st 1836, we commenced the excavations for the piers and abutments. The pits were 40 feet square and about 20 feet deep into the Solid London Clay, the stuff had to be wheeled to the embankments at each end of the viaduct, as the runs were very long, we had a strong gang on, and the barrow work required good men so we had them there.

One day as we had finished one of the pits ready for the bricklayers to commence, all the Irish labourers struck work, and as there was a flood rising in the river, it was feared it would overflow, damage and retard the work; the Engineers and builders had a consultation, and sent for me to know if I could do any thing with our men, to help them out of this [?] trouble. As our men would not carry the long tailed monkeys as they called the hods, I got some runs made with the wheeling planks, and they then went to work and rattled down the bricks & mortar and the bricklayers were hard at work. When all the Irish, returned and surrounded the pit and made a great noise, thinking they might shew fight, I ordered every man to unship his pick shaft and have it near him ready, as the Pats had their sticks with them; our men kept steady at work, but only required the word from me to go in, the bricklayers stuck to their work well also, although the Pats surrounded us all day they did not fight, and strange to say when we came onto the ground next morning the Irish were there & ready to go to work, so we let them, and there was no more striking on that contract and the Old Engineer & young Peto, now Sir M did not soon forget it.

Having finished our work there, we were making the new road under the Skew bridge and on towards Southall, when the news came that our first Son was born, this was on June 15th 1836. I galloped home to Hounslow, forgetting my coat and hat.

After this we removed from Hounslow to Maidenhead, at the end of 1836, we then commenced our work at the embankment east of the Thames Bridge, this bank was constructed with the best clean gravel ballast I ever saw, from side cutting east there were 25 feet of gravel in some parts of the field. We found several earthen pots or jars of Roman silver coins, some of which we have at the present time. There were two brothers with me on this job, and Father was often there also, but left the Management to me, he had some work on the line at West Drayton & Langley, but I had nothing to do with it. There was a five or six weeks frost and as it stopped all work, Wife & I went home to Hounslow, and to London, there we saw the ruins of the Old Royal Exchange which had just been burnt down [1838].

After the frost left and we commenced work one of our old navvies

Jesse Weakley when a empty waggon was running down the incline instead of putting a sprag in the wheel [short length of wood put through the spokes as a brake] he put his foot on the rail to stop the waggon and his foot was nearly cut off. The work went on very well and the Railway was opened on, Whit Monday May 1838, to Maidenhead the Station was at the Dumbbell below Taplow a little way west of the [turn]pike road bridge.

After the Opening we had to put some of the stage coaches into trucks to be taken to London by the rail. One day the train brought one down from Paddington, they gave it a flying shunt to sent it into the carriage shoots which was close to where the Taplow New Station is now, and as the Guard was running by the side at the brake, the poor fellow slipped & put his foot under the wheel, and it was cut off. After the hard frost they slackened the wedges under the centres of the Thames bridge and the next time in so doing found that the arch, which was 120 feet span in brick, followed the centres, and it had to be taken down & the arch rebuilt. And after it had been turned the second time, there came a very high flood which washed the centre clean out but this arch stood well, I think the frost must have effected the first.

Peter was born at Maidenhead on 22nd of April 1838.

I unloaded the North Star Loco engine from a barge and put it on to the embankment at the Thames side [at Maidenhead, 28th November, 1837].

There was a Gale of Wind one night, which drove a six wheel carriage from Maidenhead back up to Paddington which frightened a Policeman nearly to death as he thought a certain Personage was in the carriage.

After the line had been open some time, there was some wet weather and the trains began to rock and jump a good deal so they had to go at a much lower speed on the Clay at the Paddington end; And I took up a gang of men, and put both lines blocks and wedges in short length, took out all the bad burnt ballast & Clay, two feet deep and filled in with gravel, and the labour alone cost nine pounds per chain [22 yards].

The line at first was laid on thin timbers fastened down to cross timbers and these cross timbers were fastened to piles to keep the line down, so in wet weather the Engine and Carriages rose at the cross timbers & piles and of course went down in the middle, so that the Motion was like a boat in a rough sea up & down, and everything had to be cut away from the piles so as to let the lines take their bearing equally on the ballast throughout.

At the end of Septr 1838, we removed from Maidenhead to Reading, into a house near to were Palmers' biscuit works are now built. A Mr.Rainger had taken the contract at first for the Sonning Cutting [2 miles long, maximum depth 60ft], and the Twiford & Reading embankments, I think because he had to much price for the work, $2^s/6^d$ for earth work per cube, yard, and $2^s/6^d$ for soiling 10 inches thick, which would equal £605 per acre or £400 more than the cost of land, he failed, in one of the tunnels between Bath & Bristol and Spent a great deal of his time between London, Reading, Bath & Bristol, Galloping in a four horse coach. The company had taken to all his work when he failed, but there was half a mile of the deep middle of the Sonning cutting not touched. And we undertook to barrow out 40,000 cube yds 20,000 to spoil bank on each side.

[Note in the margin] The Railway Compy new [?] Engineer did not know the value of work then, and very few contractors did. [End of note]

Before we came there Raingers men became Masters of the ground, which ran through Robert Palmers, M.P., land and their men would go by daylight and shoot the game in front of his house, and kiss his daughters passing along the road.

I had two of my brothers & their house, with me and Father would come down some times, but on going home to Hounslow one Saturday night on his blood mare, she shied and threw him into a ditch and he died in a few days after through the fall. I then took the second 40,000 to be run out by horse roads and we had 42 roads on each side, which was rather close work but time then, was the most important thing, to be considered. The cutting was the longest on the GWR and was forced on. One day all the Companys men about 700 in number Struck work, and from what some of them stated they intended to Strike all the men throughout the line to London, and stopped sixteen of our gangs at the west end. I had a message as to what was going on so I had a short consultation with a lot of our old men at the east end with my brother and found they were all sattisfied, so we started and as we went along all the men followed, nearly six hundred and nearly all young, strong, and active, and we met the other men at the end of our work, but they were not like the Irish men at Hanwell these would fight, and some of their leaders stated they would strike all the work through to London, so a fight commenced and there were soon 8 or 900 men hard at it in various forms. And myself and brothers amongst them, and we drove them all into Reading, and I got nearly all our men back to work the same afternoon. The next day Mr Wm Owen and the other engineers came and thanked us for what we had done, and within a fortnight from then I had possession of all the work between Twiford and Reading.

[The following paragraph was written and then deleted by Rowland when he realised he had already mentioned this incident.]

Before we came to the Sonning Cutting Raingers men would go in a gang, and shoot the game in front of Robert Palmers MP, house in daylight, and had kissed some of his daughters when passing along the high road and they became so bad on the work and in Reading one time they were obliged to have the Guards down from Windsor. [End of deleted section]

After the fight, we had over 1000 men at work there was 42 horse roads on <u>each</u> <u>side</u> 84 of the cutting running to spoil and a large train of earth waggons running to embankment each way toward Twiford & Reading. We had nearly 200 horses on, beside locos and a good deal of the work was kept going night & day. As the men had to go so far into Reading for their provisions, and when they did go, they got too much beer and many got into very bad company, and spent or lost all their money, there was much time lost, so to alter this I put up a good shop had Tom Brown who had been a grocer in London installed. I procured from the best Markets the various groceries and supplied them with what they required in that way. I had also old Joe Manlove a Butcher down from Hounslow, we used to purchase the beef & mutton in the Carcase and let them have it at prices below what they could get it at Reading. And Mr Stephen Penton took a bakers shop in Reading, and some weeks used to bring up 3 or 4,000 loaves of good bread. To keep the men sober and at their work I contracted with the two best brewers in Reading to supply us with good beer, and put my younger brother, to serve it out who took care they did not have too much. Some days when in full work he would send out 13 to 1400, quarts [about 350 gallons] per day and it being heavy work, it did not make them drunk. The men were well sattisfied, & it paid me, the work went on well also, and there was no more kissing R.Palmers daughters and he did not forget it. The Railway opened March 1840.

Our daughter Priscilla was born at Reading on May 27th 1840, the line opened to Steventon [4 miles west of Didcot, change for 10 mile journey by coach to Oxford] June 1840.

It was at Reading where Uncle Stephin built his cart over the bakers shop and there was no way to get it down.

This was the last contract my brothers worked with me, they did a little further down, but they soon returned home to the old work, but soon after they thought they could do better in the States and made up their minds to go. And our Mother who had worked hard had been a good Wife, and a most excellent Mother to us all, against my wishes and remonstrances and that of some of her friends, made up her mind to go with them and did so, selling all off, and taking my three youngest sisters, and youngest brother a child with them, the removal of those three girls from their native homes, under such circumstances has been a sauce of trouble to my mind up to the present day. My Mother died at Milwaukee on April 9th 1859 & age 69.

We removed from Reading to the seven locks in Wootton Basset, Incline near the end of 1840. The contract had been taken by Mr Custains, who failed, and I undertook to finish the Works for his trustees, and it was the worst Clay country and Work I had ever got into. I had many of my own horses die and others killed on the incline during the progress of the works.

On the next contract as soon as they began a very shallow cutting the field uphill began to slip at least several feet deep of the surface came down, and after the first subcontractor jacked up a second went on, and when he came to be measured up, his cutting was less at the fortnights end than when he began so he jacked up also.

The old farmer where we lodged near the cutting required a new Bull, & fresh dairy Maid, and asked me to go with him to help select at the W.Bassett Mop so when we got there, there was, a long Row of Maids stood up like soldiers, and we went along the front first the Old [farmer] asked some of them many questions while I took notes and he required a strong one; we went along the back of the line, and up the front again we selected one which we thought would do. And after that, we went to the Bulls, but this was rather out of my line so I left it more to the Old farmer and he selected a young one, which turned out after, to be a bad one, and the Farmers Wife and Mary Moss, their Niece blamed me, they said I must not go again to select a Bull, but as the Maid turned out so well I should go to Mop again when one was required but I had seen enough at the fair and did not go again.

The Railway had opened to Hay lane [officially Wootton Bassett Road, about 3 miles west of Swindon] at the end of 1840, and through to Chippenham May 1841. After it was opened their was an Old Wiltshire Parson came to visit the Farmer and his wife and after tea we walked out to see a Train pass, as he had never seen one before. When it passed sharp [to time] he wanted to know if there were any [turn]pike gates and how often they stopped to pay the toll. After the line opened I had a lot of ballasting and other extra work and near the end of Octob^r being finished was having a sale of horses by auction at the White hart which was Open then, and I went up to the Station to meet some one, when the train came up Mr Hammond was in it and beg that I would go with him as there was a slip near there which had stopped the up line [for traffic towards London], so I left the sale of horses to my Old friend Brown of Reading Mr Stephen Penton & Old Tom Oxford, horsekeeper. When we arrived at the cutting west of the Skew bridge, I found there was a slip and 8 or 9000 yards of clay had come down part of it had not only blocked the up line, but was likely to stop the down also. Mr Brunel had arrived with a lot of Officials & Men from Paddington. Mr Bedbrough and sons the contractors for that part of the line were there also, and after a consultation they all press me to undertake the Management of the removial &c so I consented. It had been and was then a very wet time, and another slip occurred in an embankment west and I was there nineteen night following with 400 men and only took a little sleep in the hut by daylight, when one of the companys Engineers took charge of the men. In a short time after a deep snow and frost set in and on the night of November 18th 1841, Rowland was born, but I did not gallop home then as at Hanwell. My brother-in-law S Penton galloped for the Doctor, along the towpath on an old blind cob, and going under two low bridges they both fell into the canal, twice, and he, poor fellow took cold and was laid up a long time with Rheumatic fever through it. On the 20th Night the wind was blowing very strong, and it was very dark, when an Engin came down and ran over one of my best horses. Killed him and I then went home to bed, and slept soundly the field was still slipping and there was a large old oak tree which had been moving down from top of the hill for several weeks, as we were filling waggons, one night he fell on the Railway but missed us all, so we cleared him off out of the way of the coming train. When this work was finished, having kept my eye on the Men, the Road[?], and cash, of the Companys maintenance, I saw that I could do more work, at half the cost. So I made them an offer and it was accepted. And I took the line from Steventon to Chippenham and made it pay me very well. In the Spring of 1842, we removed to Chippenham into a house next door to Mr Collin the Millar [No. 2 New Road, Mr Collin was at 'Mill House' No. 1 New Road].

Sent January 17/82

Part 3

The first maintenance contract was only for one year. There was a good deal of extra work, and many slips to be made up, which the Company had to pay for. The line through the Clay country in the Vail of white horse [between Didcot and Swindon] required a great deal of watching, and constant care both night and day, and I had often to be out at night during the Winter.

Dureing this contract I cleaned out the little river which runs into the Thames at Pangbourne, for Squ^r Hopkings, at Tidmarsh.

Mr Wm Owen now the Cheaf Engineer, of the GWR, was the Resident, on the district between Bristol, and Swindon, and a Scotch Gentleman from Reading to Swindon. Mr Owen worked with me, and treated me very fairly, but the Scotch Man worked against me and did not use me fairly, and did all he could to make me give it up, but as I was encouraged by the Cheafs of the Company I did not care for him.

Our Son James was born in the house named above, on July 21st 1843.

At the end of the first maintenance contract the Company wished me to go on another year, but I told them I would do no more under the Scotch Gent but I would, be willing to work under Mr Owen, so a Mr Orton took the line from Reading to Swindon at my price and I took Mr Owen's district which was then extended through to Bristol.

During this contract, there were a great many heavy slips, both in cuttings and banks and a good deal of night work required to keep Matters safe. There was also a good deal of drainage and removing of bad ballast and clay from the cuttings, and a great deal of stone to remove from the Corsham Cutting as the winter affected it very much;

There was also a great lot of extra work during the year all through between Swindon & Bristol.

I likewise sunk a large well 100 feet through dry sand for Squ^r Benyon at Englefield near Pangbourne. And another at the Bradfield union [i.e. the workhouse].

When the Half yearly reports came out, they showed a great difference in the cost of maintenance not only on the GWR, but the London and South Western, & London & North Western, both had cost more than the GWR, so there was a Stir with the Share holders and at the next lettings, the contractors had to come down in price also.

Our Son Fred was born in Mr Provises sister's [Mrs Bramble?] house on April 18th 1845.

Before the end of the Second contract Mr Brunel had removed the Scotch Gentleman to the lower part of the South Wales line, and at the next letting they wished me to go in again. So I then took the line from Reading to Bristol, at a higher price, I put John Brokenbrow at the Reading end, and James Hopkings at the Bristol end. This contract was for a period of three years ending in June 1847.

Alfred was born in the same house as Fred on November 19th 1846. When the line was made there was no gravel nor stone found between Steventon and Chippenham except a little fine gravel near the river Avon and a little Iron Stone in a side cutting at Stratton which was used on the spot so that the line at first although the Vail of White horse was ballasted with burnt clay, and some of it was very bad, which in time as it will be shown hereafter had to be removed from all the cuttings, and replaced with stone and gravel ballasts, which we brought by train, we had to keep many Watchmen on in the winter both through the Clay country, Corsham Cutting and Foxe's Wood [about two miles east of Bristol towards Bath]. And one winter after a hard frost when the thaw came, large stones, fell from the crown of Box tunnel near the upper end, and we had Old Doctor Buckland over it with lights & ladders, and he told me that end would fall in, on account of the bad stone, but it has not yet done so. An Old Lady of rank going from London to Bath, would not go through the Tunnel [3,212 yards, just over $1^3/_4$ miles, long, by far the longest in the country at that time], so used to post from Corsham to Bath. We afterwards cut drains and collected the water returning it from the sides to the culvert in the centre, and cut out some parts where the stone did not stand the weather and made good with brickwork and cement and it stood very well after.

I made a large excavation on the Clifton Down [north-west Bristol] close to the Observvetory it was intended for a reservoy to supply Clifton and part of Bristol with Waters from a Strong spring which can be seen near the low water mark, when the tide is out, of the river. There was an Enginehouse built at the bottom of the rocks also. But the larger Company which proposed to supply Bristol from the Mendips swallowed it up and it was filled in, the ring on the grass can be seen at the present day. One day a slip occurred at the west end of the Chippenham bridge. When the wing wall from the bridge to the house pump fell, stopping the down line, and filling up the old Bristol Road and into Mr Provis garden, and it has never been removed. I brought several trains of stone from Tetbury road [on Fosse Way three miles south-west of Cirencester and one mile from Kemble, the station was later renamed Coates] and made up the bank and the line was soon opened, the Parrish & Provis got compensation. And I afterwards bought the house and garden [Orwell House, conveyance signed 7-4-1852] from Mr Provis and put up the flag staff & cannons in front [?].

When the great Britten Steam Ship was launched [19th July, 1843] and fowled the lock side going into the river Mr Brunel sent for me, and I took a gang down with tools and cut down the stone & brickwork and she went out next tide. There were a great many other jobs done dureing this contract but as the details are not now clear to my Mind I leave them out, this brings us to end of 1847.

Ernest was born in Mrs Brambles house May 16th 1848.

The next contract for maintenance was for a term of seven years, up to June 1854. In this Contract I had to make good all slips up to 500 cube yards find fangbolts &c and of course got a higher price accordingly, and as it was for a longer term I determined to get the line in a better permanent order & so the Engineer agreed to provide stone & gravel, at least to pay me if I would do the labour so I commenced to make side drains to all the bad cuttings, begining 7 or 8 feet deep at the end of the cuttings so as to get plenty of fall for the water from the Middle of the cuttings. I then put the lines on blocks and wedges in short lengths and took out all the old burnt ballast and soft clay reforming the bottom Surface of the Cuttings, and covered them over with flat stone with rubble on top and boxed the line full up with good gravel ballast. I had a broad gauge train going with stone from Foxe's Wood, and Tetbury road, to various parts of the line, for nearly seven years, and another train with gravel from Reading & Maidenhead at the same time, but this train was on more than fifteen years.

There was a large quantity of various works done nearly all over the line & during this contract and I made the trial shafts & borings on the South Wales line, the Sailsbury & others. The line from Swindon to Cirincestor & from didcot to Oxford was added to the contract. I relayed the whole of Box tunnel lines at the end of this contract.

John was borne in Mrs Brambles house June 11th 1850.

I planted the quickset hedges on the Bristol & Gloucester from Coalpit heath [seven miles north-east of Bristol] to Stonehouse junction [eight miles south of Gloucester] and the hedges and trees on the GWR from Bath to Swindon. On May 1st 1851 I took the mainteance of the part of Lancaster & Yorkshire Railway between Wakefield, Goole, Bradford Low Moor, Merfield &c, about 75 miles and Mr Brassey took the north end…

[Page 34 of the original was unfortunately missing by 1961 when Marcus Neal lent it to me.]

… it having been a dry time and the ground hard the Engine went all across a small field and the Carriages followed, and when I got there with a gang of men the Engine & carriage stood all upright on their wheels and only one person hurt Burton the inspector of the Company

Police. I laid down a temporary line and a couple of Engines drew all back onto the Main line at W.Bassett Station.

George was born in the house I bought of Provis March 2nd 1852

Harry – do – do – do December 6th 1853

The next contract for Mainteanence extended from June 1854 to June 1861. This embraced the lines as follows. From Reading to Bristol, Didcot to Oxford, and afterwards to Birmingham & Wolverhampton, Swindon to Stonehouse & Cirencester, Thingley to Frome Radstock & Sailsbury, Devizes, and other branches as they were finished amounting in all to about 350 miles. This contract also embraced the supply of Switches crossings, bolts and small fittings, and of course the rails were fast wearing out and required not only more labour relaying but more bolts were required and I required a higher price accordingly. The drainage and other works were continued as before, and the ballast train with gravel was kept going to the end as the banks kept settling down.

On the 350 mile farm I used to cut a large quantity of hay also fold sheep on the slopes, and keep beasts on the waste land and one year I sent one thousand fat sheep & forty fat Oxen to Market I likewise took the first prize for the largest and best fat Shorthorn beasts both at Chippenham and Warmenster shows.

[A surprising omission from his journal was the fact, reported in the *Railway Times* of 9th December, 1854, that Brotherhood had submitted to the War Department and Board of Ordnance plans for forming huts by excavations of earth and turf which is now being considered. Mr Brotherhood has sent Mr Sidney Herbert [the Minister for War] 500 Navvies for work in the Crimea who have subscribed to the 'Chippenham Patriotic Fund', £115 in addition to £50 previous.

Peter Brotherhood Ltd possesses a number of medals, mainly Peter's. However, one from the Royal Polytechnic Society Institute [of Cornwall] in 1853, First Class, with the head of James Watt on the reverse, was most probably awarded to Rowland. The reason for the award and the recipient are not known, but recognition of Rowland's activities in the Crimea War seems the most likely, bearing in mind the date, Peter then being about to leave, or having just left, school.]

When the line between Bm [Birmingham] & W[olver]hampton was being pushed on by the Redwels, I was takeing ballast up the line toward Oxford from a field of gravel I had purchased by the side of the Avon near Warrick Castle. I was induced by Mr Brunel to run some ballast down to help get the line finished, as the GWR Co was going to work it. M^r Mc,Clean was the Engineer for the line, one day as my train with twenty of my 10 ton waggons was going over an iron girder bridge down it went the engine had got over and some few waggons but the middle of the train went down into the road leaving the back part of the train on the rails. This of course stopped the Opening and the whole was put into the hands of Mr Brunel and I had to make some iron girders in great haste to Strengthen some of the bridges, before the line could be opened.

Charles was born in our old house April 25th 1855.

I was going up to Paddington one frosty Morning in the Express with Mr Lane and others it was on a board day [24th February, 1853], at Ealing Station two carriages in the middle of the train went off the line at a crossing point they ran up the slope and turned over when Mr Gibbs one of the Directors was killed he looked out of the window just as the Carriage turned over, I was in the last Carriage with Mr Lane, Hill, Dunn, Fernnis and others, our carriage run off and along the down line although shaken a little none of us were hurt.

At another time I was bringing Mrs Penton down to her daughter Priscilla, we were leaving the Reading Station by the evening express there was a Gentleman sitting by my side faceing M^{rs} P, and the Bishop of Oxford Bishop Wilberforce was sitting next to the Gentleman, just as we got to the junction of the [H]Ung[er]ford Branch we had a tremendous Shock the gentlemans head went against Mrs Pentons breast which was soon as black as my hat, both the Bishop and I were pitched forward but our heads went against the other side of the carriage it being well padded we were not much hurt. The goods Engine coming up the branch met ours at the points, which caused the Mishap. In a hard frost I was in a train going up the W.Bassett Incline when a wheel tyer broke and came through the floor close to me & out at the roof, that was rather close shaveing.

One evening I was comeing up from Birmingham by the last train and just stopped at Hayford Station when I heard a train rattleing down from Oxford which ought to have slackened and stopped at the same station it then being only a single line, I tried to jump out of the door, but before I could do so was knocked under the seat, and when I came to Myself I got out I found the two engines had met and the driver of the other train was killed.

Dureing this contract in August 1856, I undertook to build the New Station at Chippenham, [1856-58], also the New goods shed, and Engine house, and the alterations.

In November the same year, commenced to take down the timber bridges over the Thames at Newnham, and Appeford and replace them with screw piles coloms & wrought Iron girders. I had previously executed a large quantity of work at Paddington, removing 7,000 yards of earth from the Sight of the new goods shead to Bulls bridge [Hayes], building retaining walls, and also laying all the lines into the new Stations, and paveing the Passengers Station with white bricks, and other works there amounting to over Thirty thousand pounds. I made an iron bridge over the canal, and a small dock, at Bull's bridge [chief depot for receiving goods from the canal] and other works there. Also constructed the Reading fork line, to join the GWR, and [H]Ungerford branch, William was the accountant and paymaster there, and James Hopkins, managed the work.

I made the Didcot avoiding line [1856] for the Oxford expresses to miss the Didcot Station. There was a great deal of work done dureing this last Mainteance contract which I do not now remember, nor could I write it all if I did. At the end of this contract Mr Lane who was the Cheaf Engineer, then, was very anctious that I should continue, but there being so much more traffic brought on by other lines which had become lengthened, and there would be a great deal of relaying to be done, and there being so much more risk to be run, and if any accident happened through a slight neglect of my Men I should have to pay. So I required a little more price, but there had been some new directors come on the Bord dureing the last few years and they 'the Company' thought they could do it for the Old price so I let them have it, and I sold them all my tools &c. to do it.

Panic

The following troublesome item should have been written in the part No. 3 or 4 [so it has been inserted here at the beginning of 1857 in Part 3.]. It tells of Panicks or troublesome times with the Great Western Railway Company as to money matters.

Copy   Chippenham Feb 20/57

To I.K.Brunel Esqr.

Dear Sir,

I am very sorry to be compelled to trouble you with this letter, but there really is so much difficulty in getting my accounts settled and to obtain payments for the different works, when completed, that I am under the painfull necessity of doing so. I have rendered hundreds of accounts and done work to the amount of £70,000, on which I have received £37,000 and part of this in <u>Debentures</u> on which I lost very considerably for instance, in one transaction of £12,000 Debentures sent from Paddington to a Broker in Manchester to procure a loan of £10,000 notwithstanding me being kept out of the £2,000 I had to pay £80 expenses and Interest besides. The price I get for the works will not admit of such serious drawbacks.

With regard to the accounts there is one of £1,248 which was retained by the Company, on the Maintenance Contract nearly seven years since, and passed 12 month ago, but not paid, and my Factory has been at Work on Switches Crossings &c, for the last two years, and more than four hundred different accounts have been sent in and I believe passed by Mess[rs] Lee and Thomas amounting to more than £30,000 none of which have been settled, and many others of long standing. I hope you will use your influence to help me under the present circumstances.

Having been in Public Works more than 30 years and working nearly night & day for the last 20 years to put myself in a position to compete for Manufacture of Railways & fittings. And should health & strength be still granted me and if Parties under whom I may be engaged fulfill their part of the Contract nothing will be wanted on my part. And I will not stand second to many Men in this Country in carrying out works which I may undertake.

Trusting you will excuse this long letter,

> I remain, Dear Sir,
> Yours obediently
>
> R.Brotherhood.

18 Duke Street, Westminster
February 24th 1857

Dear Sir,

Your letter of the 20th on the subject of the payments by the Great Western Railway and your note to M[r] Ward declining some work on the Wilts and Somerset have surprised me very much. However incredible your statement seemed to me my reliance upon your general correctness induced me to make immediate inquiries. I cannot learn that there is any foundation for your statement. It would appear from the information sent to me that all accounts certified by me have been paid, and in fact instead of a large sum nothing is due to you.

The sooner such an extraordinary and unaccountable discrepency is cleared up the better. You must immediately explain to me what you mean, and give me the particulars of these alleged errors.

> I am, Dear Sir,
> Yours Truly,
>
> I.K.Brunel

R.Brotherhood Esqr.

Rowland wrote: On receipt of this letter I went to my old friend, D.Thomson, and we went together to Mr Woods the accountants' Office, in his absence, and we found £13,000 of my assets in a few minutes, in one drawer. I at once went to the Secretary's Office with Mr Brunel's letter and threatened to put my Lawyer on at once if some money was not at once paid to me.

And in two or three days after, I took a cheque to Mr Brunel for £10,000 which I had received from Paddington on account, and within two weeks they paid me £27,000 on acct. And Mr Brunel became my best friend at once and continued to be so until the day of his death. [Kate Brotherhood used to tell her son E.J.Lowther that Brunel had said 'Brotherhood, I will never doubt your word again.']

[End of insert]

Maud was born March 1st 1857.

I constructed the Uxbridge branch to West drayton [opened September 1856] there was an Iron bridge on screw piles over the Canal. Hopkins was manager there, after it was completed, I had the very best sale of horses there Old Tom Oxford was horsekeeper; I had bought a lot of good sound young horses in the West of England, thinking they would sell well when the work was finished, it being so near London. There was plenty of good gravel ballast for the roads so that they did not get damaged as they would have done in Clay Country. Many of them which I gave from £30 to 40, sold for £60 or 70. The sale brought £3,000

I had many good sales in London after that but none so good.

I made the East Somerset Railway to Shepton Mallet [1858]. It had then become the fashion for Contractors to take part payment in Shares, and this was my commencement to do so. I was compeled to do as others did or give up and sell all off at a great loss. Hopkins was my chief man there. The Duke of Somerset thanked me & the men, through his agent because they lost so little game and the line run through some of his best preserves.

The company gave an Opening dinner at the finish to me and the men there was a lot of Nobs there, also. One of them asked Hopkins what he would take, his reply was let me have some of that there Shakey Stuff, meaning the jelley.

I also constructed the Thame & Oxford Railway. On it there [were] two Iron bridge on screw piles and a short tunnel. My Son James was the Chief paymaster there, Brokenbrough at the Thame & Hopkins at the Oxford end to manage the works. Steggles was the horsekeeper.

We also did part of the Andover and Redbridge Railway [c.1860]. James was paymaster there. One day as he was driving me and the old Engineer from Rumsey toward Andover, the Old four wheel carriage, broke in half, leaving the Engineer with the hind part & two wheels, in the road, while the horse took the fore half with me and James forward, but there was no one hurt nor any other damage done.

Brokenbrou was at the Andover end, and Hopkins at Rumsey and this was the last Job poor Hopkins ever worked on, and I lost one of the very best men for earthworks. I ever had in my employ.

Some time after this we made the Clifton May bank Junction, with the GWR & South Western near Yeovil.

My tender for the first part of the Metropolitan under ground Railway was accepted, which ran from the junction of the GWR at Paddington to the further end of Euston Square, the price was about £295,000, a big price on account of there being so much gravel and sand, the price of building sand and gravel for concrete in London was 4ˢ to 5ˢ per cube yard it was dredged in the Thames and carted to various parts as required. In making my estimate for the brickwork, Concrete & ballast I put in the London prices, although I well knew nearly all the excavations, would [be] gravel or Sand because I had helped to sink well there in my younger days, and knew the ground well. When the line was first let there was no one in such a good position as Myself & Mʳ Jay, who was then a large builder & contractor on the Great Northern Rly that and the GWR, being the great outlet for the Stuff to be removed. I had my broad gauge plant on the GWR., and Mʳ Jay his narrow on the

Gt Northern. So the Directors left it to us to divide the Contract, to suit our selves. Mr Jay asked me how far I should like to go east. I told him to the east end of Euston Square, which he said would suit him very well, but he did not know the ground so well as me. He got into the London Clay at that point, and then into the Old rotten London, while I was on the Maiden ground composed of what I required in the work, and from which he had afterwards to purchase.

Copy Chippenham Jany 27th 1860

My Dear Sir,

Being unwell I could not reach London Town this morning or should have waited on you. I am exceedingly sorry that the untoward event should have happened so suddenly to prevent my serving under you which I was so anxious to do, but the facts are there that although I have paid a million of money through one of the Banks, here and have had thousands of pounds at different times lying idle in it, they have visited me with a piece of Base cruelty. I was induced some time since by certain parties to take some Railway contracts wherein I had to receive a large number of shares, as part payment, these being of little value caused me to overdraw my account to a small extent and although the Bank hold double the amount in security they have pressed me to pay the whole in such a short time which prevents me from going on with the contract, although all that has been said in Public or Private with reference to my price my confidence is still unshaken, but with the great prejudice that is against me with those parties whom I put my trust in, I can see clearly were I to commence as matters stand, I can see clearly I should soon be stopped which would be very injurious to all parties concerned. Therefore I was compelled to come to the conclusion of giving up – but I thank you most sincerely for the trouble and the interest you have taken in this matter and at all times on my behalf which will ever be remembered by,

      Yours very truely

My price for the earthworks was at the rate of 4^s/6^d per cube yard, the greater part I should sell at 4^s/6^d or 5^s/0, so that I should get not less than 9^s/0 for my excavation, and as I had estimated the cost of gravel for ballast, Concrete, & Sand for the building, I should get double price for that part also. The Total of the Contract was £290,000 And I was quite confident I could do the whole for less than £200,000, so there would be a net profit over £90,000 and more on Extras.

It was rather Strainge, just at the very time the contract for the Southern Outfall Sewer, for the London drainage came out in it there was to be a tunnel under Woolwich, and knowing the ground there I tendered also for it, at a high price, having made my estamate on the same principle as that of the railway, but I did not expect to get the contract, because there were so many of the big builders & others tendering, but my tender was accepted for it likewise the amount being £285,000, and a Splended job at the price, plenty of gravel & sand for the work and lots to be sold at good prices.

And just as I had worked up to the point, to commence to make a large fortune, my Bankers became frightened, and then I saw & felt, the great Mistake I had made in letting a Country Bank have my account & security, and had to thank Old Mr Piniger of Chippenham and Old Mr Privis the Wilts & Dorset Manager at Salsbury for my first fortune missed. There was no reason on their part for such conduct – the amount, I had over drawn was small when compared with the value of my deeds they had, and I had not asked them for a further advance. As both Contracts were for Cash and the payments sure at the end of every month, after I had once made a start, I should soon have paid the Bank off and, the prices being so high, had plenty of cash to spare, but no reasoning would suit them, and although bothe the contracting parties would have taken me without and [any] bond. The Two Old gents thought I must have made some error in my estimates and to my dismay I had to give both Contracts up, I turned the Railway over to Smith & Knight, who made a large sum out of it.

I then saw Webster who was then in a very small way, and advised him as he had tendered at first to go in at my price for the sewer, and that was the first foundation of his making so much money and afterward doing so much of the London public Works.

Mr Gab Goldny being my lawyer at the time, and knowing what a chance I had lost and seeing there was more London work to be done, and that my name still stood well with the Engineer and others there. He brought Mr Fowler who was then Chairman of the North Wilts Bank, to my house, and it was then arranged to pay off the Wilts & Dorset Bank which they did, and took my deeds &c as security for the amount & any further accommadation I may require.

Soon after that the contract for the great Middle Sewer over £300000 came out and I tendered for it at a good price, but this time was the lowest but one and Mʳ Brasseys tender was accepted at about £11000 below me. So the great field for London work for making money was lost to me.

When my tenders were accepted for the Railway & Sewer, bricks were cheap, but I was quite sure they would go up as soon as the work commenced so I at once made a contract with a Mʳ Smeed who was then the Largest brickmaker round London for 40,000,000 of best picked stocks, and although it was a good thing for Smeed that I could not go on with the contract and he got more money for his bricks, he was destined to try to get something more out of me for non-fullfilment of the Contract, and as his brickworks were in the County of Kent the trial came in at Maidstone there was a large show of lawyers and Counsel on both sides. Sir H.James was my chief. The trial commenced by the other side making their Statement of the case, it was then for me to reply so I told the Judge, that I should be very pleased to Carry out the Contract, and not only take all the bricks named, but would be willing to take double the number at the price if Mʳ Smeed would supply them, this put a stop to the trial as Smeed could not do it, but he was still determined to do something so the Case went to Westminster to be settled arbitration, and Smeed not only lost but had to pay all the costs on both sides which came to a very large sum, but he did very well for bricks went up 10ˢ/0 per thousand above the price he had agreed to supply me.

I was induced before by Mʳ Adam Jack, Mʳ Leonard Brustol, and other Bristol Gentlemen and friends, and also by Mʳ Ravenhill the Banker, who were all very anctious to get a Railway communication between Bristol, & South Wales. So I went to the expense of Survaying a line from the North Side of the GW Railway Station running through Queen Square with Iron bridges across the floats [harbour], and along CannonsMarsh, undr the St Vincents Rock & down alongside the river to the Avons Mouth & along at the back of the Sea bank to the New passage & to cross as at present to join the South Wales line, I got all the section & plans ready in deatail to go to parliament, which had cost me a considerable sum when to our surprise the very men who aught to have come and helped us, or at the very least have kept quiet and consulted us if they were not sattisfied, when we could have altered our plans to suit their views, but just as we were about to deposit plans they were allready to oppose, so the best line was lost and my Money also.

There was a scheme got which was to run Steamers from Bristol and the Channel [?], in connection with a Railway scheme to construct a

Railway from Halifax, to Quebec. We had a dinner at Blackwall in connection with the Railway, for which RB had to pay. There were present Lord Berry, General Williams of <u>Cars</u>, Sir Alan, McNab, Judge Haleburton, Old M^r Sm$^{l.}$ Cunard, some Members of Parliament, Gentlemen from Canada some English Engineers and others.

After that dinner I paid Lord Berry and a man well known there by the name of Nelson to act as his secretary, they were to go out and get the concession, for the Railway and I was to do the work. I also sent out My Son Peter, and Rumble with him the[y] went over the course from Halifax to Quebeck to inspect and report thereon.

Lord Berry drew a bill on me for seven hundred pounds over & above the amount we had agreed on, for procuring the concession, he got the one for a Steam line from Galway but done Nothing for me so I was sold in that little Job.

Returning to the Bristol & South Wales Railway we had a Second try and got the act to take the line in its present rout. [The Bristol & South Wales *Junction* Railway had been incorporated in 1846, but nothing happened and it was revived as the B&SW *Union* Railway in 1857, work beginning in October 1858. The 11 mile line opened from Bristol to New Passage via Filton, Patchway and Pilning on 8th September, 1863, and the mile from Portskewett pier to the South Wales main line on 1st January, 1864. The GWR worked the line from its opening, and absorbed it 'at par' in 1868. Although the ferry service ceased when the Severn Tunnel opened in 1886, some of the B&SWUR was used for the eastern approach to the tunnel.]

After we had commenced, some of the same persons who had worked hard to drive us out of the first line, went to the Chamber of Commerce Office, took a Copy of my plan & section of the first line, and made one on the very same ground, but only from the St Vensent rock to the Mud at the Avons Mouth, which never paid for the coal & oil used.

They then put out a pier into the Channel, where the Chipstow Steamer used to run through; not only did that not pay but the piles they drove silted up the Channel, and the grass soon covered the sight, where the boat went through a very short time before, this is Bristol Management all over.

We kept steady on with cuttings and banks of the [Bristol & South Wales] Union [Railway], and soon commenced the Almsbury [Almondsbury] tunnel [1,245 yards], and after that the New passage piers on south bank of Severn [nine miles north-west of Bristol], at the commencement of the one on the South Side, I took M^{rs} B, and a lot of our Children down to stay a short time at the Severn Lodge by the water side, it was arrainged that they should stay there until the first hundred piles were driven. One day all the pile drivers were seen, comeing up to the house, so I met them at the gate, and found they had Struck work and required more wages because they eat so much more than they did in land. I told them they aut to feel very much obliged to me for bringing them down to such a very healthy place, but they could not see it, and thought they aught to have six pence per day more on acct of their eating. So I proposed to give three pence per day and they should alow the other three on account of their good health, and after a little more reasoning they all went back to the work satisfied, and the first hundred piles were driven quite as soon as our Children wished them to be, as they liked the spot, and Oliver Norrises Milk, & bread & butter;

One night as we were erecting the portskewet pier [on north bank of Severn opposite New Passage, three miles south-west of Chepstow], there were some high spring tides on, when a gale of wind set in, and blew or washed away nearly £3,000 worth of work and plant, but it was not all lost, for some of the timber floated back by the down tide, and some up by the next up tide but of course RBs pocket suffered for the rest. The work was heavy. The piers cost over £40,000 and the total of the works I did amounted to over £240,000 and one fourth had to be taken in shares & debentures in payment thereof. My Son Rowland was the paymaster there. Mr J.Penton was some time at the piers, and Hopkins and Rumble attended to most of the other works.

Daughter Kate, was born in our own house next the Viaduct at Chippenham, on April 25th 1863, making fourteen. Now although Our two Fathers, & Mothers, Our four Grandfathers, & Grandmothers, as each pair had large familys, I believe there was only one who had over twelve, and they only had nine sons. So I think however Much we may have failed in carrying out other contracts, we did our duty both to Queen and Country in keeping up stock.

And I must here say that if I had not been blessed with one of the very best of Wifes I never could have gone through all I have nor carried out all the works I have done without her help. She acted as my Cashier, through out nearly all the works, sometimes drawing the money from the Banks, and collecting silver from other sauces, and often had to sit up until Midnight, counting and tying up many hundreds of pounds in small bags for me to throw out of the trains to the gangs on the Maintenance, and other works along the line. This she continued to do until the family got too large and the works so increased. When her Brother Mr E.Penton came down and took it out of her hands.

And I am bound to say that if there was any credit due in carrying out work in bringing up our family the greater share belonged to my devoted Wife.

The following item [written at the end of Part 5] should have been written also in part Three:-

One Christmas day morning while at breakfast, I received a letter from a gentleman in London, who knew I had done some large excavations stateing he had sent me a large Christmas dinner, and when I had digested it he wished to see me in Town. It was then Stated to me that himself was connected with Some Bankers in Paris, who wished to have an estimate from an English Contractor, of the costs of the proposed Suez Canal. [Concession granted 1854, Company formed 1858, canal built 1859 to 1869.] The two Engineers, had just returned from Egypt with the plan and Sections, they had taken on the ground. So it was arrainged that I should go to Paris to see them. And as there was a Railway to be made from Bourdeaux runing by the side of the River Garonne, to the Sea, which I was asked to tender for. I went over and spent a week in Paris. And one of the Bankers took me to Bourdeaux, and we went over the line and through some of the Vineyards, and at the Hotel instead of tea or coffee they gave us claret for our breakfast, quite a contrast from the breakfast at Balmoral, there they gave me Wiskey and Oat cake. At the time I was in Paris and various parts they were just about to commence the War with Prusher [the Franco-Prussian War was 1870-71; in 1859 France went to war with Austria], and I did not like the looks of so many cannons, Soldiers & Preists. So I put War prices on the Railway contract and got out of it.

I came home and thought over the canal matter and made an estimate for all the Excavations &c which came to over £8,000,000. Which the then promoters thought could be done for less, or at least they feared to bring it out before the Public, at first with that amount. So I withdrew from the Matter and I saw an account made up before the work was finished, which amounted to over £11,000,000 Sterling.

[End of insert]

Sent Feby 4/82
   Part 4

The Railway Works Chippenham Wilts, originated as follows. [*See also Appendix Two.*]

When I first commenced there in <u>1842</u>, I put up a small Smith Shop for the purpose of repairing the Maintenance tools and began with one forge, but soon had to put up another forge and start old George Whiteman on also, and in a very short time had to put on two more Smiths to keep the forges going night & day, and as the work increased we got Messrs Ayers [Eyres had a Chippenham foundry] & Silcox [?] and others to help us. I had a drilling & Screwing Machine going by hand.

Seeing there would be a great deal to do in the way of Railway fittings for Pt [permanent] way &c , I then purchased, part of a field called the Mall ground, situated between the Station and the little George [an inn]. Built an Enginehouse at the east corner and a large Smith Shop running west, and a Machine Shop going from the Enginehouse North. I ordered a twelve horse Engine from Fisher of Frome and some drilling, Screwing, and plaining machine in the North, and by the time the Shops were finished, they were all ready for fixing also. Old Mr Silcox was with me. We soon got all the Machines, Engine, blower, &c. fixed and to work onto making our own tools and Pt way fittings, &c. At the time the Railway was being Made from Swindon to Gloucester, & Cheltenham, there was a great dispute between the Great Western Railway Co & The Birmingham & Gloucester or Midland Company, as to the safe working of a Mixed gauge between Gloucester & Cheltenham, as the GWR. wished to run over their line, rather than go to the cost of another line and as the Matter was being fought in a commitee of the House of Commons, Robt Stevenson and others Stated it could not be worked with Safety at the junctions, and Mr Brunel said it could, and he sent down a plan of the proposed junction to know if I could make any switch or anything that would work safe. When I replied I could, and we got two fixed points, made and fixed one at the Cheltenham, and the other at Barnwood junction [Gloucester] which did work safely & well. Old Mr Silcocks was with me at that time [This sentence crossed out on original]. After this Mr Brunel put a lot of work into my hands, English & foreign. We had not only to Make the Pt way fittings for My own Contracts, but also for the greater part of the GWR, and for other lines connected with it.

And before the end of the year <u>1850</u>, in addition to the English work, I had sent out tools and Railway fittings to France, Spain, India and Other foreign parts.

The work increased so much that that I was not only compelled to keep my own works going day & night but I had to get Perry & Barrots of Reading, Stothert & Pitt of Bath, and Bush & Bedo [?] of Bristol, to help me.

So then I bought Mr Brinkworths land at the back of the New Shops. Put up a larger Engine house with boilar house & high chimney, also a much larger Machine Shop, a Foundry, Gas Works, sunk a deep well, put up a large & small Steam hammers & more forges, New Offices and Stores.

As these buildings were going on the new Machinery was being made. And just at the time Messrs Smith and Wilby [?] the noted iron wheel makers of Liverpool Stopped their works. So I sent Mr Silcocks to the Sale by auction, with power to arrange with the 40 theves, to bid for me, and we got a new 40 Horse beam Engine all their wheel & some other Machinery very cheap.

We also brought Mr Mackey their Foreman & about 20 of their best Smiths and wheel men to Chippenham. Mr Josiah Penton had charge of accounts out & inwards, and Management of Stores &c. Mr Silcocks had taken the Management of Engineering work department, but as soon as all was ready, Mr Mackey took the wheel, boilar & bridge work, until Mr Silcock retired when Mr Mackey took charge of all the ironwork departments. There was also a Foreman of carpenters for the wood department.

Prior to 1851, I had made a number of broad gauge Iron Tilt [open wagons with tarpaulin covering or tilt] with patent tilt & box trucks & some Carriage Trucks [flat wagons to carry road carriages], for the Bristol & Exeter Railway Co^y. Many of these can be seen working at the present day.

I bought the Patent Rights of a lattice iron bridge suitable for exportation, and carriage in forign countries from an American Engineer. And I put the first Span into the [Great] Exhibition of 1851 This bridge was erected afterwards over the Canal at Swindon to carry the road going from the Station to the Church & New Town west [Bullen's Bridge, Sheppard Street across Wilts & Berks Canal]. I also had one of my new Iron Waggons broad gauge with my patent fan tilt & a moddle railway, with Switches, Spring crossings, and distance cross bar Signals, worked with the capstan and long wires, which also worked stop blocks [instead of trap points, to prevent vehicles running out of a siding on to the main line] their were about the first worked by very long wires.

In the year 1852 there was a revision of Signals, on the Great Western Railway and I had to make and fix Signals, at nearly all the Stations on the GWR System, we were also very busy with different kinds of fittings & work both at home & abroad.

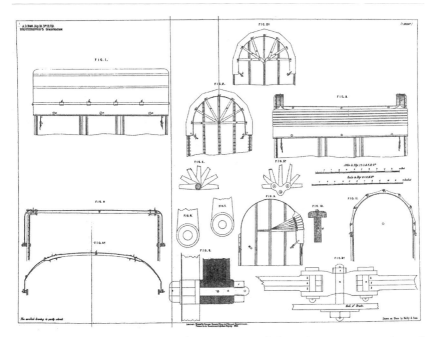

Drawing of Rowland's Patent Tilt (canvas covering) for railway wagons and canal boats, granted 10th November, 1849. The tilt could be fitted to wagons with flat or semicircular ends.   *Courtesy Patent Office*

As the bridge work increased, both in quantity and length of spans, we required still more room & I then bought Squire Eastmeads [Note on copy of original: Monkton House] field for erecting bridges and other large work. During the year 1853 & 54, we were very busy, in foreign work, and we also supplied Peto & Bits [Betts] with a lot of Switches, Crossings, Signals &c for the Oxford Woster [Worcester] & Wolverhampton Railway, and the GWR Co required a great deal of various fittings.

We also Manufactured and erected the Putney Acquaduct over the River Thames, at a cost under £19,000. [Constructed in 1856 for Chelsea Waterworks Company who pumped water from Kingston-on-Thames to reservoirs on Putney Heath, and thence by gravity to Putney Hill & High Street. The aqueduct was constructed to carry mains across Thames to Chelsea. It had eight piers, each six hollow cast-iron screw piles screwed about 14ft into bed of river, carrying wrought-iron girders. Piers protected by timbers. A brick tower at each end covered the junction with the underground pipes. The existing timber road bridge

Bullens Bridge, Swindon, carrying Sheppard Street across the Wilts & Berks Canal, looking north. Rowland had exhibited this span at the 1851 Great Exhibition.

Courtesy Swindon Central Library

Lattice bridge of 140ft span under construction. Note the overhead crane on its timber supports and the crude ladders for its operator. It looks as though he turned a handle to make the crane travel. The crane carriage sitting on the supports probably carried the winch, operated by the workman standing beside it.   *Courtesy Chippenham Museum*

was pulled down in 1886 and replaced by stone bridge on site of aqueduct, with water pipes beneath footways. This bridge was widened in 1932 and is still in use, for road and water.]

In 1855 we were full of work, and amongst the rest we made a wrote [wrought] iron girder bridge and erected the same over the Dee at Balmoral, for His Royal Highness, Prince Albert. There was a great many coal waggons made this year also.

[In the summer of 1854 I.K. Brunel was invited to design a bridge at Balmoral, and the plans were submitted for approval in November. The list of tenders was agreed in May 1855 for 'Contract for Wrought Iron Bridge over the River Dee near Balmoral'. Brotherhood's figure of £1,650 was substantially less than the other six received. Brunel issued instructions in July for masonry work, but delays in completion kept Brotherhood waiting, and so in September 1856 he asked for payment on account. The bridge was complete except for painting by the autumn of 1857, and was opened 8th September, 1857, although wrangles about excess payments incurred by delays etc. outside Brotherhood's control continued until 18th November, 1858 when the Royal Factor was advised to pay them. This bridge carries the B976 across the River Dee from the A93 at Crathie past the entrance to Balmoral Castle to become the South Deeside route eastwards to Aberdeen. It comprises two riveted wrought-iron girders, 125ft clear span, with a 13ft wide timber deck covered with tarmac. Three plates on the bridge read 'R.BROTHERHOOD CHIPPENHAM WILTS.' 1856. See article with drawing by Angus Buchanan & Stephen K.Jones in *Industrial Archaelogy Review*, Volume 4 Number 3 Autumn 1980.]

Dureing 1856 we were full of work, and as we had done before sent out a lot of the patent lattice bridges to Ceylon. We had improved them by substituting wrote iron in some parts in the place of cast. The Designs for the Muswell, made by Mr J.Spencer & myself. In 1857 the Indian Government had built a large Stone bridge over the River Indian, near Delia [Delhi?], and when they Struck the centres the arches fell into the River and Col.Hart of the Royal Engineers was sent to visit various bridge builders in England, with a view to acertain where the most suitable one in Iron could be got in the shortest time, and as he passed Chippenham he saw us busy on some for Ceylon, and after he sent in his report the Order was sent to me for four large spans of the latticebridge to be sent out at once.

Twelve of us known to each other formed a Company to build works and smelt the iron ore at Westbury Station, and I made the Sidings, fittings &c. also the large boilars, blast tubes, Hoists, Furnacebands, and

Top: Brunel's bridge over the River Dee close to Balmoral, constructed by Rowland Brotherhood. Its functional simplicity did not please its royal patrons! Although the girders were ready in 1855 the abutments delayed completion by nearly two years. Aberdeenshire County Council now maintains this bridge as part of the public road network.

Right: View along deck
Above: Rowland's plate.

other works.

And after that there was a larger company formed of Wiltshire Gentlemen to work the ore at Seend, all these were very respectable men, but there were two more came in from London or elsewhere, with a coal pit scheme. I was to do all the work &c. as at Westbury, and also to make coal and ore waggons to the extent of £10,000. The Coal pit was to be purchased at Ruhabron [Ruabon near Wrexham], the Coal was to be taken from there to Seend and to kill two birds with one stone, the waggons were to take back with ore from Seend and iron was to be Smelted at both ends. Mr Meak of Devizes was one & the Lawyer for all. The leases & deeds were all drawn and there was one for paying the GWR Co. from £30 to 40,000 per annum for Carriage. The day was named for all to meet at Devizes, to ratify the agreements, but as I did not like the looks of the two Straingers, I made some little private enquiries in London & Ruhabron. We all met on the day appointed, The London gents brought down an old gent who they stated was a rich merchant and was willing to take a large nomber of Shares in the Concern, all seemed to be going on smoothly until it came to the agreement with me. When I told them that not a single thing would be done by me untill I had been down and had a look at the coal in the pit, I had before seen the old merchant as a cad in a scheming office in the City, and when Mr John Spencer and others who know me found I was determined to stand firm they stuck to me, there was a divition and a great noise, but it was arranged to meet and go down the pit at Ruhabron, which we did and soon found it was a dead Sell, and the whole thing burst up, it turned out that there was a very little coal in the pit and and and [twice on original] one or two parties had been Swindled before we came in.

Some little time after another company was got up at Seend [three miles west of Devizes], and I did all the work for them as at Westbury.

In September 1857 being a Shareholder in the great Eastern Steam Ship Company I let them 500 tons of new rails for the launching ways, and I sent up many little pieces of work to Mr Brunel at the time of launching.

In this year we sent 1200 sets of carriage & waggon Iron work to the East India Railway Co & a lot of Switches &c.

In the year 1858 I sent out four Spans of my latticebridge, with Screw piles & colomns to erect a bridge 100 feet high, to cross the Quina [?] River in Mysor.

And a lot of 42 feet Engine turntables to the east India Railway, and other works.

I bought a Strip of land by the side of the works fronting the Station at Chippenham, and built a new shop for Peter to make his Small Loco Engines in, he had made the broad gauge Moloch in an old shop outside.

In 1859, I agreed with H.G.E.Childers, Esqr, M.P., to make the Moovaboo [Moorabool?] River Viaduct for the Victorian Government [Australia], which I erected in the works and delivered the same on board ship in London for the sum of £40,060 Mr Brunel was the Engineer & Mr C. the agent at the time.

In 1860 we were very full of work, and sent out many lattice bridges to Ceylon.

In 61 there was a very great variety of work done amongst it the Great Western Railway Co took to about £2000 of my Maintenance tools, Waggons, to the amount of £14,990, Switches crossings &c £8,500, and carriage wheels, £3,000.

The Victorian Railway had waggon work over £3000 with sundries.

In the year 1862, I made the *Great Eastern* Steam Ships paddle new

The double track Moorabool Viaduct over the Moorabool River on the railway from Geelong to Ballarat, Victoria, Australia. Having 10 spans of 130ft, resting on piers about 90ft high, it was opened in 1862. Later it was strengthened to carry heavier locomotives by having a steel lattice girder tower erected under the midpoint of each span (see *The Commonwealth Engineer*, 1st August, 1918).   *State of Victoria, via R.Davidson*

wheels after the Storm, She had encountered. They [were] 52 feet in diameter. I also made the new rudder post a piece of rivetted ironwork 8 tons weight. Peter took some Men down and fixed all on to the Ship at Milford. She was a most unfortunate Ship for some of us holders. Mr Brunel had taken a large number of Shares, and as others had done I went in to the amount of £4000 to help him out. I not only this but also another £2000 to help her off at the Second launch, but I did not care so much about it at the time, because I well knew that if Mr Brunel put me into one bad job he would put me into two good ones, to help me out. He had been a good friend to me.

In that year the GWR Co had in switches crossings and fittings £2500 in carriage & waggon wheels £3000 and £5000 in sundry jobs.

In 1863 amongst other things, the Bristol & South Wales line had Switches & Crossings & Signals £3440 Mr Jay the Contractor for the east end of the under ground Railway £1550 in Switches & crossings, and the Somerset & Dorset Ry for the same kind of fittings £1000. And there were a lot of coal waggons made that year. And a lot of similar done for the GWR also.

In 1864 in addition to other works, Mr E.Price the Contractor who made the Cocklbury Cutting at Chippenham, took wt [wrought] iron Girders for bridges on the Smyrna Railway [now Ismir, Turkey] £2100, The East India Ry Turntables £1200, The Wycombe Ry Switches Crossings & Signals £2100, and the South Devon Co £1300, The Bristol &

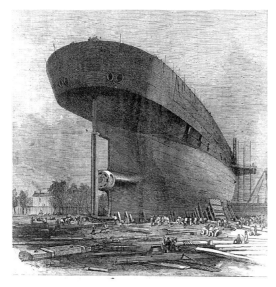

Stern view of the *Great Eastern* under construction with one paddle wheel in the distance. The rudder post carrying the rudder has not yet been hung aft of the propeller, itself not yet fitted.
Courtesy Illustrated London News

South Wales extra accts during the year, The New passage piers Construction £40,200. Iron roofs over ends of the piers £1,477. The gas house £525. The Engin house at port Skewet £644, Signals at the junction £1000 Permanent way acct £26,690. Stations £6855 New passage Station platform £1600 sundries £1975. Son James used to sell Agricultural Implements & Machinery in the Markets, but that work was much too slow. It used to take some of the Old Wiltshire Farmers nearly all day considering as to the purchase of a plough.

In 1865 The GWR Co. took narrow gauge waggons to the amount of £31,000. Mr Price for Smyrna £6600 The Indian Government bridge work £4500 Natal bridge work £1000 the South Devon Railway Co £2000 and the South Eastern Ry Co £1000. There was also a lot of other work done during the year.

Although I had made fair profits on nearly all the works I had done. As there had been a large amount of money paid for land, buildings, Machinery, tools &c &c on the works at Chippenham. And also for Horses Plant & tools &c for the Railway construction, the maintenance contracts & other works, with the expences of a large family, and cost of investments I had made, I required a little more Capital. And also afterwards, having in two Contracts to follow the fashon of taking part payment in shares, viz East Somerset Railway, Bristol & S.W. Railway, to the extent of over £70,000 I had made an arrangement with the North Wilts Bank, for a further over draft, giving them my deeds, Shares, &c as security and paid them a good interest for the advance, but as they had lost my old friend Mr Fowler their Chairman, who was not only a Quaker & a rich man, but was also a man of business, and connected with Dimsdales & Co Bankers of London who understood such matters. But two or three of the N.W.B Directors, Shopkeepers & some others of the same class, Shareholders in Melksham, became nervous and pressed me for repayment, which could not be done just then, without a most ruinous sacrifice. So I consulted an Old friend Mr Ch^{ls} Cammell who I had done a large business with and was a creditor at the time. And as he had just been Successful in forming his business into a limited company. Although the time was getting more unfavourable for such. [Recent years had seen a lot of speculation in railway schemes, with subsequent reaction, and in the near future, in early May 1866, the major bank Overend, Gurney & Co failed, causing a panic and the collapse of a number of other banks and finance houses, numerous railway contractors including the large firm Peto & Betts, and saw several railway companies, including the Great Eastern, London Brighton & South Coast and London Chatham & Dover in difficulties.] He very strongly advised me to try and do as he had done.

And at the end of June I had Mr Radford, Engineer of Manchester, who had valued Sir John Browns Works, which was also Successful in forming a company, to value the Railway Works for me, and on the 4th of July 1865, he rendered his valuation and report as follows,

Land & Buildings, The Fixed Plant, Loos Tools, Stock in Trade, the Rolling Stock &c at or on the Works near the GWR Station only, amount £103,812. And after that several Gentlemen and friends looked into the Matter, and we had a meeting, when it was proposed to form a limited company to carry on the works. The temporary Offices was at the South Sea House, City. The prospectus was printed. The Company was called the General Contract Company Limited. And Sir Dn^l Gooch, had put his name down as Chairman, and the amount required. And M^r McShell, one of the GWR Directors, had put his name as a Director with £10,000 in Shares. And Mr Fowler of Dimsdales Bankers London, Mr Ravinell Banker, Mr Gab Goldney, Mr T.P.Pocock, Mr Jones Timber Merchant since Mayor of Bristol, and some other good names, as Directors & Shareholders. And it was thought with such a good list of names, and with the Interest that such could bring in both English and foreign, that the company would take and do well. But the Panic set in just at the time, and we were too late to float or raise the capital required. There were many Firms failed at that time. But I kept the Railway Works going, and as I had taken a large contract for bridge and Waggon work, in the year 1866 I built the two large shops in the field and put a Saw Mill &c so as to do the work under cover & to contract time. And in addition to other works The GWR Co took narrow gauge waggons that year to the amount of £34,000, and the Ceylon Government bridges £10,000. I also made a Small bridge that year for Lord Cowley at Draycot [knocked down by US Army vehicles in the Second World War when they occupied Draycot House]. But although I was doing very well some of the Melksham gents became uneasy again, and one day M^r GG & T.P. came to my house and wished to see me in private, So we went & sit under the walnut tree at the bottom of the garden, when they brought out an assignment, or bill of Sale, and pressed me very much to sign it, and cheat my trade friends & creditors, who were very few but all first rate firms. I at once refused and sent for my friends, we had a private meeting and desided to call in Messrs Barnard Thomas & Co, Accountants of Bristol to examine the books & the State of affairs, and report there on, and on 25th of August we had another meeting, including those Connected with the Bank, when the accountants rendered their report, and after due consideration it was arrainged that I should go on under an inspection, which would keep the Bank quiet until I could recover myself. And Mr Freeman, for the Lowmoor Co, Mr Almond for the Coalbrookdale Co, and Mr Palmer for the Bank, should be the three Inspectors. I had an arrangement with Mr Saunders & others of the GWR, that they would amalgamate their line with the Bristol & S.Wales Union, and then I should get all my money back in full. We were then making a good trade profit, and all went on smothly and the first 5^s/0 in the pound [i.e. 25%] was soon paid to all.

Some time after this a Gentleman well known to Mr Goldney came to me with a contract to be let for the drainage of Receife in Brazil [now Pernambuco, on the coast, near the tip of the bulge towards Africa], but as I would have nothing to do with it then Myself he went to Mr G. He being still a Director of the Bank. And in a few days Mr Goldney made a clear agreement with me to effect that if I would again get him returned at the coming Election he would, himself arrainge with the Bank to finance the Debentures. And it can now be seen by the Devizes Gazette, of August 20/68, that I took the Chair at a large Meeting of Electors, and strongly advocated his cause, and it will be seen by the following letter which I have, that he would not have been returned to Parliament without my help.

[Summary of a cutting from a local paper, enclosed with the handwritten manuscript Marcus Neal borrowed for me from E.C.Lowther in 1961, but not with the copy now held by Wiltshire Record Office. The paper is presumed to be *Devizes & Wilts Gazette*, 20th August, 1868.

Enthusiastic meeting at Chippenham in favour of Mr Goldney, M.P., held on Monday in the large room of the White Lion Inn, upwards of 300 principal inhabitants present despite the heavy rain, and people overflowed into the passage.

Mr West Audry proposed Mr Brotherhood 'who was one of the most influential inhabitants of the town' should be asked to take the chair. Cheers, carried with acclamation.

Mr Brotherhood took the chair, said he felt concerned for future of the country then proceeded to describe the man he would like to see in Parliament, and proposed Mr Goldney, 'the present member for the borough of Chippenham'.

Mr Goldney began by referring to the downpour because 'it is doing immense benefit to the country at large'. He referred to Mr Brotherhood 'I have known him for the third of a century, and I believe there is no man more upright in his conduct, more desirous of doing justice to all who work under him, or more anxious to uphold the interests of this town, than he is (cheers).' He went on to talk on many subjects:- government expenditure, electoral reform, rates, education, unemployment, pure water supply. 'He would hold out no delusive hopes to them. He would not say his getting into Parliament would make the loaf cheaper or their wages higher (hear, hear). But he would say that no man was more desirous of maintaining and upholding the trade of the town of Chippenham than he was; and his worthy friend Mr Brotherhood knew that three weeks before he left England, he gave up the whole of his time in endeavour to secure a large contract for him; and he might tell them that so recognised are Mr Brotherhood's habits of industry and knowledge of his business, so great was the opinion entertained of him, that his contract was accepted before that of any other man. It was a large question connected with the Government of Brazi,l and the only thing pending within the last week had been the comparative value between the mill real (reis) in Brazil and England – the Government of Brazil contending that they should pay Mr Brotherhood in the coin of their own country, whereas Mr Brotherhood contended that he ought to be paid according to the value of English money. I hope and trust however that long before the election is over the contract will be in full force, and I shall then be glad to claim some share of credit for having brought to the town what I believe to be of benefit not to Mr Brotherhood alone, but to the inhabitants generally. (Cheers)'

Mr Phillips moved a vote of thanks to Mr Brotherhood for taking the chair, 'and alluding to his having been selected to carry out the extensive foreign contract to which Mr Goldney had referred, said that to have such a man amongst them was not only a benefit to the town, but a matter of which they ought to feel proud.'

Mr Brotherhood thanked the company for compliments paid to him, and 'hoped (they would) support their staunch friend and the friend of the working men of Chippenham (hear, hear) – one who was doing all he could to fill their family cupboards and their breeches' pockets (cheers)'.

End of summary of newspaper report]

Beachfield, Chippenham Nov 17/68

My dear Sir,

I cannot sleep to night without first offering to you, my thanks for kind and unremitting exertions during the Contest, which has ended so happily for me, to your kind efforts and exertions I am indebted for a very considerable portion of the results. Many thanks for it, and happiness to you & yours in esteem.

I remain Yours Truly,

Gab. Goldney

The Contract was soon arrainged for the draining[?] and I sent out My Sons, Fred & Ernest first to Receife, and Rowland followed and joined them to carry out the works.

The Works at Chippenham had been going on satisfactorily. The Inspectors did not trouble me, dureing the time in addition to other work we had sent out £24,500 bridge work to Ceylon and a lot to India & other parts. And then as things were were [twice on original] going on to pay, Mr Goldney, advised the Bank and the other Inspectors to release me to carry on the works again myself. To which they all agreed, and I proceeded accordingly. And by the end of Decr 68 I had sent out Tools & Materials to Recife to the value of £4337 and in Jan^{ry} 69 materials £2410. And it was all arrainged for me to go out to Brazil. I had paid my passage and one day just as I was about to start for Southampton to take the Mail on March 9th When a Message came from the Bank to say I must stay, they would not finance the Debentures. I then saw that I had allowed M^r GG. to deceive me, I had served his purpose, and sold myself. So as the Bank and those connected with it, had then got nearly all I had, I was compelled to Stop the works. A meeting was called. There were only Nine Trade creditors, and they were all ready and willing to forgo there amounts, to keep me going. But the Bank and party, were determined to realize, although at a very bad time, so on the 31st of March 1869 I made an assignment of nearly everything I then possessed for the benefit of my Creditors & the Bank.

And to say nothing of good will & loss of the connection which had taken me so long to create. The loss through forced sales in bad times were very grievous, for Instance take one item. The Bristol & South Wales Shares, No 1740 and each cost me £25 £43500 which were thrown on the market when they were down to £5 each, and with such a glut knocked them down to £4, and sold or taken away from me at that price, and which in a very short time when the line was amalgamated went up to par as above. And it was very galling soon after that when the GWR Stock went up to £138.

[Paragraph follows on the copy Marcus Neal borrowed for me, but not on the copy now held by Wiltshire Record Office.]

To know that some persons who who took my shares each four at on for £16 sold them at £138 and my £43,500 which had been credited to me by the Bank at £6,960, were then worth then in the market £60,230, with such a loss and the sacrifice of the Railway works, Plant, Stock in Trade, and including the Land and House property at Chippenham which had been valued just before at £119,255 was to me at the time most appalling. I cannot write more now on the subject.

[End of additional paragraph]

Sent on Feby 21ˢᵗ
    Part 5

At the end of the year <u>1869</u>, I made an agreement, with Messʳˢ Herbet & Charles Maudslay, to be their General Manager at the Bute Iron & Engineering works at Cardiff, for a term of ten years, subject to 12 months notice, on either side, and should the firm give RB notice after three years to pay him £500. And the following are some of the Works we executed during the time I was there. The Old dock gates at Newport, originally being constructed of cast iron & timber, had for some time been very defective, and being strengthened with heavy oak & Iron from time to time they had become so heavy, some of them each <u>120</u> to <u>130</u> tons and at last they could scarcely be moved. And we undertook to make two wrot [wrought] Iron gates with watertight compartments, which would float enough to take the weight off the roller paths, and work easy. When the two first gates were finished we floated them round by sea from Cardiff to Newport. We lifted the old gates up bodily, out of the pivot hole, threw them down flat, put two lighters over each made them fast, and then floated them out of the lock, across the river to be broken up. We then floated the new gates in, raised and erected them in place. As the docks were closed, during the operation, and a heavy fine to be put on us in case the work was not finished in the contract time, it being short we had to work day and night, and I did not get much sleep dureing the time the work was going on.

As the above two gates worked so well the Directors gave us another Order for two more, on the same plan. The four gates cost £8200. <u>Charlie</u> was with me at the erection of these gates. <u>Fred</u> and <u>Harry</u> were at the Bute works also.

We also supplied and erected Six new gates, in the new locks, at the Bristol docks. Fred, with a Foreman, attended to the erecting of these, they were put up in the dry locks. There was no floating nor night work with these, so I was not required to be there so much, only when they were being removed back into the hollow quoin, These six gates cost £<u>13,500</u>.

We made an iron pontoon landing Stage for the Bristol docks. 'It was <u>225</u> feet long', floated it from Cardiff to the Hot Wells, and it is fixed by side of the river above the bridge.

We <u>likewise</u> erected four of these gates at the New Bute docks at Cardiff at a cost of £<u>10,200</u>.

And the two sea gates at the new Alexandra Dock Newport at a cost

of £6,500, * as the tide rises so very high in the Bristol Channell most of
these gates had to be over 40 feet deep.

[* Footnote on original] Each of 20 new Iron gates required at the new
docks in the Bristol Channel We made 16.

And a day or two after these two were finished, the outer dam burst
with a high spring Tide, and the water rose nearly 40 feet against the
outside of the gates in a very short space of time, and it was most
fortunate for the Contractor and the Dock Company that our gates were
finished in time, because the work in the dock was nothing like finished,
and besides the damage to it, the water would have flooded a large track
of land between Newport & Cardiff. Sir George Elliot, and the other
chief men, were much pleased with the way I had pushed on the gates
to finish.

We also sent out nearly £5000 of Iron roof and bridge work to Brazil.
We made some steam Hopper dredge barges, and a good deal of other
work dureing the time I was at the Bute Works. But Messrs Maudslay
Brothers did not feel inclined to go into large foreign bridge nor Railway
Contracts offered. So they gave me Notice before the five years expired.
I left and they had to pay.

[Whilst at Cardiff Rowland wrote a letter entitled 'Sewage & Water
Supply' which was published in *The Builder* on 20th January, 1872.

Having suffered when young with fever, and since lost several friends
... and knowing others who are sick with typhoid fever, I venture to pen
these lines. During 45 years, constantly having something to do with
well-sinking, drainage, sewering, waterworks, etc my experience has
shown me that as gunpowder is dangerous when put in contact with
fire, so is nightsoil when in contact with water, where old wells, drains,
cesspools, and inferior traps, and badly fitted water closets, are allowed
to remain in use.

I enclose you section, showing the drainage and water supply of a
house on a small piece of land I purchased in Chippenham, Wiltshire,
twenty years ago [Orwell House], and on investigation at the time found
a large number of other cottages in the same condition. [The section
shows a well, lined with rough pieces of stone, between the cesspits of
two privies, the contents of which percolate to the water.]

Knowing the danger, and having a large body of workmen, also my
own family, located there, I endeavoured, with other persons, to obtain
a public water supply for the town; but not succeeding, I sank a private
well for the use of ourselves and workmen, procuring most excellent
water from the deeper springs, and from this well most of the
inhabitants of the town are now supplied. As to rivers, I well remember

Rear of Orwell House, the Brotherhood family home in Chippenham, *c.*1870. The GWR viaduct is on the left, with Chippenham station buildings in the distance. Charles plays croquet on the lawn while Kate sits on the verandah. Mrs Bramble's house, where several of the children were born, is next door on the right.

Courtesy Wiltshire Local Studies Library.

seeing fine salmon taken from the Thames between Isleworth Ferry and Richmond Bridge, and often watched the gradual pollution of its waters since with regret...

[He suggested sinking deep wells so as to avoid impure surface water. Mentioning the fine crops grown by his father and others after the enclosure of Houslow Heath, 'by the use of nightsoil, urine and the contents of cesspools' he said that it was a waste to send sewage into the sea; instead it should be used as manure and so enable many areas of waste land, commons, downs, etc to be brought into cultivation.]

At the end of <u>1874</u> we left Cardiff and came to Bristol.

And early in the year <u>1875,</u> I recommenced work for the Great Western Railway Company. I had a small amount of cash left with which I procured a little plant & some tools, and as there was a new goods shed to be built on the west side of the Old one, at the Bristol Station I tendered, and obtained the Contract.

And as a great part of the Shed was composed of Iron, I let the cast coloms to My Old Friends the Coalbrookdale Co, the Wrot Iron to the Patent Shaft Co. The Galvinized roof to John Lysaight, and the Timber for platforms &c to Messrs Jones & Nash, who were all pleased to give me a little credit until I got my payments from the Company, so I got on again fairly well. Harry and Charlie was my cheif helpers there, during the time.

We drove a lot of piles and made some Steam and Hydraulic crane Jetties by the Water Side, filled in the old dock which I had excavated nearly 40 years ago. We also raised all the goods yard, floors of the Sheds & Platforms 3ft 6in. I took all the Old platforms and erected new, at the higher level. All the new platforms were reversed to run from east to west, and we also took out all the Old Sidings, and laid down new reversed same as the platforms, with Inclines from the Sheds, to the main line at the Float bridge so that the Loco Engines now take up all goods from the Sheds. And all the waggons by rail inward are let down the incline to the unloading platform, which is a very great Improvement on the Old plan. And after it was finished we took down all the Old Hydraulic lifts & Machinery, and cleared out the engine houses and converted them into use for the new works. At the time we lengthened the down platform at Corsham and erected a large crane for the Stone work. We also erected a crane at the new good station at Bath.

At the time the above work was going on the company, required a new grain Store built near the goods Shed. I tendered at £15000 a splendid job, the tender was accepted but just at the time the company took to the Bristol & Exeter Railway, and cancelled the contract, giving me a few more little jobs to compensate the loss of that of the Store contract.

So all the work I did at the Bristol Goods Station, amounted to over £30,000 out of which I made a very fair trade profit, it being the last work done by me, for the company.

Dureing the time the above work was going on, the Contract for the Construction of the Severn Tunnel Railway, was advertised giving contractors one month to make their Estimates. [Severn Tunnel Railway Act passed in 1872 for eight miles of railway between Pilning and Rogiet, having a tunnel about $4^1/_2$ miles long of which a little over half was under the river. Early in 1873 the GWR began work by sinking the Old Shaft close to the river bank at Sudbury, and then driving a heading – initial tunnel – under the river. However, progress was very slow, so in August 1877 the Directors advertised for tenders.] And it being a cash contract and the payments sure, some of my Old friends advised me to tender, and they would help me should I get the contract. So I made my estimate and in August 1877 I tendered, at the amount of £987,372-10-0. The Heading was then driven about two thirds under the river and about seven feet square.

On August 22nd-77 I received the following note.

(copy, Great Western Railway Paddington, August 21/77

Dear Sir,

I should like to see you in London if you can come up on Friday morning.

      Yours truly
      Dan[l] Gooch

I went up, and found privately that although in most cases, when a Railway contract in these days, is to be let there is generally from <u>20</u> to <u>30</u> Tenders in for it. But in this case there was only <u>three</u> and one of them M[r] Webster the Gentleman, who I had let into the London drainage some years ago, was considered so very high that he was put out of the race. And then it lay between Mess[rs] Walker and Myself. I was about £<u>3000</u> below him, but I would not undertake to do it in any thing less than <u>five years</u> when he offered to do it in <u>four</u>. So that the difference of one years interest on such a large sum brought him below me, and as I would not alter my time I was out also. But at that time the Directors Report came out at the Halfyearly meeting to the effect that the Tenders for the Tunnel Railway was such that they could not accept. So they went on again themselves. At the Old Shaft. Two small contracts were then let, to Rowland Brotherhood (third son) and Oliver Norris of New Passage, [probably the same person whom the family met when Rowland was making the New Passage piers.] And some time after I helped my Son Rowland to undertake and carry on, some of the Heading Work until the water broke in. When M[r] Walker undertook the works. And the four years has expired since I tendered, and not much of the Tunnel yet completed.

    [MacDermot says Rowland Brotherhood had contracts to sink Marsh and Hill Shafts on the Monmouthshire bank, west of Sudbrook, and drive headings from them each way. By mid-October 1879 work was progressing well and the headings under the river had nearly met, when men driving the heading (under land) west from the Old Shaft hit the Great Spring, which flooded many of the workings and brought all work to a standstill. Subsequently, in December 1879, the GWR let the whole contract to T.A.Walker. The tunnel was eventually opened in 1886 after more inundations, from the river bed, an exceptionally high tide, and the Great Spring again.]

So I commenced the first excavation of the Great Western Railway in Feby 1836. And the last contract I did for the company at Chippenham was 700 narrow gauge waggons £65,800 finished in August 1866. And the last work of all done by Myself for the GWR, was the new works at the Bristol goods Station, amounting to £30,000, which was finished in August 1876.

Being taken ill soon after and unable to undertake work. And as I did not get better but worse, Peter came down early in Decr and boldly advised me not to undertake more work. Stateing that he would not only assist me then, but would continue to do so, which promise I am thankful to say he has most nobily kept up to the present hour.

I assisted Rowland with his Tunnel heading work until the company Stopped him at Christmas 1879. And thus ended my Career in connection with the Great Western Railway, which commenced 46 years ago.

[Rowland died at his home, Everton Villa, (now 5) Chertsey Road, Bristol on 4th March, 1883, aged 70. His wife Priscilla died 28th December, 1888. Their grave is in Arnos Vale Cemetery, Bristol, plot Q156.]

A scene very familiar to Rowland Brotherhood, Railway Contractor. As a loaded earth wagon approaches the tipping point the driver of its horse uncouples and leads it from between the rails. Meanwhile the wagon continues under its own momentum to the end of the track, where the waiting navvy will stop it, probably by thrusting a sprag (stout piece of wood with tapered ends) through the spokes. Behind, two navvies shovel the remaining dirt out of the previous wagon, while the horse driver waits to right the tipped body before setting back for the next load. Frontispiece of *Aid Book to Engineering Enterprise Abroad*, Part II – Ewing Matheson, 1881.]

APPENDIX TWO

WAGONS CONSTRUCTED FOR BRISTOL & EXETER, GREAT WESTERN AND SOUTH DEVON RAILWAYS

Wagon Descriptions for List Below

Ballast/permanent way truck – open wagon with drop side used by staff maintaining the track.

Box – either an open wagon or closed van.

Break [sic] van – a covered wagon at the very rear of a train for the guard, fitted with a screw brake which the guard used to help control the train on gradients or when stopping, often in response to whistle signals from the driver. Brake vans were in regular use on British freight trains until the late 1980s, by which time British Railways had at last fitted all its freight rolling stock with continuous brakes under the control of the driver. Until then the brakes on most wagons could only be applied when the wagon was stationary, and the only brakes available while most freight trains were moving were on the locomotive and brake van, thus keeping freight train speeds low. Brake vans remain in use where a train is propelled for any distance, so that the guard, with better visibility than the driver, can stop it if necessary by using his continuous brake valve. They are also used at the rear of trains carrying hazardous goods, for example toxic gases or nuclear flasks, so that in the event of an accident the guard can go back to protect his train without having to pass the hazard.

Carriage truck – a flat wagon designed to carry road vehicles, particularly gentlemen's carriages, often attached to a passenger train, sometimes with its passengers still inside if they preferred their privacy.

Coal – an open wagon to carry minerals, probably with a door in one end as well as both sides.

Open goods – an open wagon, with a central door on each side, for general use.

Stone truck – a flat or very low sided wagon with heavy duty springs and securing rings to fasten blocks of stone to prevent movement in transit.

Tilt wagon – an open wagon with a frame to support a canvas or tarpaulin covering to keep goods dry. Rowland's folding patent tilt is described in the main text.

Timber – a flat wagon, having a single (possibly two) bolster fitted with stanchions, used in pairs to carry long lengths of timber, possibly with a flat wagon between to provide sufficient distance between the bolsters.

Bristol & Exeter Railway

Date	No. Built	Load	Type	Tare Ton-cwt-qtr	Cost	Gauge	Running Nos.* *not consecutive	Notes
5/1849	10	6 tons	Carriage truck	4-9-0	£130	4ft 8$\frac{1}{2}$ in.	1-10	Rebuilt to 7ft gauge 12/1860
5/1849	18	6 tons+	Tilt	6-8-0		7ft	11-24*	12, 13, 17 patent tilt, + 7 beasts or 30 sheep
						7ft	25-9	Iron
5/1849	1		Goods			7ft	30	Wood
5/1849	48	6 tons	Box	5-18-0	£140	7ft	76-100*	Iron
							151-175	
5/1849	10	6 tons	Timber	4-5-0	£90	7ft	501-510	
1/1850	8	6 tons	Coal	5-5-0	£110	7ft	301-310*	
5/1851	9	6 tons	Tilt		£150	7ft	1-9	
Total	104							

Great Western Railway

Date	No. Built	Load	Type	Gauge	Running Nos.* *not consecutive	Notes
10/1851	1	7 tons	Iron Tilt	7ft		Rebuilt to NG** Open Goods 1874
11 & 12/ 1852	6	7 tons	Wood Tilt wood frame	7ft	1704-9	Rebuilt to NG** Open Goods 1874-6 (3)
11 & 12/ 1852	6	7 tons	Wood box wood frame	7ft	1710-15	Rebuilt to NG** Open Goods 1874-77 (2)
11/1852- 1/1853	22	10 tons	Wood box wood frame	7ft	1716-32, 1758	Rebuilt to NG** Open Goods 1875-77 (6); Rebuilt to 8 ton Timber truck (3)
12/1852- 1/1853	19	10 tons	Wood Coal	7ft	1757-76*	Rebuilt to NG** Open Goods 1872-77 (8)
4/1853- 9/1853	100	10 tons	Wood Box	7ft	2157-2256	Sold to Cornwall Rly (1)
12/1853	1	15 tons	Stone truck	Mixed	2657	6 wheels, late P/W truck

Great Western Railway

Date	No. Built	Load	Type	Gauge	Running Nos.* *not consecutive	Notes
12/1853	10		Wood Box	7ft	2658-67	
2 & 3/ 1854	20	10 tons	Wood Coal	7ft	2988-3007	2992 altered to mixed gauge for Windsor line 11/62
5/1854- 2/1855	250	12 tons	Wood coal	7ft	3008-3257	Sold to Cornwall Rly (13), to South Devon Rly (8), to South Wales Rly (15), to West Cornwall Rly (19)
2 & 3/ 1860	12	6 tons	Goods Break [sic] vans	7ft	3261-72	
7/1861	1	6 tons	Iron Tilt	7ft	1373	
7/1861	104	10 tons	Wood Box	7ft	323-36, 1203, 1334-97*, 1400-41*, 2457-99*	Sold to Cornwall Rly (36), South Wales Rly (5), to West Cornwall Rly (5), Rebuilt to NG** Open Goods (32)
9/1861	1		Timber truck		2522	
9 & 10/ 1861	30	10 tons	Wood Box iron frame	7ft	2501-41*	Sold to Cornwall Rly 1873-74 (8), to South Devon Rly 1870-73 (7), to West Cornwall Rly 1871 (5) Rebuilt to NG** Open Goods 1873-76 (22)
5/1865- 12/1865	300	8 tons	Low side Open	4ft 8½in.	10634-10933	Model at Peter Brotherhood Ltd.Order value £31,000
5/1865- 12/1865	50	15 tons	Rail truck	7ft	4942-4991	6 wheels, some sold to Cornwall and West Cornwall Rlys
1-8/1866	400	8 tons	Low side Open	4ft 8½in	11454-11853	
Total	1,333	plus 6 (see South Devon Rly 823-828 below), making 1,339				

** NG narrow gauge (in contemporary GWR terminology), i.e. 4ft 8 1/2 in. (standard gauge to everyone else!)

South Devon Railway

Brotherhood wagons in traffic in 1876 from Broad Gauge Society records. All 7ft gauge.

Qty	Wagon No	Date	Type	Description (load, material, outside length & breadth, inside height, wheelbase, tare: ton-cwt)
1	25	1870	Tilt	6 tons, iron, 17ft x 9ft 9in. x 2ft 9in., 9ft 9in., 6-0
12	159-170	1847	Ballast truck	8 tons, wood, 14ft x 6ft x 2ft 3in., 7ft 7in., 3-12
30	249-278	1859	Box truck	10 tons, wood, 15ft 2in. x 9ft 9in. x 2ft 4in., 9ft 6in., 5-5
45	291-335	1860	Box truck	10 tons, wood, 14ft 9in. x 9ft 6in. x 2ft 6in., 9ft 6in., 5-9
6	823-828	1871	Timber truck	15 tons iron, 27ft x 8ft 4in. x 8in., 18ft (6 wheels), 9-4, ex-GWR (not in list above, obviously I missed it)
4	829-832	175	Rail truck	15 tons, iron, 24ft 6in. x 8ft 6in. x 1ft, 14ft (6 wheels), 8-17, ex-GWR presumed 4942-91 series above
10	1-10	1851	Loco coal	10 tons, iron, 17ft 6in. x 9ft 10in. x 2ft 4in., 10ft 6in., 6-2
Total	108		(98 when second-hand GWR wagons are excluded) over 23 years.	

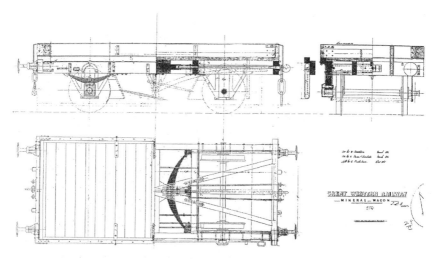

The Railway Works constructed 400 of these standard gauge wagons for the GWR in 1865. Note the single wooden brake block on each side and the safety chains either side of the coupling. See illustration on page 33.

Collection S.A.Leleux

APPENDIX THREE

ROWLAND BROTHERHOOD'S FAMILY

Rowland (Senior) was the eldest of seven sons and five daughters, the two youngest sons dying in infancy. His mother, Charlotte, three daughters and the youngest son emigrated to the USA around 1840. These notes are mainly derived from notes written by Alfred in 1904, and the history of James Brotherhood's family written by family members in 2000.

William	1836-91	Milwaukee, at Allis Works
Peter	1838-1902	Inventor of Brotherhood 3-cylinder engine
Priscilla	1840-?	Married William Renny, Chippenham
Rowland	1841-?	Was a rover. At one time was in charge of government works at Gibraltar, but later disappeared and nothing more was heard of him.
James	1843-1930	A member of the Hudson Bay Company. Earlier he had been an agricultural implement salesman. Was for many years Civil Engineer on Grand Trunk RR in Canada, retired and living in Montreal (1904). Married twice, having eight children by his first wife and two by his second. His eldest son and grandson were both called Rowland, and a great grandson is Peter Rowland Brotherhood, born 5-2-1946.
Fred	1845-1906	For many years in business in Charleston South Carolina and in 1904 was a mechanical engineer living in New York.
Alfred	1846- post 1923	An engineer who emigrated to Buffalo, Canada. He had eight children by his first wife and two by his second. Assisted with the Balmoral Bridge project and later inherited a sterling silver tea service given to Rowland by Queen Victoria as a token of thanks, later inherited by his son Francis.
Ernest	1848	Since early 1870s filled the position of City Engineer in charge of water works and drainage works at Pernambuco (i.e. Recife), Brazil. His father put in the drainage works there and Ernest stayed to take charge of them.

John	1850-1938	Engaged in making cloth at Chippenham. Lived in a house there called 'Oakleigh'.
George	1852-1880	Died at Wilkes Barre, Pennsylvania. Was a Teamster.
Harry	1853-1894	Died in Charleston South Carolina. Was in the phosphate dredging business with his brother Fred.
Charles	1855-1921	With Crossley Brothers, gas engine manufacturers of Manchester. Became their West of England agent.
Maud	1857-1923	Never married, lived at Bristol.
Kate	1863-1908	Married Howard Townshend, Chepstow and then Edward J.Lowther, mother of E.C.Lowther (1893-1962) in the shipping business at Bristol.

Traction Engine (possibly for hauling artillery) fitted with the electric light for French Military Service, with a 3-cylinder engine and dynamo mounted on top of the unusual design of boiler. *Engineering*, December 30th, 1881

APPENDIX FOUR

PETER BROTHERHOOD'S NOTEBOOK

Note that facing pages have the same number. Unrecorded pages were blank and have been ignored.

Pages   Contents

44   Cost of Pass^r Engines & Tenders made at Swindon Works
       [typically £2,500 to £3,350, plus £400 to £500 for the tender.]
45   Cost of Goods Engines & Tenders made at Swindon Works
       [typically £2,100 to £2,600, plus tenders as above. There was little
       cost difference between narrow (standard) and broad gauge
       locomotives.]
46-7   Cost of Trucks Carriage Frames &c made at Swindon Works
       [4-wheel wagons cost £100 to £130 each, with wheels apparently
       costing only about £5 per wagon, while First or Second Class
       coach frames cost £126 or £115 respectively, with wheels an
       extra £85!]
57-68 Piece work prices now in use at Swindon July 1859 [Angle iron
       Fire Boxes to Warming cocks with flanges]
69-70 More detailed rates for Smiths and Turners &c [for various
       wheels]
71-2   Various costs for six monthly periods ending Dec 1855 to June
       1859, with passenger and goods trains shown separately.
73   Average Coke per Mile in lbs
       Average Oil & Tallow in lbs per Mile
74   Average Cost of Repairs per Mile including Management and
       other general charges   Average Cost of Coke per Mile in pence
75   Average Cost of Enginemen and Firemen's Wages
       Average of General Charges per Mile
76   Average Total Cost per 55 to 58 tons, 0.14d., 0.48 to 0.54 average
       0.51 lb coke, goods 258 to 286 tons, 0.04d., 0.23 to 0.26 lb coke
77   Total Mileage for half years
78   Wage costs [average £1-2-11 (about £51.50) and engine mileages]
79   Abstract of Locomotive Expenditure Half Year ending 30th June
       1859 [broad & narrow shown separately, and combined]
80   Miles run for Half Year ending 30th June 1859 [as above]
82   Scale for Enginemen's Extra Miles [basic rates 5/- to 7/6 per day
       i.e. £11.25 to £16.87] and Firemen's Extra Miles [basic rates 3/- to
       4/6 per day i.e. £6.75 to £10.13, with an ordinary day's work about
       160 Miles]
83   Scale of Coke and Coal Premiums 1859 [standard fuel
       consumption for various types of traffic over various routes and
       allowance for changes to the number of vehicles in the train.]
84   Comparison between consumption of Coke and Coke & Coal
       [half-years ending June 1856, 1858 & 1859.]
85   Railway Works Chippenham – Prices of Wheels &c
86   Weights & prices of Wro^t Iron Lattice Bridges, with cross girders

& all iron work complete the lengths between inside of piers – Oct 1857: [Listed bridges for common roads with clear spans 50 to 200ft, railway bridges with clear spans 50 to 140ft 100 feet span Trellis Bridge actual weights and dimensions as taken from the bridge made in March 1857 for Ceylon]

87   Estimated cost of one Pair of Tyres for retyring Locomotive wheels 5ft diameter –Bowling [Iron Co.] tyres – 'say 40-0-0', Patent Shaft Co tyres – 'say 30-10-0'

88-9   Small Locomotive Engines – weight of forgings in the rough Net, cost of materials with percentage added for Coals &c – not including wages June 10th 1862 – [Material costs totalled £301-3-10, and net cost of wages was estimated at £300-0-0]

Engine room of the first diesel-electric tug, *Acklam Cross*, with two Brotherhood-Ricardo 300hp diesel engines, *c*.1933.

APPENDIX FIVE

JAMES & FREDERICK HUNT

Thomas Sewell sent me this information in 1963, from notes supplied by Mrs J.W.Purdy, who was Peter's wife's niece.

James Hunt engineered the first railways in India. He had at least three sons and two daughters. The eldest son was Frederick Seager Hunt, born 1838. After leaving Westminster School he joined his father in India, and married his cousin Alice, daughter of his father's brother Alfred, in 1867. They had no children. He died in 1904. He became chairman of the distillery business Seager Evans . In addition, he was Member of Parliament for Marylebone (London) and later Maidstone, and sometime around 1890 was created a Baronet.

The third son, Walter Freeman, married and had at least one daughter, Mrs Purdy. Another son was married and had a daughter Gertrude.

James' daughter Eliza (born 1839) married Peter Brotherhood (in 1866) and another daughter Harriet married Arthur Guillan Scott.

In 1961 H.C.Hughes, a member of the RCTS who had researched Indian railways, wrote to me about James Hunt. The contract for the first $25\frac{1}{2}$ miles of the East Indian Railway (EIR) from Howrah (Calcutta) to Raneegunge was awarded in September 1850 to Messrs Hunt, Bray & Emslie of London. Construction was completed in November 1853 and the line opened in 1854. Intervening sections of the line were awarded to other contractors, but the last $35\frac{1}{2}$ miles was also awarded to Hunt, Bray & Emslie, in November 1851. In June 1854 the contract for another section of the EIR, from Mogul Serai to the Jumna River near Allahabad, 95 miles, was awarded to Messrs Hunt & Emslie. It included the Tonse Bridge, seven spans of 150ft. Construction was interrupted by the Mutiny (1857) and subsequent disorders, and the line was eventually completed by EIR engineers and opened in 1864. (Presumably Eliza aged about 19 went to India at the end of 1857 or early 1858, and with her father came back to England after the line was opened.) In 1862 the EIR contract for 223 miles of line to Jubbulpore was divided between Waring Brothers and Hunt of London. This line was completed in 1863. Mr Hughes thought that Rowland's girder bridge for Mysore in 1859 was probably on the Bangalore branch of the Madras Railway, sanctioned 1858 and completed 1864, as there were no other railways in Mysore at that time.

APPENDIX SIX

RESTORATION AND DESCRIPTION OF MODEL LOCOMOTIVE *PEARL*

When I entered King's College, Strand, London, in 1958 *Pearl* stood on the half-way landing of the main staircase. Paintwork had turned grey with age, bright steelwork had a hard coating of rust, and once polished brass looked as though it was painted black. A few small parts, and a plaque which presumably had given its history, were missing. The smokebox and well tank were full of paper and the safety valve cover was crammed with nut shells. Altogether *Pearl* was in a sorry state. This caused a new member of the College Railway Club to suggest, on 16th October, 1959, that the Club should seek permission to give *Pearl* a thorough clean.

The necessary permission was obtained from the College Authorities, and further permission was granted to do the work in a corner of the Mechanical Engineers' workshop. Arrangements were made and a team of about 10 Club members and friends assembled on the morning of Saturday 28th November, 1959 to move *Pearl*. About 6ft long, and weighing about $10^{1}/_{2}$ cwt (although that was not known at the time), *Pearl* was lifted bodily on to old door mats to protect the stone floor, and then on to scaffolding planks laid on the stairs. An L-shaped anchor of scaffold poles was put across the head of the stairs, bearing against the newel posts. A rope fastened to *Pearl's* front buffer beam was wound a couple of times round the anchor for added braking power, and *Pearl* was lowered down the main flight. *Pearl* was held in check on the short bottom flight without any additional anchor. Once at ground level, *Pearl* was pushed out into the quadrangle, along the Strand for a few yards and then down the alley Strand Lane to the back entrance to the workshop, old door mats being constantly taken from behind and laid in front. Including clearing up, the operation took about two hours.

Over the next 18 months *Pearl* was completely stripped down, cleaned, repainted in its original colours and reassembled. Plans to use it on a pleasure railway to raise funds for charity collapsed immediately the boiler was filled with water preparatory to a hydraulic test. Eight of the twelve 1in. boiler tubes were found to be damp and water flowed from another, even without applying any pressure. When completely reassembled *Pearl* was weighed on pressure capsules. As the weight was now known to be within the capacity of the College lift it was used on 6th May, 1961 to take *Pearl* up to the ground floor. Planks were laid on the stairs. The short bottom flight was rushed, but the main flight was taken in a similar way as for the descent. A pulley system attached to the anchor hauled *Pearl* up, and a safety rope wound round the anchor was kept taught in case the pulley system failed. Soon *Pearl* was back on the plinth, and generated very favourable comment. The Engineering Workshop staff were particularly helpful throughout the whole restoration period.

Pearl reflects 1860s locomotive practice. The outside frames are $^3/_4$ in. thick wood sandwiched between $^1/_4$ in. iron plates, the whole being rivetted together. The inside frames are $^3/_8$ in. iron, and extend from the front buffer beam to the front of the firebox. All the wheels have shrunk-on tyres, outside bearings and leaf springs above the footplate. The diameter of the flangeless driving wheels is 20in. and of the carrying wheels $11^1/_2$ in. The cylinder block consists of two castings bolted together with a lead seal. The two cylinders are 4in. x $5^1/_2$ in. stroke, with a single steam chest between them having a brass slide valve moving over the vertical face on each side. The crossheads each have four slide bars, and a boiler feed pump is driven directly from each. The brass big and little end bearings are secured to the connecting rods by straps and wedges. None have any identification, and each has minor variations in size. This was brought home forcibly when, at a late stage in the reassembly, it was discovered that the left-hand piston had been put into the right-hand cylinder and the big ends would only fit their proper cranks. It was not feasible, due to lack of symmetry in its bearings, to turn the driving axle round, and there was insufficient time to strip everything down, so the brasses were machined to fit. This introduced a little play, which was bad engineering but by then we knew *Pearl* would not steam again. Stephenson's link motion is fitted, operated by a reversing lever on the footplate. The original had been mislaid so a replacement was made. A surprising feature was the lack of any facility to adjust the valve setting. By the time the motion had been fully assembled the popularity of outside cylinders and valve gear on modern locomotives was fully appreciated, since the space between the frames was extremely limited, making components hard to see, let alone reach!

The boiler barrel, 12in. in diameter and 32in. long, is made of two sheets of $^1/_4$ in. iron, rivetted together. The outer firebox is slightly raised and carries a Salter safety valve whose spring is calibrated in tens 0-60. A lug on each side of the firebox rests on the frame and is bolted to it. Lugs bolted to the foundation ring supported the firebars, but none remained. The inner firebox is $11^1/_2$ in. long x $10^5/_8$ in. wide and 14in. high. A row of four trycocks on the back of the firebox enable the driver to estimate the water level. The regulator valve is at the base of a copper trumpet-shaped pipe within the dome. The blast pipe is a parallel tube with the upper end flanged over to restrict the size of the orifice. The original boiler lagging was thin brown hairy sheeting which fell to pieces when *Pearl* was dismantled, so was replaced by material obtained on a Club visit to Swindon works, applied as a paste and allowed to dry.

Under the cab floor is a small water tank, estimated capacity $1\frac{1}{2}$ gallons. A pipe on each side, with a stop valve just below the tank outlet, feeds the water to the appropriate feed pump, and thence to the boiler clack valves. Nowhere is there any provision for connection to a tender.

The old livery, discovered as paint was removed, was followed. Boiler, firebox, wheels and springs are royal blue, frames and front buffer beam dark red (with a bright red panel edged with black) and other parts black. Lining is red. All the brightwork was varnished to delay tarnish and rust.

As nothing seemed to be known about *Pearl*, research into its history was done alongside its restoration, which eventually resulted in the publication of the first edition of this book.

Pearl in January 1959 before restoration.   *S.A.Leleux*

Down the stairs, 28th November, 1959. Author grasping the top of the chimney.   *T.L.Gilchrist*

Turning in the entrance hall. Note the rubbish in the smokebox, layers of dust on the frames, and doormats to protect the floor.   *T.L.Gilchrist*

Totally dismantled in the Mechanical Engineers' workshop. Note pile of scale beside boiler from firebox water space. Note, too, the separation of the plates forming the sides of the frames, with wood between them.
S.A.Leleux

The frames and motion. Even allowing for the fact this is a model, the attraction of outside cylinders and valve gear is obvious. Either side are the composite frames, an iron, wood, iron sandwich, with inside them the iron inner frames. The driving wheels fit into the space between them. Within the inner frames are two cylinders, whose crossheads each run between two pairs of slide bars and each crosshead drives a feed water pump. Each crosshead is attached to a connecting rod, with its big end bearing, and between the two cranks are eccentrics driving four straps to operate the Stephenson link motion valve gear. *S.A.Leleux*

Back up the stairs, 6th May, 1961. Note scaffold planks for the wheels, chain block and safety rope, and doormats on the floor.   *S.A.Leleux*

Some 40 years later (21st February, 2001), bright work is starting to tarnish or rust, although the protective varnish applied in 1960 seems to have been quite effective. Note the set of four try cocks to determine water level in the boiler, and the oval opening for the water tank under the footplate.   *S.A.Leleux*

APPENDIX SEVEN

SUMMARY OF STANLEY BROTHERHOOD'S DIARY 1899

Amazingly, Stanley's diary for 1899 survives. It cost 1/- and like modern diaries had pages of useful information at the beginning, but there was also pink blotting paper bound in between each page. During the week he appears to have lived at the family home 15 Hyde Park Gardens (the address on his marriage certificate), but until his marriage spent the weekends with his fiancee at Sunningdale (near Windsor), leaving the works at about 1pm on Saturdays. As 1st January was Sunday the following Monday was a Bank Holiday in Scotland only; for Stanley it was 'Came up from Sunningdale 9.29 [half an hour later than usual]. [At] Works all day.'

He noted visits to various shipyards in Glasgow, Liverpool, Portsmouth, Newcastle and Sunderland, as well as to the Admiralty. Sundry events around the works, such as experiments with aluminium valves in a small 3-cylinder air compressor appeared satisfactory and trials of equipment for various ships and other customers, were also recorded. An unexpected entry was on Friday 24th February when he 'Went on footplate of 11.30 train to Bristol & returned by the 5.50 arriving Padd[n] 8.30 Very enjoyable ride each way.'

The works closed for Easter holidays 5pm on Maundy Thursday, 30 March, so Stanley went to Eastbourne from the Thursday evening to the following Wednesday morning.

Some diary entries refer to financial affairs, for example on 10th April 'Received cheque from Japanese for £7646-18-11 on air compressing machinery' and on 22nd April "Rec[d] cheque from Whitehead for £1,000 for torpedo engines.'

On Tuesday 25th April he noted 'E.K.B's wedding' (his sister) and on Thursday 27th 'PB very bad with gout & left at 11 o'cl'. Peter was in the next day but went to Eastbourne in the afternoon until Monday. At Whitsun, the works closed 1pm on Saturday 20th May, reopening at 6am Wednesday 24th May. Peter Brotherhood was in Paris for this weekend. Sporting events were also noted, Stanley attending Ascot on both Thursday and Friday, 15th & 16th June, and on the Saturday 'cricket at Broadlands', with his future in-laws.

On 27th June, 1899 Stanley married Vera, the fourth daughter of Charles Durrant Kemp-Welch of Broadlands, Sunningdale, at Holy Trinity church, Sunningdale,at 2.30pm. Stanley and Vera had a continental honeymoon. On Wednesday 28th June they went to Paris, staying until Friday when they left for Neuchatel, arriving Saturday and leaving Monday for Spiez. Continuing to spend one or two days in each centre, they travelled on to Interlaken, Lucern, Basle, Rheims and Boulogne. They left Boulogne on Friday 21st July at 2.15pm, arriving at Charing Cross at 5.40pm, and on Saturday Stanley was 'Back at office.' By the time of the 1901 census, and probably from their wedding, Stanley and Vera lived at Windlesham, about three miles from Sunningdale towards Bagshot.

The works closed at 5pm on Friday 4th August, and remained closed for the 'August holiday' until it reopened on Thursday 10th August at 6am. (The Bank Holiday was then the first Monday in August.)

On Saturday 4th November a 'Collection for Widows & Orphans of men in Transvaal for Daily Telegraph fund started in works'. Around this time Stanley spent some weekends on the South Coast, at Brighton, Eastbourne, and Folkestone. A month later, on Saturday 2nd December he noted 'Not at works today – went Charterhouse.' This was the date of the London Charity Cup football match, Old Carthusians v London Caledonians, which OCs won 4-1. The report of the match in *The Carthusian* says that their crowd at the match cheered their side on with a cry 'Now then, Charterhouse, give 'em a bit of Baden Powell' [he too was an Old Carthusian and at that time was one of the heroes of the Boer War in South Africa, having then been besieged in Mafeking for about six weeks, tying down large Boer forces, and would not be relieved until the following May].

The works closed for Christmas holidays on Friday 22nd December, at 5pm, reopening Thursday 28th at 6am. On the following Saturday, 30th December, there was a 'Staff' dinner at Dover Castle (presumably a nearby hotel) at 6.30pm.

It can be seen that, ignoring Sundays and counting Saturday as a half day, for most of the employees, holidays at this time comprised: Good Friday to Easter Tuesday (inclusive, $3\frac{1}{2}$ days), Whitsun Monday and Tuesday (2 days), August Bank Holiday Saturday to Wednesday ($3\frac{1}{2}$ days), Christmas ($3\frac{1}{2}$ days – probably normally a half day on Christmas Eve, Christmas Day, Boxing Day and the day after). The normal working day was 6am to 5pm (1pm Saturday). With half an hour for breakfast and an hour for lunch this gave a working week of 54 hours.

APPENDIX EIGHT

OUTLINE OF THE MANUFACTURING PROCESS

A broad outline of the Manufacturing Process follows, beginning in the drawing office, where the new machine is designed (or modifications are designed for an existing one). Every component, apart from nuts and bolts etc. is drawn to scale. The designers and draughtsmen also do any necessary calculations for performance and strength requirements. All this work is now done using CAD (computer aided design) software, but then calculations were done using slide rules or tables of logarithms, possibly very occasionally aided by a hand-operated mechanical calculator, with drawings made using pencil, paper and specialized drawing instruments. When old drawings showed signs of wearing out due to heavy use, or amendments had to be made just to a small area, the original was copied by tracing in the Tracing Department. Until about 1970 drawings were made on paper cut to a convenient length and wound on to a stick for storage. A standard requirement when making a new drawing was to keep figures off fold lines on the paper. Copying drawings used to involve an exposure an hour long by the sun on the roof. Alternatively, the drawing was wrapped round a glass cylinder containing an arc lamp which was moved along the cylinder to give an even exposure.

Drawing Office c.1960: Of some 40 people in the photograph only two are women. The drawing board in the foreground has the paper with the new drawing firmly clipped to it, and a set square (which could double as a protractor), pencil and eraser lie on it. The draughtsman at the desk behind has a T-square to keep his horizontal lines parallel, and to support his set square when necessary.

Women in pattern shop in the First World War, with examples of patterns – wooden masters for making the moulds for castings – behind and in their hands.

The finished pattern for a compressor crankcase. The different colours indicate the surface finish required. Red areas will be left as cast, black will be machined away, and yellow denotes a surface which will require machining so it will be made larger than required, with additional material on it, to ensure that machining will leave a perfect surface when the surplus is removed.

Components then had to be made. Many were castings, made by pouring liquid metal into a suitable mould. The mould was made using patterns, usually of wood, which were slightly larger than full size replicas of the components (to allow for shrinkage when the liquid metal solidified and cooled). They often comprised several detachable pieces to facilitate withdrawing the pattern from the mould without disturbing the impression.

The pattern was then put into moulding boxes and special sand was packed down hard all round, so that when the pattern was removed it left its exact shape in the mould. The moulders had to use their skill to create channels in the mould so that the liquid metal would enter easily and also permit air and gases to escape quickly. Moulds for small items would be made in special robust iron boxes, while the mould for a large item would have to be made in the foundry floor. Molten metal was poured into the mould in the foundry, to fill the shape of the pattern. When cold, the casting would be lifted from the mould and the sand knocked off.

Some parts were forgings, made by hammering red hot metal into the desired shape (like a blacksmith making a horse shoe), but for many years these were mainly purchased from specialist firms instead of being made on site.

Iron foundry (1): While the mould for a small item could be made in a suitable box, the mould for a large one had to be made in the floor of the foundry. Here foundry staff show the size of the mould for an engine casing. A core, well reinforced with metals bars and hooks, would then be placed over this mould to form the space for the metal.

Other parts were cut, by saw, guillotine or oxy-acetylene burner, from thick metal plates or thin sheets of metal, or from various standard sections of rod, angle, girder or tube.

Each rough part then needed finishing to make surfaces smooth and to the required size. Small components could be finished by hand, by scraping or filing, but most were machined. Basically, milling and planing machines produce flat surfaces while lathes and boring machines produce curved ones. Grinding is another smoothing method. In view of the size of many of the firm's products the machine tools to make them were correspondingly large. Sometimes parts needed to be annealed during their manufacture. This was heat treatment, to bring the part to a state of uniform hardness/softness prior to further machining, or to relieve any stresses which had developed in it during manufacture.

Inspection followed most stages of manufacture, to ensure the components met the required specification.

Parts which rotated as high speed such as turbine rotors were balanced to prevent any possibility of vibration or excessive wear in bearings when running at speed.

The machine then had to be assembled and tested, and finally transported to the customer.

Iron foundry (2): Pouring liquid cast iron into a tower of mould boxes, with excess metal flowing out at the other end. The tower arrangement meant that the sand could be packed uniformly firm throughout the height of the mould.

Smiths' shop: Hearths to heat the metal and adjacent anvils are against the wall on the left, and a steam hammer is in the centre. The plate with holes in the foreground is to facilitate making accurate bends in metal sections. Despite the risks from sparks and hot metal, the only protective clothing is leather aprons.

Machining a large connecting rod. It is secured with T-bolts placed in slots in the large rotating baseplate to hold it still against the action of the cutting tool. As it turns, the cutting tool, initially positioned by the hand wheels, will remove a thin, narrow strip of metal. The tool is progressively lowered each revolution so that the whole surface of the bearing is machined.

Oxy-acetylene burners cut steel quickly. The machine shown has four burners, each one following the outline on the drawing which is being automatically scanned in front of the operator.

Grinding to smooth the metal forming a turbine base plate, using a tool powered by compressed air supplied by the air line. In the background are two Dorr-Oliver filters.

APPENDIX NINE

BROTHERHOOD PATENTS

Rowland

Number	Date	Description
12713	10-11-1849	Apparatus for covering trucks and wagons on railways, also road wagons and canal boats
Total	1	

Peter

Number	Date	Description
2826	9-11-1857	Boilers and furnaces
825	16-4-1858	Construction of locomotive and other steam boilers
710	17-3-1860	Improved methods of steam generation in locomotive, stationary, marine and other boilers
2408	31-7-1868	Apparatus for cooling, heating or tempering fluids
107	14-1-1869	Valves
47	6-1-1870	Packing of pistons, glands, pipes and other joints
2174	4-8-1870	Apparatus for accumulating hydrostatic pressure
2909	4-11-1870	Boilers for heating liquids, generating steam and like purposes
143*	20-1-1871	Regulation etc. flow of liquids
648*	11-3-1871	Steering vessels, valves
287	24-1-1873	Propelling machinery [the 3-cylinder radial engine]
2003	5-6-1873	Fluid pressure engines
3883	1874	Slide valves
999	18-3-1875	Forcing fluids, etc.
4230	7-12-1875	Steering apparatus
4546	30-12-1875	Motor engines
3164	10-8-1876	Compressed air, etc.
2300	7-6-1880	Compressed air or other elastic fluid
3826	21-9-1880	Launching torpedoes
697	17-2-1881	Rotating slide valves
4451	12-10-1881	Discharging torpedoes under water
2494	18-5-1883	Multiple-cylinder engines
4943	17-10-1883	Coupling for shafting
13756	17-10-1884	Multiple-cylinder engines
944	22-1-1885	Pistons

2965	6-3-1885	Admission valves and gear
3989	17-3-1887	Three-cylinder engines
3485	4-3-1890	Slide valves for steam, etc., engines
18909	9-10-1893	Air compressors
11027	4-6-1895	Water trap
20311	28-10-1895	Air compressors
7766	25-3-1897	Packing rings for pistons and plungers
17832	29-7-1897	Pump and compressors
17833	29-7-1897	Compressing or exhausting elastic fluid
22649	2-10-1897	Triple-cylinder engines
11060	14-5-1898	Steam engines
6354	23-3-1899	Centrifugal governors
7496	18-4-1899	Air-compressing engines
24719	4-12-1901	Cylinder engines
Total	39	

Stanley

Number	Date	Description
25328†	18-11-1902	Compressors
25644†	21-11-1902	Clutches
13826	20-6-1903	Cylinder engines
4891	27-2-1904	Internal combustion engines
7315	26-3-1904	Fluid pressure motors
11464	18-5-1904	Carburettors
6789	30-3-1905	Fluid pressure engines
20304	7-10-1905	Torpedo engines
23519	15-11-1905	Torpedo propulsion
20333	12-9-1906	Ships' pumping plant
20980	21-9-1906	Internal combustion engine ignition
25096	7-11-1906	Internal combustion engine ignition
2999	6-2-1907	Internal combustion engine ignition
3117	7-2-1907	Air-compressing plant etc.
5205	4-3-1907	Internal combustion engines
16881	23-7-1907	Internal combustion engines
4801‡	3-3-1908	Ignition devices
14423	7-7-1908	Torpedoes
23900	7-11-1908	Valve spindle etc. packing
16632	16-7-1909	Testing gauges etc.
Total	19	

Subsequent patents taken out in name of Peter Brotherhood Ltd.

Notes

*	Peter Brotherhood & G.D.Kittoe
†	Stanley Brotherhood and another
‡	First patent of Peter Brotherhood Ltd

MEDALS

Royal Polytechnic Society Institute 1853 First Class.On reverse, head of James Watt. Reason for the award and the recipient are not known, but recognition of Rowland's activities in the Crimea War seems the most likely, bearing in mind the date, Peter then being about to leave, or having just left, school.

World Exhibition 1873 Wien (Vienna) For Merit.On reverse, head of Franz Joseph I, Kaiser (Emperor/ King) of Austria, Bohemia, Hungary etc.

For Progress World Exhibition 1873 Wien.On reverse, head of Franz Joseph I as above.

International Exhibition Paris MDCCCLXXVIII (1878). The central figure is Marianne, the national symbol of the French Republic, a personification of liberty and reason, and a portrayal of the Goddess of Liberty.On reverse, around the rim French Republic Plans for Buildings for the Universal Exhibition of Champs de (Field of) Mars (later site of Eiffel Tower) and Trocadero (Gardens). Either side of the central feature the text reads 'MDCCCXXVIII, the eighth year of the [Third] French Republic [1870-1940], [6th] Marquis of MacMahon [1st] Duke of Magenta, President. Teisserenc De Bort (Minister of Commerce & Agriculture), Jean-Baptiste Kranz, Senator nominated as Commissionaire General of the Universal Exhibition.'

Universal International Exhibition 1878 Paris with Marianne and the name Brotherhood on the banner carried by the small figure.

International Electricity Exhibition Paris 1881 with Brotherhood across the centre.On reverse, French Republic and head of Marianne.

Universal Exhibition 1889 Note the Eiffel Tower, constructed from 1887–89 as the entrance to this exhibition.On reverse, French Republic and Peter Brotherhood displayed below Marianne.

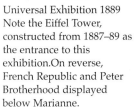

Royal Agricultural Society of England Incorporated 26th March 1840 (having been established in 1838) and its motto 'Practice with Science'. On reverse, head of His Majesty King George V Patron. Awarded 1920 for tractor.

Bibliography

The Balmoral Bridge of I.K.Brunel, *Industrial Archaeology Review*, Vol 3 No 3, A.Buchanan & S.K.Jones, 1980

British Battleships, Dr Oscar Parkes (Seely Service & Co., 1970)

The British Internal Combustion Locomotive 1894-1940, Brian Webb, (David & Charles, 1973)

British Railway Bridges & Viaducts, Martin Smith, (Goose & Son, 1994)

British Steam Locomotive Builders, J.W.Lowe, (Goose & Son, 1975)

The Canals of the East Midlands, Charles Hadfield, (David & Charles, 1970)

Chronicles of a Country Works, R.H.Clark, (Percival Marshall, 1952)

The Chronicles of Boulton's Siding, A.R.Bennett, (Locomotive Publishing Co., 1927)

The Commercial Motor

Crewe Works Narrow Gauge System, Edward Talbot & Clive Taylor, (LNWR Society, 2005)

Daily Telegraph

Daily Mail

Development of the English Steam Wagon, R.H.Clark, (Goose & Son, 1963)

The Devil's Device, Edwyn Grey, (Purnell Book Services, 1975)

Drum Roll, James Blades, (Quality Book Club, 1977)

The Early Days of the Power Station Industry, R.H.Parsons, (Cambridge University Press, 1939)

Engineering

Engines & Enterprise (Biography of Sir Harry Ricardo), John Reynolds, (J.H.Haynes & Co., 1999)

Garrett Wagons – parts 1, 2, 3, R.A.Whitehead, (R.A.Whitehead & Partners, 1994)

Heat Engines, D.A.Low, (Longmans, 1926)

Industrial Railway Record (Society magazine), Industrial Railway Society

Industrial Locomotives of Central Southern England, Industrial Railway Society, 1981

Industrial Locomotives of East Anglia, Industrial Railway Society, 1993

Industrial Locomotives of Bucks, Beds & Northants, Industrial Railway Society, 2001

James Brotherhood – Genealogy & Family History, Mary Lard Silvia, 2000 (privately published in USA)

Locomotives of the London Chatham & Dover Railway, D.L.Bradley, (RCTS or Railway Correspondence & Travel Society, 1960)

Machinery Handbook, HMSO, 1941

Nelson to Vanguard – Warship Design & Development 1923-45, D.K.Brown, (Chatham Publishing, 2000)

Patent Specifications, Patent Office

Peterborough Standard

Proceedings, Institution of Civil Engineers

Proceedings, Institution of Mechanical Engineers

Reminiscences of a Lance-Corporal of Industry, Edward Barford, (Elm Tree Books, 1972)

Shipping Wonders of the World, Clarence Winchester (ed.), (Amalgamated Press & Fleetway House, 1936)

Steam on the Road, David Gladwin, (Batsford, 1988.)
Take the Strain, Tim Nicholson, (Alexandra Towing Co., 1990)
The Times
The Undertype Steam Waggon, Maurice A.Kelly, (Goose & Son, 1975)
Who Was Who – various volumes (Bloomsbury Yearbooks)

In addition, a wide range of Catalogues, Correspondence, Minutes, Order Books, etc. for Peter Brotherhood Ltd and its predecessors has been made readily available. Photographs not otherwise credited are from the firm's collection, many having come from the private collections of Ernest Dewar, Andrew Eyre and Peter Roy.

Turning a gas engine piston and cutting grooves for its piston rings in a lathe. The operator appears to be using callipers to check the diameter of the piston. The cutting tool is basically the point at the apex of an irregular pyramid formed at one end of a hardened steel bar, firmly bolted into the tool holder in front of the machinist. The hand wheels enable the tool holder to be moved in relation to the work piece, and the long screw (if engaged) enables the tool holder to be moved steadily along the lathe and so take a uniform cut from the work piece. The swarf (cuttings) has accumulated in the sloping tray beneath the work piece. Note the stepped pulley with the leather drive belt positioned on an intermediate size pulley. A downward pointing pipe by the machinist's elbow could be used to direct white cutting fluid, a soluble oil known as suds, over the cutting tool. It had better cooling properties than oil although it did not lubricate as well. The lubricating action saved some machine power, and its cooling effect helped to prevent the heat generated by cutting from welding the chips on to the tool and so destroying its cutting ability. As a result, higher cutting speeds can be used. A heavy flow of coolant can be used to wash away chips. The use of coolant depends on circumstances, not least the material being used as some, like cast iron, are always machined dry.

Index

Note: An asterisk with a page reference denotes an illustration.

British Railways Standard Class 5 4-6-0 73050, later named *City of Peterborough*, under restoration in Brotherhood's workshops. 1978. The tender wheels and frame are beside the boiler in the foreground with the locomotive's frames and driving wheels by the tender body beyond them.